STANDARD CATALOGUE

OF

BRITISH COINS

I. ENGLAND AND UNITED KINGDOM

that is, excluding
Scottish, Irish and the Island Coinages

Editor

PETER SEABY

1968 EDITION

B. A. SEABY LTD.

Numismatists

59-65 GREAT PORTLAND STREET, LONDON, W.1

FIRST EDITION 1962

SECOND EDITION 1963/64

THIRD EDITION 1964

FOURTH EDITION 1965

FIFTH (enlarged) EDITION 1966

SIXTH EDITION 1967

SEVENTH EDITION 1968

Printed in England by ROBERT STOCKWELL LTD., Baden Place, London, S.E.1

INTRODUCTION

Britain's coinage extends over a period of more than 2000 years. Some of these coins are valuable historical records of this country's early history: they also mirror in miniature the artistic achievements of the times. In recent years the fascination of numismatics has attracted an increasing number of devotees. It is hoped that this catalogue will be of use both to collectors and students, and also to the casual enquirer who wishes to identify and value his coins.

FOR nearly forty years B. A. Seaby Ltd. have been publishing the only comprehensive priced catalogue of British coins. Early editions were based on our stock, giving prices of coins we had for sale at the time of going to press. However, as our stock is constantly changing and as the price of a coin varies considerably according to its exact variety and its state of preservation, we decided to make the catalogue more useful to the collector by giving prices for coins in an average state of preservation and by including all the main varieties of coins so as to make it a comprehensive type catalogue, irrespective of whether or not they were all in stock. In 1945, therefore, our first *Standard Catalogue of the Coins of Great Britain and Ireland* was compiled. In 1962 a new catalogue was produced in a smaller format and with photographic illustrations in place of line drawings; Scottish and Irish coins were omitted, but it is hoped to deal with these series in a separate volume. In this edition we have included a list of Latin legends with translations.

In Part I of this catalogue we have endeavoured to cover each reign up to 1816 according to its numismatic range, but as limitations of space preclude the listing of every variety this part of the catalogue is essentially a type list. In many cases we have followed the arrangement of the excellent reference work by J. J. North, *English Hammered Coins*, in two volumes (Vol. I, price 80s., deals with Anglo-Saxon from *c.* 650 A.D. to the end of the reign of Henry III, and Vol. II, price 50s., covers the period 1272-1662.) All advanced collectors of English coinage will wish to have these in their library.

In Part II we have covered the coinage issued since 1816 and have listed all dates with their individual prices.

ACKNOWLEDGEMENT. We should like to record our thanks to the many numismatists who have given us their advice during the compilation of this catalogue or who have lent us coins for illustration. All the coins have been photographed by Frank Purvey.

THE VALUE OF A COIN. Except in a very few instances this catalogue will not give the exact value of any coin. Its purpose is to give a general value for a particular class of coin in an average state of preservation and also to give the collector an idea of the range and value of coins in the English series. The value of any particular piece depends on three things:

Its exact design, legend, mintmark or date.

Its exact state of preservation; this is of prime importance.

The demand for it in the market at any given time.

Some minor varieties are much scarcer than others, and, as the number of coins issued varies considerably from year to year, coins of certain dates and mintmarks are rarer and of more value than other pieces of similar type. The prices given for any type are for the commonest variety, mintmark or date of that type. **Values given are our selling prices at the time of going to press** and *not* the price we would pay.

ORDERING COINS. It is for the above reasons that collectors should not, generally, order from this catalogue but from the lists published monthly in our *Coin and Medal Bulletin*. If, however, collectors wish to order from this catalogue, they are requested to make this clear in their order.

CONDITIONS OF A COIN

(i.e. grade of preservation) in order of merit as generally used in England.

Proof. See page 12.

FDC = *Fleur-de-coin*. Mint state, unused, flawless, without any wear, scratches or marks.

Unc. = *Uncirculated*. A coin in new condition as issued by the Royal Mint, but, owing to modern mass-production methods of manufacture, not necessarily perfect.

EF = *Extremely Fine*. A coin that shows little sign of having been in circulation, but which may exhibit slight surface marks on very close inspection.

VF = *Very Fine*. Only slight traces of wear on the raised surfaces; a coin that has had only slight circulation.

F = *Fine*. Considerable signs of wear on the raised surfaces, or design weak through faulty striking.

Fair. A coin that is worn, but which has the inscriptions and main features of the design still distinguishable, or a piece that is very weakly struck.

Poor. A very worn coin, of no value as a collector's piece unless extremely rare.

EXAMPLES OF CONDITION GRADING

Edward III groat   *Elizabeth I sixpence*   *George II halfcrown*

FAIR

FINE

VERY FINE

EXTREMELY FINE

For more details about varieties, dates and classification of English coins see some of our other publications:

Coinage of Roman Britain (17/6)

Roman Coins and their Values (30/-)

Notes on English Silver Coins 1066-1648 (*out of print*).

The English Silver Coinage from 1649 (*new edition in preparation*).

British Copper Coins and their Values (15/-).

Other works we have consulted in compiling this catalogue are:

BROOKE, G. C. *English Coins*. (3rd Ed., 1951).

HAWKINS, E. *Silver Coins of England*. (3rd Ed., 1887).

KENYON, R. Ll. *Gold Coins of England*.

GRUEBER, H. A. *Handbook of the Coins of Great Britain and Ireland*.

MACK, R. P. *The Coinage of Ancient Britain*.

ALLEN, D. *The Origins of Coinage in Britain: A Reappraisal*.

DOLLEY, R. H. M. (Ed.). *Anglo-Saxon Coins; studies presented to Sir Frank Stenton*.

LAWRENCE, L. A. *The Coinage of Edward III from* 1351.

WHITTON, C. A. *The Heavy Coinage of Henry VI*.

BLUNT, C. E. and WHITTON, C. A. *The Coinages of Edward IV and of Henry VI (Restored)*

MORRIESON, Lt.-Col. H. W. *The Coinages of Thomas Bushell, 1636-1648.*

SPINK & SON, LTD. *The Milled Coinage of England, 1662-1946.*

PECK, C. W. *English Copper, Tin and Bronze Coins in the British Museum, 1558-1958.*

and other authoritative papers published in the *Numismatic Chronicle* and *British Numismatic Journal*.

SEABY'S COIN AND MEDAL BULLETIN. This is a magazine published monthly for all interested in Numismatics. It contains papers, articles and notes on coins and medals; news from numismatic societies; answers to questions; letters to the Editor; cuttings from the Press, etc., etc.; also many pages of coins and medals of all kinds offered for sale. These are well catalogued and act as a good guide to help collectors to catalogue and classify their own coins. The subscription price for 1968 is 15/- inland (17/6 overseas). Cloth bound copies of 1966 are available at 30/- each, the bound copy of the 1967 Bulletin is available early in 1968, and further volumes should also be available each subsequent year.

LATIN LEGENDS ON ENGLISH COINS

A DOMINO FACTUM EST ISTUD ET EST MIRABILE IN OCULIS NOSTRIS. (This is the Lord's doing and it is marvellous in our eyes: *Psalm* 127, 23). First used on " fine " sovereign of Mary.

AMOR POPULI PRAESIDIUM REGIS. (The love of the people is the King's protection). Reverse legend on angels of Charles I.

ANNO REGNI PRIMO, etc. (In the first year of the reign, etc.). Used around the edge of many of the larger milled denominations.

CHRISTO AUSPICE REGNO. (I reign under the auspice of Christ). Used extensively in the reign of Charles I.

CIVIUM INDUSTRIA FLORET CIVITAS. (By the industry of its people the State flourishes). On the 1951 Festival crown of George VI.

CULTORES SUI DEUS PROTEGIT. (God protects His worshippers). On gold double crowns of Charles I.

DECUS ET TUTAMEN. (An ornament and a safeguard). This inscription on the edge of all early large milled silver was suggested by Evelyn, he having seen it on the vignette in Card. Richelieu's Greek Testament, and of course refers to the device as a means to prevent clipping.

DOMINE NE IN FURORE TUO ARGUAS ME. (O Lord, rebuke me not in Thine anger: *Psalm* 6, 1). First used on the half-florin of Edward III and then on all half-nobles.

D[OMI]NUS DEUS; OMNIPOTICE REX. Lord God, Almighty King.

DUM SPIRO SPERO. (Whilst I live, I hope). On coins struck at Pontefract Castle during the Civil War after Charles I had been captured by the Parliamentarians.

EXALTABITUR IN GLORIA. (He shall be exalted in glory). On all quarter-nobles.

EXURGAT DEUS ET DISSIPENTUR INIMICI EIUS. (Let God arise and let His enemies be scattered: *Psalm* 68, 1). On the Scotch ducat and early English coins of James I (VI) and was chosen by the King himself.

FACIAM EOS IN GENTEM UNAM. (I will make them one nation: *Ezek.* 37, 22). On unites and laurels of James I., also on Scottish unites of Jas. VI. and Charles I.

FLORENT CONCORDIA REGNA. (Through concord kingdoms flourish). On gold unite of Charles I and broad of Charles II.

HANC DEUS DEDIT. (God has given this, *i.e. crown*). On siege-pieces of Pontefract struck in the name of Charles II.

HAS NISI PERITURUS MIHI ADIMAT NEMO. (Let no one remove these [letters] from me under penalty of death). On the edge of crowns and half-crowns of Cromwell.

HENRICUS ROSAS REGNA JACOBUS. (Henry [united] the roses, James the kingdoms). On English and Scottish gold coins of James I (VI) and second issue Irish shillings of James I

INIMICOS EJUS INDUAM CONFUSIONE. (As for his enemies I shall clothe them with shame: *Psalm* 103, 19). On shillings of Edward VI struck at Durham House, Strand.

JESUS AUTEM TRANSIENS PER MEDIUM ILLORUM IBAT. (But Jesus, passing through the midst of them, went His way: *Luke* iv. 30). The usual reverse legend on English nobles, ryals and hammered sovereigns before James I; also on the very rare Scotch noble of David II of Scotland and the unique Anglo-Gallic noble of Edward the Black Prince.

JUSTITIA THRONUM FIRMAT. (Justice strengthens the throne). On Charles I half-groats and pennies and Scottish twenty-penny pieces.

LUCERNA PEDIBUS MEIS VERBUM EST. (Thy word is a lamp unto my feet: *Psalm* 119. 105). Obverse legend on a rare half-sovereign of Edward VI struck at Durham House, Strand.

NUMMORUM FAMULUS. (The servant of the coinage). The legend on the edge of the English tin coinage at the end of the seventeenth century.

O CRUX AVE SPES UNICA. (Hail! O Cross, our only hope). On the reverse of all half-angels.

PAX MISSA PER ORBEM. (Peace sent throughout the world). The reverse legend of a pattern farthing of Anne.

PAX QUÆRITUR BELLO. (Peace is sought by war). The reverse legend of the Cromwell broad.

PER CRUCEM TUAM SALVA NOS CHRISTE REDEMPTOR. (By Thy cross, save us, O Christ, our Redeemer). The normal reverse of English angels.

POST MORTEM PATRIS PRO FILIO. (For the son after the death of the father). On siege pieces struck at Pontefract in 1648 (old style) after the execution of Charles I.

POSUI DEUM ADJUTOREM MEUM. (I have made God my Helper: *comp. Psalm* 54, 4). First used on groats of Edward III and continued as the reverse legend of all the large English silver coins until the reign of Elizabeth, also on many Irish. Altered to POSUIMUS and NOSTRUM on the coins of Philip and Mary.

PROTECTOR LITERIS LITERÆ NUMMIS CORONA ET SALUS. (A protection to the letters [on the face of the coin], the letters [on the edge] are a garland and a safeguard to the coinage). On the edge of the rare fifty-shilling piece of Cromwell.

QUÆ DEUS CONJUNXIT NEMO SEPARET. (What God hath joined together let no man put asunder: *Matt.* 19, 6). On the larger silver English and Scotch coins of James I after he succeeded to the English throne.

REDDE CUIQUE QUOD SUUM EST. (Render to each that which is his own). On a Henry VIII type groat of Edward VI struck by Sir Martin Bowes at Durham House, Strand.

RELIGIO PROTESTANTIVM LEGES ANGLIÆ LIBERTAS PARLIAMENTI. (The religion of the Protestants, the laws of England, the liberty of the Parliament). This is known as the " Declaration " and refers to Charles I's declaration to the Privy Council at Wellington. 19th Sept., 1642; it is found on many of his coins struck at the provincial mints during the Civil War. Usually abbreviated to REL : PROT : LEG : ANG : LIB : PAR :

ROSA SINE SPINA. (A rose without a thorn). Found on small silver coins of Henry VIII and some later reigns, which also have it on some gold.

RUTILANS ROSA SINE SPINA. (A dazzling rose without a thorn). As last but on small gold.

SCUTUM FIDEI PROTEGET EUM *or* EAM. (The shield of faith shall protect him *or* her). On much of the gold of Edward VI and Elizabeth.

TALI DICATA SIGNO MENS FLUCTUARI NEQUIT. (Consecrated by such a sign the mind cannot waver: from a hymn by Prudentius written in the 4th cent., entitled " Hymnus ante Somnum "). Only on the beautiful " George noble " of Henry VIII.

TIMOR DOMINI FONS VITÆ. (The fear of the Lord is a fountain of life: *Prov*. 14, 27). On many shillings of Edward VI.

TUEATUR UNITA DEUS. (May God guard these united, i.e. kingdoms). On many English, Scottish and Irish coins of James I.

VERITAS TEMPORIS FILIA. (Truth, the daughter of Time). On English and Irish coins of Mary Tudor.

Some Royal Titles:

REX ANGL*orum*—King of the English.

REX SAXONUM OCCIDENTALIUM—King of the West Saxons

DEI GRA*tia* REX ANGL*iae* ET FRANC*iae* D*omi*N*us* HYB*erniae* AQVIT*aniae*—By the Grace of God, King of England and France, Lord of Ireland and Aquitaine.

D*ei* G*ratia* M*agnae* B*ritanniae*, FR*anciae* ET H*iberniae* REX F*idei* D*efensor* BR*unsvicensis* ET L*uneburgensis* D*ux*, S*acri* R*omani* |I*mperii* A*rchi*-TH*esaurarius* ET EL*ector* = By the Grace of God, King of Great Britain, France and Ireland, Defender of the Faith, Duke of Brunswick and Luneburg, High Treasurer and Elector of the Holy Roman Empire.

BRITANNIARUM REX—King of the Britains (i.e. Britain and British territories overseas).

BRITT : OMN : REX : FID : DEF : IND : IMP—King of all the Britains, Defender of the Faith, Emperor of India.

Although not *Latin* legends, the following Norman-French mottos might usefully be added here:

DIEU ET MON DROIT. (God and my right). On halfcrowns of George IV and later monarchs.

HONI SOIT QUI MAL Y PENSE. (Evil to him who evil thinks). The Motto of the Order of the Garter, first used on coins in the reign of George III. It also occurs on the Garter Star in the centre of the reverse of the silver coins of Charles II, but being so small it is usually illegible.

MINTMARKS ON ENGLISH COINS

A MINT-MARK (mm.), a term borrowed from Roman and Greek numismatics where it showed the place of mintage, was generally used on English coins to show (and a religious age preferred a cross for the purpose) where the legend began. Later, this mark, since the dating of coins was not usual, had a periodic significance, changing from time to time. Hence it was of a secret or " privy " nature; other privy marks on a coin might be the code-mark of a particular workshop or workman. Thus a privy mark (including the mm.) might show when a coin was made, or who made it. In the use of precious metals this knowledge was necessary to guard against fraud.

A table of mintmarks is given on the next page. Where mintmarks appear in the catalogue they are sometimes referred to only by the reference number, in order to save space, i.e. *mm*. 28 (=mintmark Sun), *mm*. 28/74 (=*mm*. Sun on obverse, *mm*. Coronet on reverse), *mm*. 28/– =*mm*. Sun on obverse only).

9

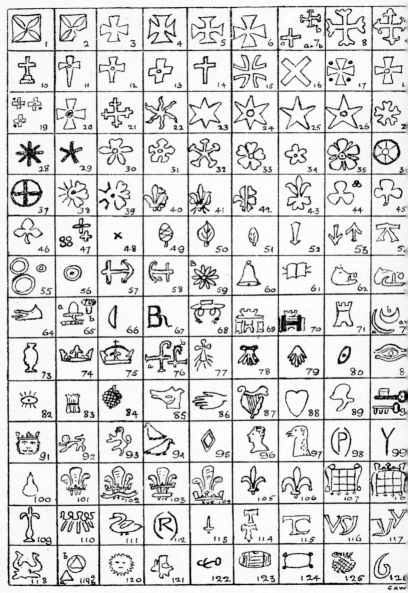

MINTMARKS ON ENGLISH COINS

MINTMARKS ON ENGLISH COINS

1 Edward III, Cross 1 (Class B+C).
2   ,,   broken Cross 1 (Class D).
3   ,,   Cross 2 (Class E).
4   ,,   Cross 3 (Class G).
5 Cross Potent (Edw. III Treaty).
6 Cross Pattée (Edw. III Post Treaty, Rich. III).
7 (a) Plain or Greek Cross.
   (b) Cross Moline.
8 Cross Patonce.
9 Cross Fleurée.
10 Cross Calvary (Cross on steps).
11 Long Cross Fitchée.
12 Short ,,   ,,
13 Restoration Cross (Hen. VI).
14 Latin Cross.
15 Voided Cross (Henry VI).
16 Saltire Cross.
17 Cross and 4 pellets.
18 Pierced Cross.
19 Pierced Cross & pellet.
20 Pierced Cross & central pellet.
21 Cross Crosslet.
22 Curved Star (rayant).
23 Star.
24 Spur Rowel.
25 Mullet.
26 Pierced Mullet.
27 Eglantine.
28 Sun (Edw. IV)
29 Mullet (Henry V).
30 Pansy.
31 Heraldic Cinquefoil (Edw. IV).
32 Heraldic Cinquefoil (James I).
33 Rose (Edw. IV).
34 Rosette (Edw. IV).
35 Rose (Chas. I).
36 Catherine Wheel.
37 Cross in circle.
38 Halved Sun (6 rays) & Rose.
39   ,,   ,, (4 rays) & Rose.
40 Lis-upon-Half-Rose.
41 Lis-upon-Sun & Rose.
42 Lis-Rose dimidiated.
43 Lis-issuant-from-Rose.
44 Trefoil.
45 Slipped Trefoil, James I (1).
46   ,,   ,,   ,,   (2).
47 Quatrefoils.
48 Saltire.
49 Pinecone.
50 Leaf (-mascle, Hen. VI).
51 Leaf (-trefoil, Hen. VI)
52 Arrow.
53 Pheon.
54 A.
55 Annulets.
56 Annulet-with-pellet.
57 Anchor.
58   ,,   & B.
59 Flower & B.
60 Bell.
61 Book.
62 Boar's Head, (early Richard III.
63   ,,   ,, (later)   ,,

64 Boar s Head, Charles I.
65 Acorn (a) Hen. VIII (b) Elizabeth.
66 Bow.
67 Br. (Bristol, Chas. I).
68 Cardinal's Hat.
69 Castle (Hen. VIII).
70 Castle with H.
71 Castle (Chas. I.)
72 Crescent (a) Henry VIII (b) Elizabeth.
73 Pomegranate. (Mary; Henry VIII's is broader).
74 Coronet.
75 Crown.
76 Crozier (a) Edw. III (b) Hen. VIII.
77 Ermine.
78 Escallop (Hen. VII).
79   ,,   (James I).
80 Eye (in legend; Edw. IV).
81 Eye (Parliament).
82 Radiate Eye (Hen. VII).
83 Gerb.
84 Grapes.
85 Greyhound's Head.
86 Hand.
87 Harp.
88 Heart.
89 Helmet.
90 Key.
91 Leopard's Head.
92 Lion.
93 Lion rampant.
94 Martlet.
95 Mascle.
96 Negro's Head.
97 Ostrich's Head.
98 P in brackets.
99 Pall.
100 Pear.
101 Plume.
102   ,,   Aberystwith.
103   ,,   Oxford.
104   ,,   Shrewsbury.
105 Lis.
106 Lis.
107 Portcullis.
108   ,,   Crowned.
109 Sceptre.
110 Sunburst.
111 Swan.
112 R in brackets.
113 Sword.
114 T (Henry VIII).
115 TC monogram
116 WS monogram
117 Y.
118 Dragon (Henry VII).
119 (a) Triangle (b) Triangle in Circle.
120 Sun (Parliament).
121 Uncertain mark.
122 Grapple.
123 Tun.
124 Woolpack.
125 Thistle.
126 Figure 6. (Edw. VI).

N.B. The reign after a mintmark indicates that from which the drawing is taken. A similar mm. may have been used in another reign and will be found in the chronological list at the beginning of each reign.

SOME NUMISMATIC TERMS EXPLAINED

Obverse. That side of the coin which normally shows the monarch's head.

Reverse. The side opposite to the obverse.

Blank. The coin as a circular, blank piece of metal, i.e., before it is struck.

Flan. The whole piece of metal after striking.

Type. The main, central design.

Legend. The inscription.

Field. That flat part of the coin between the main design and the inscription or edge.

Exergue. That part of the coin below the main design, usually separated by a horizontal line, and normally occupied by the date.

Die. The block of metal, with design cut into it, which actually impresses the coin blank with the design.

Die variety. Coin showing slight variation of design.

Mule. A coin with the current type on one side and the previous (and usually obsolete) type on the other side, or a piece struck from two dies that are not normally used together.

Graining. The crenellations around the edge of the coin, commonly known as ' milling.'

Proof. Specially struck coin from new dies with a mirror-like or matt surface. (In this country ' Proof ' is not a term used to describe the state of preservation).

Hammered. Refers to the old craft method of striking a coin between dies hammered by hand.

Milled. Coins struck by dies worked in a coining press.

ABBREVIATIONS

Archb.	Archbishop	laur.	laureate
Bp.	Bishop	*mm.*	mintmark
cuir.	cuirassed	mon.	monogram
d.	penny, pence	quat.	quatrefoil
diad.	diademed	qtr.	quarter
dr.	draped	*O., obv.*	obverse
ex.	exergue	pl.	plume
grs.	grains	rad.	radiate
hd.	head	℞., *rev.*	reverse
i.c.	inner circle	s.	shillings
illus.	illustration	var.	variety
l.	left	wt.	weight

Part I

BRITISH COINS

FROM THE 1st CENTURY B.C. UNTIL 1816

CLEANING COINS. Speaking generally, *don't* clean coins. More coins are ruined by cleaning than by any other cause, and a badly cleaned coin loses most of its value. A nicely toned piece is usually considered desirable. Really dirty gold and silver can, however, be carefully washed in soap and water. Copper coins should never be cleaned or washed, they may be lightly brushed with a brush that is not too harsh.

CELTIC COINAGE

PERIOD OF BELGIC MIGRATION

The earliest (Gallo-Belgic) uninscribed Celtic coins found in Britain may have been made in Gaul, but they circulated extensively in this country as a result of the migration of Belgic peoples from the continent. These and other British coins were ultimately derived from the gold staters (M) of Philip II, king of Macedonia (359-336 B.C.). It is not possible to ascribe all these coins to particular tribes during this period of tribal movement. In the following list we have followed D. Allen, *The Origins of Coinage in Britain: a Reappraisal,* for the uninscribed series. For the later inscribed coins see R. P. Mack, *Coinage of Ancient Britain.*

M   1   5   6

Gallo-Belgic Issues   *Fine*

1	" Bellovaci," *c.* 130-80 B.C. Gold *stater*. A. Good copy of Macedonian stater, large flan	£50
2	— — B. Somewhat similar, but small flan and " defaced " *obv.* die	£42
3	— *Quarter stater*. A. As last	£38
4	— — B. " Defaced " *obv.* die	£28
5	" Gaulish Atrebates," *c.* 110-70 B.C. *Stater*. C. Disintegrated face and horse	£32
6	" Morini," *c.* 65-45 B.C. *Stater*. E. O. Blank. ℞. Disjointed curved horse	£30
7	— *Stater*. Xc. O. Blank except for A (or VE mon.). ℞. s below horse r.	£45
8	— *Quarter stater*. O. Similar. ℞. Horse l.	£30

15

9   12

Armorican (Channel Isles and N. W. Gaul), *c.* 75-50 B.C.   *Fine*

9   Billon *stater*. Classes I, II and III. Head r. with curly hair. ℞. Horse, boar below   ..   35/-

10   — Classes IV and V. ℞. Horse with reins, cornucopiae (?) below 50/-

11   — Class VI. Similar, but boar below horse with reins..   90/-

12   Billon *quarter stater*. Similar types   ..   .. *from*   75/-

Early British Uninscribed Issues

Gold staters

13   A, Westerham type, *c.* 95-65 B.C. As 5, but horse more disjointed £38

14   B, Chute type, *c.* 85-55 B.C. Similar, but crab-like figure below horse £50

15   C, Yarmouth (I.O.W.) type, *c.* 80-70 B.C. Crude var. of 5   £55

16   D, Cheriton type, *c.* 80-70 B.C. Var. of 5 with large crescent face   ..   ..   .. *Extr. rare*

17   20

17   E, F and G (Clacton) types, *c.* 90-70 B.C. E. Anglian varieties of 5   ..   ..   £40

18   H, N.E.Coast type, *c.* 75-30 B.C. Variety of 5; horse r.   £40

19   I. — — Horse l. £45

21   23

Gold Staters   *Fine*

20 J, Norfolk Wolf type, *c.* 65-45 B.C. ℞. Crude wolf r.
or l. £100

21 K, Coritani, South Ferriby type, *c.* 30 B.C.-10 A.D. Crude
wreath. ℞. Disjointed horse l. Illustrated on p. 16   £45

22 — — Trefoil pattern and horse r.   ..   *Extr. rare*

23 L, Whaddon Chase type, *c.* 45-20 B.C. ℞. Spirited
horse r. of new style. Illustrated on p. 16   ..   £35

24 Lx, North Thames group, *c.* 40-20 B.C. O. Blank
apart from reversed ss. ℞. As above £70

25 Ly, North Kent group, *c.* 45-20 B.C. O. Blank. ℞.
Similar horse l. £60

26 Lz, Weald group, *c.* 35-20 B.C. O. Blank. ℞. Horse,
panel below £65

27 M, Wonersh type, *c.* 35-20 B.C. Crossed wreath design.
℞. Spiral above horse, wheel below £40

28 Na, Iceni, *c.* 30 B.C.-10 A.D. Double crescent design. ℞.
Horse r. £70

29 Nb — Trefoil on cross design. ℞. As above £65

30 Nc — Cross of pellets. ℞. As above £85

31 Qa, British "Remic" type, *c.* 45-25 B.C. Crude laur. head.
℞. Triple-tailed horse, wheel below. Illus. below ..   £42

32 Qb — Similar, but blank *obv.* £38

           31   33

33 R, Dobunni, *c.* 30 B.C.-10 A.D. Similar, but ear of corn
on *obv.* £70

Quarter Staters

34 Lx, North Thames group. Floral pattern or wreath.
R. Horse r. or l. £38

35 Ly, North Kent group. O. Blank. R. Horse r. £40

36 Lz, Weald group. Wreath or blank. R. Horse r. or l. .. £37

37 N, Iceni. Floral pattern. R. Horse r. £70

38 O, Geometric type, Sussex group, c. 80-60 B.C. Unin-
telligible patterns as illustration below £24

39 P — Kentish group, c. 65-45 B.C. O. Blank. R.
Trophy design £30

38 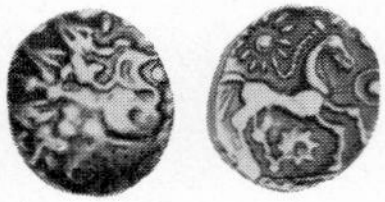   40

40 Qc, British " Remic " type. O. Head or wreath pattern.
R. Triple-tailed horse £28

41 R, Dobunni. O. Blank. R. Triple-tailed horse.. .. £48

Silver

42 Lx, North Thames group. Head l. R. Horse or deer £30

43 — — Two horses or two beasts £35

44 — — Wreath pattern. R. Horse £35

45 Lz, South Thames group. Wreath, head of serpent.
R. Horse £30

45A — Helmeted head r. R. Horse £30

45B — Quarter denomination. Similar £40

46    49

46 Durotriges, c. 60 B.C.-20 A.D. Size and type of Westerham staters (no. 13 above) £16

47 — Size and type of 38 .. .. £24

48 — Very thin flans, c. 55 B.C. £40

49 Dobunni, 30 B.C.-10 A.D. Head r., some of good style,
others very crude (as illustration). R. Triple-tailed horse £18

Uninscribed Silver

50	Coritani, *c.* 30 B.C.-10 A.D. As illustrated below..	..	£50
50A	— Half-denomination. Similar		£50
51	— *O*. Blank. ℞. Horse		£40
52	— Half-denomination. Similar		£50

50   53

53	Iceni, *c.* 30 B.C.-10 A.D. Boar r. ℞. Horse ..	..	£30
54	— — Similar, but half-denomination	..	£45
55	— Head r. ℞. Horse	..	£20
56	— Double crescent and wreath pattern. ℞. Horse	..	£15

55   61

Bronze

57	Lx, North Thames group. Head l. with braided hair. ℞. Horse l.		£22
58	— — Other types .. .. *from*		£24
59	Ly, North Kent group. Boar. ℞. Horse ..	..	£28
60	Durotriges, *c.* 20-50 A.D. Debased form of Æ stater (46)		£14
61	— Cast coins, *c.* 50-70 A.D. As illustration ..	..	£10

Tin or pale bronze, *c.* 50 B.C.-50 A.D.

62	Thames and South. Cast. Crude hd. ℞. Lines representing bull		£14

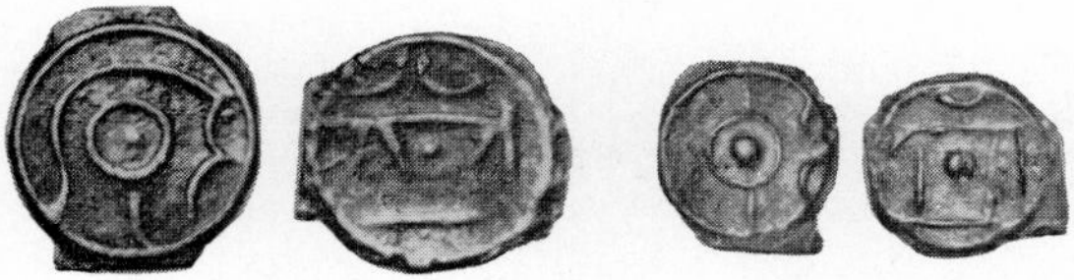

62   63

63	N. Thames var. Smaller flan, large central pellet..	..	£22

CELTIC DYNASTIC ISSUES

The dates given for the various rulers are, in most cases, very approximate. Staters and quarter staters are gold coins of varying quality.

SOUTHERN BRITAIN

Atrebates and Regni. *Berks., Hants., Surrey and Sussex.*   *Fine*

64 **Commius,** *c.* 35-20 B.C. *Stater.* As 31, but COMMIOS
around horse £125

65 **Tincommius,** *c.* 20 B.C.-5 A.D. Celtic style. *Stater.*
Similar, but TINC COMMI F around horse £125

66 — *Quarter stater* TINCOM. ℞. Horse £85

67   74

67 Classical style. *Stater.* TINC or COM · F on tablet. ℞.
Horseman £140

68 — *Quarter stater.* O. Similar. ℞. Medusa head or
animal £85

69 — *Silver.* Head. ℞. Bull or eagle £70

69A — *Silver quarter unit.* .. .. .. *Extr. rare*

70 **Eppillus,** *c.* 5-10 A.D. (*see also under Cantii*). *Quarter
stater.* EPPI over animal. ℞. Star over CALLEV (*Silchester*)
Extr. rare

71 *Silver.* EPP, eagle. ℞. REX crescent CALLE *Extr. rare*

72 **Verica,** *c.* 10-40 A.D. *Stater.* Group I. COM · F on tablet.
℞. VIR below horseman £140

73 — II. Similar, but title REX added £125

74 — III. Vineleaf. ℞. Horseman £125

75 *Quarter stater.* I. COM · F, etc. ℞. Horse, VIR, etc. .. £65

76 — II. VERIC COM · F. ℞. Horse, REX £70

77 — III. Vineleaf. ℞. Horseman. Illus. above .. £75

78 — — Head or seated figure. ℞. Horseman £80

79 *Silver.* I. Crescents, COM · F. ℞. Boar £60

80 — II. Name around circles. ℞. Lion £60

81 — III. Horseman with spear. ℞. Horseman with shield £60

82 — — Seated figure. ℞. Two cornucopiae £55

83 — — Head r. ℞. Seated or stg. figure £60

84 *Silver quarter unit.* I. O. Various. ℞. Animal £50

85 — III. Head, VIRI. ℞. C · F in wreath £55

Atrebates and Regni. *Fine*

86 **Epatticus,** *c.* 25-35 A.D. *Stater.* TASCI · F, ear of wheat.
   R. Horseman £180
87 *Silver.* Head of Hercules r. EPATI R. Eagle, ..   £60
87A — Victory seated. R. Boar £100
88 *Silver quarter unit.* O. EPATI. R. Lion's head (?) ..   £65
89 *Bronze.* Head r. R. Horseman £40

90 **Caratacus,** *c.* 35-40 A.D. *Silver.* As 87, CARA *Extr. rare*
The above two rulers were brother and son of Cunobelin (see Catu-vellauni), but their coins appear in the same area as Verica's.

87    97

Cantii. *Kent.*

91 **Dubnovellaunos,** *c.* 15-1 B.C. (*see also under Trinovantes*).
  Stater. O. Blank. R. Horse r., DVBNOVIILLAVN .. £100
92 *Silver.* Animal. R. Horse or seated figure £65
93 — Head l. R. Pegasus £65
94 *Bronze.* Boar. R. Eagle, horseman or horse .. £40
95 — Animal. R. Horse £40

96 **Vosenios,** *c.* 5 A.D. *Stater.* O. Blank. R. Serpent
  below horse .. .. *Extr. rare*
97 *Quarter stater.* Similar, VOSE. Illustrated above .. £100
98 *Silver.* Griffin and horse. R. Legend retr., horse .. £120
99 *Bronze.* Boar l. R. Horse l., SA below £45

101

100 **Eppillus,** *c.* 5-10 A.D. (*see also under Atrebates*). *Stater.*
  COM · F in wreath. R. Horseman l., EPPILLVS .. £180
101 — Victory in wreath. R. Horseman r. Illus. above.. £250
102 *Quarter stater.* EPPIL / COM · F. R. Pegasus.. .. £85
103 — EPPI around wreath, or COM · F. R. Horse .. £85
104 *Silver.* Head. R. Lion, horseman, Victory or capricorn £70
105 *Bronze.* Head. R. Victory holding wreath £40
106 — Curved figure or bull. R. Eagle £40

Cantii.

				Fine
107	**Amminus,** *c.* 15 A.D.? *Silver.* Plant. ℞. Pegasus		..	£100
108	— A within wreath. ℞. Capricorn	..	..	£100
109	*Silver quarter unit.* A within curved lines. ℞. Bird..			£70
110	*Bronze.* Head. ℞. Capricorn ..	..	..	£55

Durotriges. *W. Hants., Dorset, Som. and S. Wilts.*

			Fine
111	**Crab.** *Silver.* CRAB in angles of cross. ℞. Eagle	..	£120
112	*Silver quarter unit.* CRAB on tablet. ℞. Star shape	..	£100

NORTH THAMES

Trinovantes. *Essex and counties to the West.*

113 **Addedomaros,** *c.* 15-1 B.C. *Stater.* Crossed wreath, or spiral. ℞. Horse, wheel or cornucopiae below .. £75
114 — Double crescent ornament. ℞. Horse, branch below £85

115   117

115 *Quarter stater.* Similar, but rectangle below horse .. £85

116 **Diras?,** *c.* 1 A.D.? *Stater.* O. Blank. ℞. DIRAS and snake (?) over horse, wheel below .. *Extr. rare*

117 **Dubnovellaunos,** *c.* 1-10 A.D. (*see also under Cantii*). *Stater.* Wreath design. ℞. Horse l., branch below.. £100
118 *Quarter stater.* Similar £100
119 *Bronze.* Head r. or l. ℞. Horse r. or l. £50

Catuvellauni. *N. Thames, Herts., Beds., spreading E. and S.*

Tasciovanus, *c.* 20 B.C.-10 A.D., and associated coins.

120 *Stater.* As 23, but TASCIAV and bucranium over horse .. £90
121 — O. Similar, sometimes with VER (*Verulamium*). ℞. Horseman r., TASC £100
122 — — ℞. Horse, CAMV monogram (*Camulodunum*) .. £175
123 — TASCIOV / RICON. ℞. Horseman l. £175
124 — TASCIO in panel. ℞. Horseman r., SEGO £175

Tasciovanus *Fine*

125	*Quarter stater*. Wreath, TASCI or VERO. ℞. Horse, TASC	£70
126	— *O*. As 122. ℞. CAMVL mon. over horse	£85
127	— *O*. As 123, omitting RICON. ℞. Pegasus l. ..	£75
128	— *O*. As 124. ℞. Horse l., omitting SEGO	£75
129	*Silver*. Bearded or laur. hd. ℞. Horseman or bull ..	£75
130	— Pegasus or eagle. ℞. Griffin	£75
131	— Panel on crossed wreath. ℞. Pegasus or boar ..	£75
132	— VER across field. ℞. Horse or horseman	£65
133	— TASC on panel. ℞. Horseman	£65
134	— SEGO on panel. ℞. Horseman	£90
135	— DIAS / C / O. ℞. Horse, VIR (?) below	£85
136	*Bronze* (TAS or VIR, etc.). Bearded hd. or two conjoined heads. ℞. Horse or Pegasus. Illustrated below ..	£40
137	— Unbearded head. ℞. Horseman, seated figure, Pegasus, lion, or boar	£40
138	— Interwoven lines. ℞. Bull, sphinx, or horse ..	£35
139	— Wreath design. ℞. Boar	£35
140	— Lion (?). ℞. Griffin	£40
141	— Head r., RVIIS. ℞. Horseman, VIR	£37
142	— RVIIS on tablet, or over lion. ℞. Winged lion or eagle	£40
143	— Head r., TASC and DIAS. ℞. Centaur	£40

136    144

144	**Andoco,** *c.* 5-15 A.D. *Stater*. Crossed wreath design. ℞. Horse r., AND	£125
145	*Quarter stater*. Crossed wreaths, ANDO. ℞. Horse ..	£100
146	*Silver*. Bearded hd. l. ℞. Pegasus, ANDOC	£90
147	*Bronze*. Head r., ANDOCO. ℞. Horse r., ANDOCO ..	£50

148   150   158

148	**Cunobelin** (Shakespeare's *Cymbeline*), *c*.10-40 A.D. *Stater.* CAMVL on panel. ℞. Leaf above two horses	*Fine* £175
149	*Quarter stater.* Similar	£100
150	*Stater.* Ear of corn, CAMV. ℞. Horse, CVNO ..	£80
151	*Quarter stater.* Similar	£80
152	*Silver.* Head r. or l. ℞. Victory seated, sphinx, horse, or figure with lyre	£65
153	— CVNO / BELIN. ℞. Horseman	£70
154	— CVN or CVNO. ℞. Griffin, Pegasus, Hercules, centaur, horse, or she-wolf on serpent	£65
155	— Pegasus. ℞. Seated figure	£70
156	— Two horned serpents entwined. ℞. Horse ..	£70
157	— Hercules. ℞. Female with lion, or figure with dog	£70
158	— Leaf or plant design. ℞. Horse, or horseman ..	£70
159	— SOLIDV in circle. ℞. Standing figure	£100
160	*Bronze.* Name in wreath. ℞. Horse	£40
161	— CVNOBE / LINI. ℞. Victory seated	£40
162	— CAMVL / ODVNO. ℞. Sphinx	£40

163   164

163	— Head r., l. or facing. ℞. Boar, bull, eagle, centaur, or metal-worker .. .. *from*	£40
164	— Pegasus. ℞. Horse, or Victory stg. or sacrificing bull *from*	£40
165	— Sphinx. ℞. Figure with shield	£45
166	— Horseman. ℞. Armed figure	£40
167	— Horse, or Victory with wreath. ℞. Horseman ..	£42
168	— Horned serpent. ℞. Horse	£42
169	— Hd. of Jupiter Ammon. ℞. Horseman, or lion ..	£42
170	— Janus head. ℞. Boar beneath tree	£42

For Epatticus and Caratacus, see under Atrebates.

S.W. MIDLANDS

Dobunni. *Glos., Here., Mon., Oxon., Som., Wilts. and Worcs.* *Fine*

171	**Anted.**	*Stater.* As 33, but ANTED over horse ..	..	£140
172	*Silver.*	As 49, AN / TED added ..	..	..	£40
173	**Eisu.**	*Stater.* As 33, EISV over horse ..	..	..	£200
174	*Silver.*	As 49, EI / SV added ..	..	..	£45
175	**Catti.**	*Stater.* As 33, CATTI over horse	..	..	£150

176   180

176	**Comux.**	*Stater.* Similar, but COMVX ..	..	..	£200
177	**Inam.**	*Stater.* Similar, but INAM ..	*Extr. rare*
178	**Corio.**	*Stater.* Similar, but CORIO ..	..	..	£150
179	*Quarter stater.*	COR. R. Triple-tailed horse	..	£90
180	**Bodvoc.**	*Stater.* BODVOC. R. Triple-tailed horse			*Extr. rare*
181	*Silver.*	Head l., BODVOC. R. Horse ..	*Extr. rare*

EASTERN ENGLAND

Iceni. *Cambs., Norfolk and Suffolk.*

182	**Duro.**	*Silver.* Boar. R. Horse r., DVRO below, CAN above	£85
183	**Anted.**	*Stater.* Triple-crescent design. R. ANTED in two monograms below horse	£300
184	*Silver.*	As illust. below, but with ANT ED monograms..	£16
185	*Silver half unit.*	Similar	£35
186	**Aesu.**	*Silver.* Similar, AESV below horse	£25

184   187

187	**Ecen.**	*Silver.* Similar, ECEN or ECE	£20
188	*Silver half unit.*	Similar	£40
189	**Saemu.**	*Silver.* Similar, SAEMV below horse	£30

Coritani *Lincs., Yorks. and E. Midlands.* *Fine*

190 **Aun Ast.** *Stater.* Crude wreath type. ℞. Disintegrated
    horse (as 22), AVN AST £150
191 *Silver.* As 51, but AVN over horse l. £85
192 *Silver half unit.* Similar £65

193   198

193 **Vep Corf.** *Stater.* As 190, but VEP CORF £150
194 *Silver.* Crude wreath. ℞. Horse r., VEP CO £85
194A *Silver half unit.*   ..   .. *Extr. rare*
195 **Esup Asu.** *Stater.* As 190, but IISVP ASV £150
195A *Silver.*   ..   .. *Extr. rare*
196 **Dumno Tigir Seno.** *Stater.* DVMN across wreath. ℞.
    Horse l., TIGIR SENO £175
197 *Silver. O.* DVMNO across wreath. ℞. As above..   .. £80
198 **Dumnocoveros.** *Stater.* VOLI / SIOS across wreath. ℞.
    Horse l., DVMNOCOVEROS £120
199 *Silver. O.* VOLI / SIOS. ℞. Horse r., DVMNOCO   .. £80
200 **Dumnovellaunos.** *Stater.* As 198, but DVMNOVELLAVNOS
    around horse £125
201 *Silver.* As 191, but DVMNOVE £70
202 **Cartivel.** *Silver.* As 191, but CARTIVE   *Extr. rare*

ROMAN OCCUPATION

For over four hundred years the currency of the Roman Empire was the only coinage of these islands and therefore no representative collection of the coinage of Great Britain is complete without some Roman coins. Our *Roman Coins and Their Values* (price 30/-) describes the coins of each emperor, and gives historical notes and illustrations.

Here we give four lists:

Roman emperors and usurpers whose coins were current in Britain or who counted " Britannia " as one of their possessions.

Some coins that are particularly related to Britain by type or inscription.

Some of the coins struck in Britain at London, Colchester, or elsewhere.

British imitations of Roman coins.

The Roman imperial coins have usually the head or bust of the emperor or relative on the obverse. The reverse types described below are representative of the commonest of each emperor—there are a great number of varieties.

ROMAN EMPERORS
whose coins were current in Britain or who counted Britannia as one of their possessions.

The prices here are for one or two of the cheapest denominations of each reign. The denarius is the " d " of our £ s. d.

Fine

203 **Julius Caesar** (†44 B.C.). Æ *denarius*, without portrait. Elephant r. ℞. Sacrificial implements £5

204 — With portrait. ℞. Calf stg. l. £25

205 **Augustus** (27 B.C.-14 A.D.). Æ *denarius*. ℞. Caius and Lucius Caesars to front holding shields and spears .. 85/-

206 — Æ *as*. ℞. Altar 55/-

204   207

207 **Tiberius** (14-37 A.D.). Æ *denarius*. ℞. Livia seated r. (This coin circulated during Ministry of Our Lord and may be the " Tribute penny " of the Bible).. .. £9

208 **Caligula** (37-41).   Æ *quadrans*, without portrait.   Cap
of Liberty.   R.   Inscription 35/-

209

210

209 **Claudius** (41-54).   Æ *quadrans*, without portrait.
Hand holding scales.   R.   Inscription 30/-

210 **Nero** (54-68). Æ *denarius*. R. Salus seated l. .. £7/10/-

211 — Æ *as*. R. Victory flying l. 50/-

212 **Galba** (68-69). Æ *denarius*. R. Livia standing l. .. £7/10/-

213 **Otho** (69). Æ *denarius*. R. Security standing l. .. £17/10/-

214 **Vitellius** (69). Æ *denarius*. R. Tripod with dolphin £8

215 **Vespasian** (69-79). Æ *denarius*. R. Emperor seated l. 37/6

216

224

216 — Æ *as*. R. Victory stg. r. on prow 45/-

217 **Titus** (79-81). Æ *denarius*. R. Throne 50/-

218 **Domitian** (81-96). Æ *denarius*. R. Minerva r. .. 30/-

219 — Æ *as*. R. Virtus r. 40/-

220 **Nerva** (96-98). Æ *denarius*. R. Clasped hands .. 55/-

221 **Trajan** (98-117). Æ *denarius*. R. Equity l. .. 25/-

222 — Æ *as*. R. Victory flying l. 40/-

223 **Hadrian** (117-138). Æ *denarius*. R. Fides stg. r. holding
basket of fruits 30/-

224 — Æ *dupondius*. R. Pietas stg. r. 45/-

225 **Antoninus Pius** (138-161). Æ *denarius*. R. Equity l. 22/6

226 — Æ *dupondius*. R. Annona r. 42/6

227 — **Faustina Senior**, wife of Antoninus Pius. Æ
denarius. R. Ceres l. 25/-

Roman *Fine*

228 **Marcus Aurelius** (161-180). Æ *denarius*. ℞. Salus l. feeding serpent rising from altar 25/–

229 — Æ *sestertius*. ℞. Providence l. 75/–

230 — **Faustina Junior,** wife of Marcus Aurelius. Æ *denarius*. ℞. Juno l. 27/6

231 **Lucius Verus** (161-169). Æ *denarius*. ℞. Equity seated. 37/6

232 **Commodus** (177-192). Æ *denarius*. ℞. Salus seated l. 30/–

233 **Pertinax** (A.D. 193) *one time Governor of Britain*. Æ *denarius*. ℞. Emperor l., sacrificing at altar £28

234 **Clodius Albinus** (195-197), *Governor of Britain on the death of Pertinax, was proclaimed emperor by the legions he commanded*. Æ *denarius*. Minerva l., holding olive-branch and spear £6

236 **Septimius Severus** (193-211), *died at York*. Æ *denarius*. ℞. Roma seated l. 17/6

237 — **Julia Domna,** wife of Sept. Severus. Æ *denarius*. ℞. Piety l. 18/6

238 **Caracalla** (198-217). Æ *denarius*. ℞. Mars walking r. 17/6

239 **Geta** (209-212). Æ *denarius*. ℞. Security seated l... 25/–

240 **Macrinus** (217-218). Æ *denarius*. ℞. Salus seated l., feeding serpent rising from altar 70/–

241 **Elagabalus** (218-222). Æ *denarius*. ℞. Emperor l., sacrificing at altar 22/6

242 **Severus Alexander** (222-235). Æ *denarius*. ℞. Sun-god l. 18/6

243 — Æ *sestertius*. ℞. Pax l. holding olive branch 45/–

244 — **Julia Mamaea,** mother of Sev. Alexander. Æ *denarius*. ℞. Venus standing l. 30/–

245 **Maximinus I** (235-238). Æ *denarius*. ℞. Fides l., holding two standards 35/–

246 — Æ *sestertius*. ℞. Victory advancing r. 55/–

247 248

		Fine
Roman		
247	**Gordian III** (238-244). Æ *antoninianus*. ℞. Jupiter with Emperor	15/–
248	— Æ *sestertius*. ℞. Liberty stg. l.	42/6
249	**Philip I** (244-249). Æ *antoninianus*. ℞. Roma seated l.	17/6
250	— Æ *sestertius*. ℞. Equity l.	45/–
251	**Trajan Decius** (249-251). Æ *antoninianus*. ℞. Dacia	20/–
252	**Trebonianus Gallus** (251-253). Æ *antoninianus*. ℞. Felicity l.	21/–
253	**Valerian I** (253-260). Æ *antoninianus*. ℞. Victory l. ..	15/–
254	**Gallienus** (253-268). Æ *antoninianus*. ℞. Antelope ..	10/6
255	**Postumus** (259-267). Billon *antoninianus*. ℞. Moneta l.	12/6
256	**Victorinus** (265-270). Æ *antoninianus*. ℞. Salus r., holding serpent in her arms	8/6
257	**Tetricus I** (270-273). Æ *antoninianus*. ℞. Laetitia l.	8/6
258	**Claudius II** (268-270). Æ *antoninianus*. ℞. Providence l.	8/6
259	**Aurelian** (270-275). Æ *antoninianus*. ℞. Emperor and empress hand in hand	15/–
260	**Tacitus** (275-276). Æ *antoninianus*. ℞. Security l.	20/–
261	**Probus** (276-282). Æ *antoninianus*. ℞. Emperor and Concordia	10/6
262	**Carus** (282-283). Æ *antoninianus*. ℞. Pax l. ..	25/–
263	**Carinus** (283-285). Æ *antoninianus*. ℞. Jupiter and Carinus	20/–

Roman   *Fine*

264 **Numerian** (283-284). Æ *antoninianus*. Providence l.   22/6

Diocletian (284-305)
Maximianus Herculius (286-305 and 306-308)
Carausius (287-293)
Allectus (293-296)
Constantius I, Chlorus (305-306)
Licinius I (307-324)
Constantine I, the Great (308-337)
Constantine II (337-340)

> See
> Roman Coins
> Struck
> in Britain,
> pages 27-29

265 **Constantius II** (337-361). Æ *siliqua*. ℞. Inscription
within wreath 30/–

266 — Æ 17. ℞. Soldier l., spearing fallen horseman ..   10/6

267 **Magnentius** (350-353). Æ 22. Two Victories holding
wreath 20/–

268 **Julian II** (360-363). Æ *siliqua*. ℞. Inscription within
wreath 35/–

269 **Valentinian I** (364-375). Æ *siliqua*. ℞. Similar   ..   45/–

270 — Æ 18. ℞. Victory l. 12/6

271 **Gratian** (367-383). Æ *siliqua*. ℞. Roma seated l.   ..   30/–

272 **Theodosius I** (379-395). Æ *siliqua*. Similar 40/–

273 — Æ 14. ℞. Victory l., dragging captive 10/6

268   274

274 **Magnus Maximus** (*Commander of the legions in Britain,
Usurper 383-388*). Æ *siliqua*. ℞. Roma seated facing   65/–

275 **Honorius** (393-423). Æ *siliqua*. Similar 47/6

ROMAN COINS RELATING TO THE CONQUEST OR OCCUPATION OF BRITAIN

See: *Coinage of Roman Britain*, by Gilbert Askew now available again, price 17/6.

276   280

		Fine
276	**Claudius.** *N aureus.* His head r. ℞. DE BRITANN on triumphal arch	£135
277	— *R denarius.* Similar	£50
278	— *R didrachm* of Caesarea. Laur. hd. l. ℞. Emperor in quadriga r., DE BRITANNIS in ex.	£45
279	**Hadrian.** Æ *sestertius.* ℞. BRITANNIA, Britannia seated half-left	£100
280	— Æ *as* or *dupondius.* Similar, but sometimes with longer legend	£25
281	— Æ *sestertius.* ℞. ADVENTVI AVG . BRITANNIAE, Emperor and Britannia .. .. *Extr. rare*	
282	— ℞. Emperor addressing soldiers, EXERC . BRITANNI in ex.	£100
283	**Antoninus Pius.** *N aureus.* ℞. IMPERATOR II BRITAN. Victory on globe	£100

| 284 | — Æ *sestertius.* ℞. BRITANNIA. Britannia seated l. (sometimes with longer legend) ..   .. | £40 |

Fine

285 — — ℞. BRI TAN across field, Victory l. on globe .. £20

286 — Æ *as*. ℞. Victory l., holding shield inscribed BRI/TAN £10

287 — Æ *as* or *dupondius*. ℞. BRITANNIA COS IIII. Britannia seated l. in attitude of sadness £8

288 **Commodus.** Æ *sestertius*. ℞. Britannia standing l., BRITT, in ex. .. .. *Extr. rare*

289 — ℞. Victory seated r., VICT. BRIT. in ex. £12

290 **Septimius Severus.** N *aureus*. ℞. VICTORIAE BRIT, Victory r., carrying trophy and dragging captive.. .. £125

291 — Æ *denarius*. Similar, but Victory r. or l., holding palm and wreath 75/-

292 — Æ *sestertius*. ℞. VICT . BRIT . P . M . TR . P . etc., or VICTORIAE BRITANNICAE. Two Victories and two captives £28

293 **Caracalla.** N *aureus*. ℞. VICTORIAE BRIT. Victory r. as on 290 .. .. £150

294 — Æ *denarius*. As 291 .. .. 85/-

295 — Æ *sestertius*. ℞. VICTORIAE BRITANNICAE, Victory, trophy, Britannia and captive £30

296 — Æ *dupondius* or *as*. Victory seated l. on shields .. £12

297 **Geta.** Æ *denarius*. As 291 .. .. 95/-

298 — Æ *sestertius*. ℞. VICT . BRIT . etc., or VICTORIAE BRITANNICAE, Victory standing or seated £30

299 — Æ *as*. ℞. VICT . BRIT . etc. Victory seated r. .. £15

300 — *Bil. tetradrachm* of Alexandria. ℞. NEIKH KATA BPETAN, Victory l. £15

ROMAN COINS STRUCK IN BRITAIN

301 **Carausius** (usurper in Britain and Gaul, 287-293). N *aureus*. ℞. Pax stg. l. .. .. .. *Extr. rare*

302 *London.* Æ *denarius*. ℞. Emperor riding l. £110

303 — Æ *antoninianus*. ℞. PAX AVG, Pax stg. l. 65/-

304 — ℞. Other types .. .. *from* 75/-

305 *Colchester.* Æ *denarius*. ℞. Joined hands £125

306 — Æ *antoninianus*. ℞. Various .. .. *from* 85/-

307 *Other mints.* Æ *denarius*. ℞. As 302 .. .. .. £100

308 — Æ *antoninianus* .. .. .. *from* 55/-, barbarous 45/-

309 **Allectus** (usurper in Britain, 293-296). *N aureus.* ℞.
Pax stg. l. .. .. *Extr. rare*
310 *London.* Æ *antoninianus.* ℞. Similar 85/-
311 — ℞. Other types .. .. *from* 95/-
312 — Æ *quinarius.* ℞. VIRTVS AVG. Galley 40/-

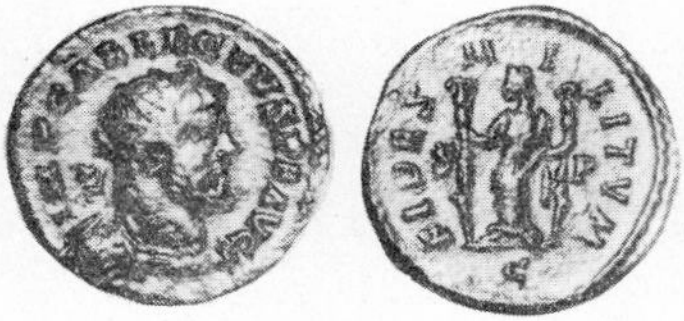

313 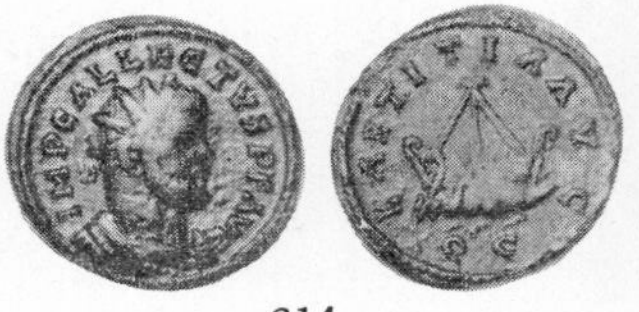 314

313 *Colchester.* Æ *antoninianus.* Varied .. .. *from* 85/-
314 — Æ *quinarius.* As 312 .. .. 40/-
315 **Diocletian.** Æ *follis.* ℞. GENIO POPVLI ROMANI. Genius
l., no mintmark 27/6
316 — With London *mm.* 35/-
317 **Maximianus.** Æ *follis.* As 315 .. .. .. 27/6
318 — As 316 .. .. 25/-
319 *Struck by Carausius in London.* Æ *antoninianus.* ℞. Various £5
320 — *Colchester.* Æ *antoninianus.* ℞. Various £6

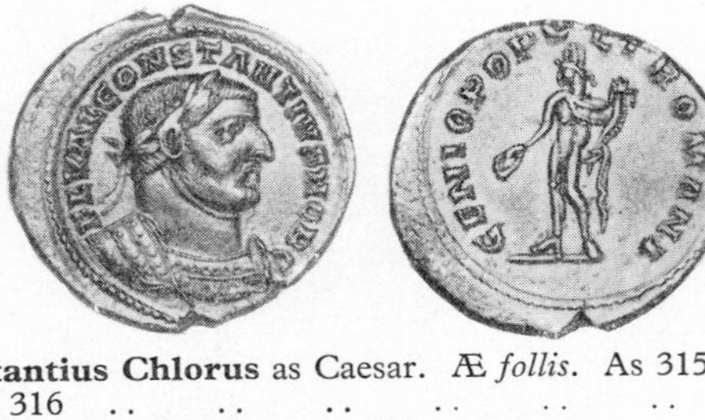

321 **Constantius Chlorus** as Caesar. Æ *follis.* As 315 .. 30/-
322 — As 316 .. .. 50/-
323 As Augustus. Æ *follis.* As 315 .. .. 45/-

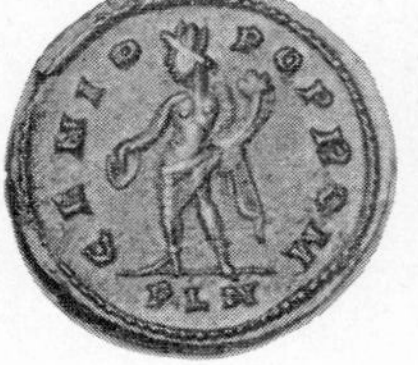

318 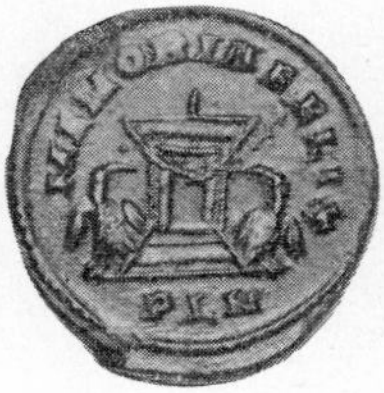 324 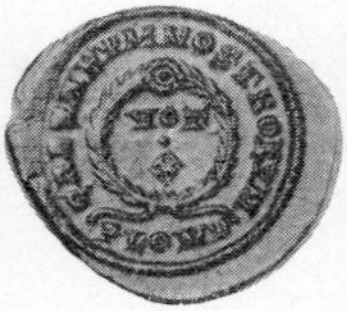 337

324 — Veiled bust. ℞. MEMORIA FELIX. Two eagles beside
altar, PLN in ex. 45/-

325 **Galerius** as Caesar. Æ *follis.* As 315 .. .. .. 27/6
326 — With London *mm.* 50/–
327 As Augustus. Æ *follis.* As 315 .. .. 37/6

328 **Severus II** as Caesar. Æ *follis.* As 315 .. .. 65/–
329 As Augustus. Æ *follis.* Similar 70/–

330 **Maximinus II Daza** as Caesar or Augustus. Æ *follis.*
As 315, with or without mintmark 30/–

331 **Licinius I.** Æ 2. ℞. Similar to 316 .. .. .. 20/–

332 **Constantine I, the Great.** Æ *follis.* ℞. Mars advancing
r., with London *mm.* 37/6

333 — Æ small (about 17 mm.). ℞. Various, with London
mm. .. .. *from* 15/–

334 **Helena** (mother of Constantine I). Æ small. ℞. Pax l.,
with London *mm.* 75/–

335 **Fausta** (wife of Constantine I). Æ small. ℞. SALVS
REIPUBLICAE. Fausta with two children, with London *mm.* 65/–

336 **Crispus.** Æ small. Hd. or bust r. or l. ℞. Altar, with
London *mm.* 17/6

337 **Constantine II.** Æ small. Similar. ℞. Inscription
around wreath, with London *mm.* 15/–

338 **Constantius II.** Æ small. ℞. Camp-gate, with London
mm. 40/–

BRITISH IMITATIONS OF ROMAN COINS

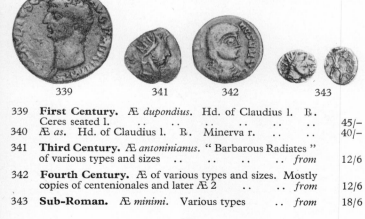

339   341   342   343

339 **First Century.** Æ *dupondius.* Hd. of Claudius l. ℞.
Ceres seated l. 45/–
340 Æ *as.* Hd. of Claudius l. ℞. Minerva r. 40/–

341 **Third Century.** Æ *antoninianus.* " Barbarous Radiates "
of various types and sizes .. .. *from* 12/6

342 **Fourth Century.** Æ of various types and sizes. Mostly
copies of centenionales and later Æ 2 .. .. *from* 12/6

343 **Sub-Roman.** Æ *minimi.* Various types .. *from* 18/6

ANGLO SAXON

EARLY PERIOD
circa A.D. 575-775

GOLD

344	**Solidus.** Copies of Roman types	..	*Extr. rare*	
345	**Thrymsa.** Various types ..	..	.. *from*	£250

345   350   351

SILVER

346	**Sceat.** *Br.* 1. Bust r. between A, N and cross. ℞. Victory between two Augusti	£65
347	— 2. Helmeted bust r. ℞. ' PADA ' in Runic to r. of standard	£75
348	— 3. Similar but ' PADA ' on standard	£100
349	— 4. Diad. bust r. ℞. ' PADA,' cross and annulets ..	£80
350	— 5. Rad. bust r. ℞. Standard	£18
351	— 6. Similar but degraded style, with Runic legends such as APA, EPA or WIGRAED	£35
352	— 7. Similar, without runes	£20
353	— 7*. Degraded type. *O.* Curved figure, as illustration, but each differs in details	£17
354	— 7a. *O.* As last. ℞. Cross on steps pattern ..	£27
355	— 7b. As 7*, but head has been further changed until it has really become a bird	£25

353   355   356

356	— 8. *O.* As 7*. ℞. AETHILRAED in Runic	£150
357	— 9. Crude hd. r. ℞. Cross and pellets	£17
358	— 9a. Standard type. ℞. As last	£20

Early Silver Sceats   *Fine*

359 — (*B.M.C.*, pl. II, 1). Hd. of fine style r., cross before.
R. Annulet and four crosses in square £22

360 *Br.* 10. Diad. hd. r. R. Annulet at each end of cross .. £25

361   365

361 — 11. Similar. R. Bird above cross £24

362 — — Somewhat similar but without legend £22

363 — 12. Facing hd. R. Similar to 361 .. .. £30

364 — 13. Hd. r., cross before. R. Two birds £35

365 — 13a. Two heads face to face, cross between. R.
Floral design formed of four birds £35

366 — 14. LVNDONIA, bust r. R. Man holding two crosses £75

367 — 14a. Similar. R. Crowned figure with bristles .. £75

368 — 15. Similar. R. Seated figure £75

369 — 16. Similar but bust l. R. Shield with four bosses £75

370 — 17. Bust r. of fine work, usually something before. R.
Man standing £40

371 — 18. Victory standing. R. Similar.. .. .. £60

372 — 19. Two men holding cross. R. Degraded standard £35

373   376

373 — 19a. Similar. R. Shield with bosses £35

374 — 20. Bird standing in vine. R. Wolf and Twins .. £50

375 — 21. Bust r., cross before. R. Wolf curled head to tail £40

376 — 21a. — Similar, but wolf's head £40

377 — 22. Man with cross. R. As 375 .. .. .. £30

378 — 22a. *O.* Similar. R. Bird £30

379 — 22b. Shield. R. As 375 .. .. .. £30

380 — 22c. Shield. R. Bird £30

381 — 23. Winged centaur. R. Whorl of wolves' heads and
tongues £45

382 — 24. Bust r. of fine work, no legend. R. Shield with
bosses £40

383 — 25. Shield with bosses. R. Whorl of wolves' heads £35

384 — 25*. Similar. R. Fantastic animal £30

385   388

385	*Br.* 25**. As illustration	£35
386	— 25a. Bust r., ARIP before. ℞. Bird pecking at branch	£65
387	— 26. Crude sun head facing. ℞. Two men holding cross	£35
388	— 27. Similar. ℞. Fantastic animal	£30
389	— 28. Hd. r. in wreath. ℞. Bird on two steps ..	£35
390	— 28a. Similar. ℞. Bird in torque ..	£35
391	— 29. Four annulets in square. ℞. As last ..	£35
392	— 30. Dragon-like animal. ℞. Profile r. ..	£35
393	— 31. Similar. ℞. Man with crosses ..	£35
394	— 32. Similar. ℞. Two men	£35
395	— 33. Similar. ℞. Bird r.	£35
396	— 33a. Similar but crude, bird l.	£40
397	— 34. As *Br.* 30. ℞. Quatrefoil design ..	£40
398	— 34a. Similar. ℞. Wolf's hd. facing ..	£40
399	— 35. Facing bust. ℞. Arabesque pattern ..	£40

This is not a complete list, but includes the main types and follows Brooke's *English Coins.*

KINGS OF NORTHUMBRIA

400 **Ecgfrith** (670-685). Æ *sceat.* *O.* Small cross. ℞. LVXX in angles of a cross radiant .. .. *Extr. rare*

401 **Aldfrith** (685-704). Æ *sceat.* *O.* Boss of pellets. ℞. Fantastic quadruped .. .. .. *Extr. rare*
The attribution of these coins to the kings of the dates given is doubtful.

402 **Eadberht** (737-758). Æ *sceat.* *O.* Small cross. ℞. Fantastic quadruped to l. or r. £60

Aethelwald Moll (759-765). See Archbishop Ecgberht

400   403

403 **Alcred** (765-774). Æ *sceat.* As 402 .. .. .. £100

404 **Aethelred I,** first reign (774-779). Æ *sceat.* As last .. £125

405 **Aelfwald I** (779-788). Æ *sceat.* As last £100
406 — — *O.* Small cross. ℞. With name of moneyer CVDBEVRT £50

407   **Aethelred I,** second reign (789-796). *Æ sceat.* Similar.
      ℞. SCT CVD. (St. Cuthbert), shrine .. *Extr. rare*
408   — — ℞. With moneyer's name £25

The last and the rest of the *sceats*, except where otherwise stated, have on the *obv.* the king's name, and on the *rev.* the moneyer's name: in the centre on both sides is a cross, a pellet, a rosette, etc. During the following reign the silver sceat becomes debased and later issues are only brass or copper.

409   411

409   **Eanred** (810-41). Base *Æ sceat* £10
410   — *Æ sceat* 60/-

411   **Aethelred II,** first reign (841-844). *Æ sceat* 40/-
412   — ℞. Quadruped £30

413   **Redwulf** (844). *Æ sceat* £9

414   **Aethelred II,** second reign (844-849). *Æ sceat,* mainly of the moneyer EARDWVLF 80/-

415   **Osberht** (849-867). *Æ sceat* £20

Coins with blundered legends are worth less than those with normal readings, and to this series have been relegated those coins previously attributed to Eardwulf and Aelfwald II.

ARCHBISHOPS OF YORK

416   **Ecgberht** (732 *or* 734-766). *Æ sceat,* with king Eadberht. As illustration, or holds cross and crozier £70
418   — — with Alchred. Cross each side .. *Extr. rare*

420   **Eanbald II** (796-*c.* 830). *Æ sceat* £20
421   — *Æ sceat,* as last £15

416   420   423

422   **Wigmund** (837-854). Gold *solidus.* Facing bust. ℞. Cross in wreath   ..   ..   *Unique*
423   — *Æ sceat,* various £5

424   **Wulfhere** (854-900). *Æ sceat* £35

SILVER PENNIES

All of the Anglo-Saxon coins are now silver pennies unless otherwise stated. The silver penny (the Latin *denarius*) is the *d* of our £ s. d. The first pennies were made of the same size and weight as the denier of Pepin, father of Charlemagne, king of the Franks. The weight was raised a little later to 24 grains or one pennyweight (dwt.).

KINGS OF KENT

Fine

426 **Heaberht** (*circa* 765). Monogram for REX. ℞. Five annulets, each containing a pellet, joined to form a cross

Unique

The first English silver penny.

427 **Ecgberht** (*circa* 780). O. Similar. ℞. Varied *from* £350

428   430

428 **Eadberht Praen** (796-798). As illustration. ℞. Varied £150

429 **Cuthred** (798-807). *Canterbury*. Various types without portrait   ..   .. *from* £70

430 — As illustration £90

431   432

431 **Anonymous** (*c.* 822-823). *Canterbury*. As illustration £100

432 **Baldred** (*c.* 823-825). *Canterbury*. Head or bust r. ℞. Varied £200

433 — Cross each side £175

434 *Rochester*. Diademed bust r. ℞. Varied   *Extr. rare*

ARCHBISHOPS OF CANTERBURY

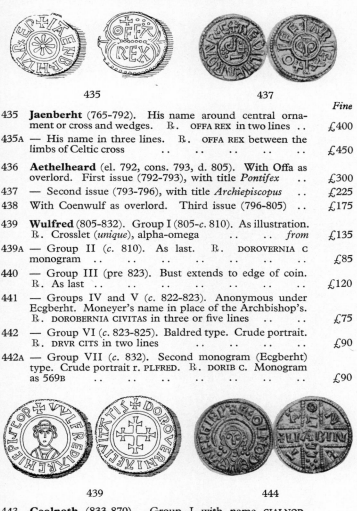

435   437

Fine

435 **Jaenberht** (765-792). His name around central ornament or cross and wedges. ℞. OFFA REX in two lines .. £400

435A — His name in three lines. ℞. OFFA REX between the limbs of Celtic cross £450

436 **Aethelheard** (el. 792, cons. 793, d. 805). With Offa as overlord. First issue (792-793), with title *Pontifex* .. £300

437 — Second issue (793-796), with title *Archiepiscopus* .. £225

438 With Coenwulf as overlord. Third issue (796-805) .. £175

439 **Wulfred** (805-832). Group I (805-*c.* 810). As illustration. ℞. Crosslet (*unique*), alpha-omega .. .. *from* £135

439A — Group II (*c.* 810). As last. ℞. DOROVERNIA C monogram £85

440 — Group III (pre 823). Bust extends to edge of coin. ℞. As last £120

441 — Groups IV and V (*c.* 822-823). Anonymous under Ecgberht. Moneyer's name in place of the Archbishop's. ℞. DOROBERNIA CIVITAS in three or five lines .. £75

442 — Group VI (*c.* 823-825). Baldred type. Crude portrait. ℞. DRVR CITS in two lines £90

442A — Group VII (*c.* 832). Second monogram (Ecgberht) type. Crude portrait r. PLFRED. ℞. DORIB C. Monogram as 569B £90

439   444

443 **Ceolnoth** (833-870). Group I with name CIALNOÐ. Tonsured bust facing. ℞. Varied .. .. *from* £60

444 — Group II. Similar but CEOLNOÐ. ℞. Types of Aethelwulf of Wessex £65

41

446 448

445	— Group III. Diad. bust r. ℞. Moneyer's name in and between lunettes	£90
446	**Aethered** (870-889). Bust r. ℞. As illustration or with long cross with lozenge panel	£300
447	— Cross pattée. ℞. ELF / STAN	*Unique*
448	**Plegmund** (890-914). DORO or XDF in circle. ℞. As illustration above, various moneyers	£60
449	— Cross pattée. ℞. Somewhat as last	£50
450	— Crosses moline and pommée on *obv.*	£90

KINGS OF MERCIA

452	**Offa** (757-796). Gold *dinar*. Copy of Arabic dinar of Caliph Al Mansur, dated 157 A.H. (A.D. 774), with OFFA REX added on *rev.*	*Unique*
452A	Gold *penny*. Bust r., moneyer's name. ℞. Standing figure, moneyer's name	*Unique*

SILVER

453 454

453	*Canterbury.* Group I (*c.* 784-*c.* 787). Early coins without portraits, small flans. Various types *from*	£200
454	— Group II (*c.* 787-*c.* 792). Various types with portrait, small flans *from*	£350
455	— — — Various types without portrait, small flans *from*	£200
456	— Group III (*c.* 792-796). Various types without portrait, large flans (one illustrated, p. 37) *from*	£200
457	*East Anglia.* Copies of Group II and III, possibly struck *c.* 790. Ornate, crude, and sometimes with runic letters	£175

456   458

458   **Cynethryth** (wife of Offa). Coins as Group II of Offa.
As illustration £650

459   — *O*. As *rev*. of last. ℞. EOBA on leaves of quatrefoil   £500

460   **Eadberht** (Bishop of London, died 787/789). EADBERHT
EP in three lines. ℞. Name of Offa   ..   *Extr. rare*
The attribution to this particular cleric is uncertain.

461   **Coenwulf** (796-821). Group I (796-805). *Canterbury*
and *London*. Without portrait. His name in three lines.
℞. Varied £140

462   — *Canterbury*. Name around ⋔ as illus. below. ℞.
Moneyer's name in two lines   ..   ..   *Unique*

462A   — *Both mints*. 'Tribrach' type as illustration £120

462A   463

463   Group II (*c*. 805-810). *Canterbury*. With portrait. Small
flans. ℞. Varied but usually cross and wedges   ..   £135

464   Groups III and IV (*c*. 810-820). *Canterbury*. Similar but
larger flans. ℞. Varied £135

465   — *Rochester*. Large diad. bust of coarse style. ℞. Varied.
(Moneyers: Dun, Ealhstan) £135

466   — *London*. With portrait generally of Roman style. ℞.
Crosslet £150

467   — *E. Anglia*. Crude diad. bust r. ℞. Moneyer's name
LVL on leaves in arms of cross £120

468   **Ceolwulf I** (821-823). *Canterbury*. Group I. Bust r.
℞. Varied. (Moneyers: Oba, Sigestef) £120

469   — — Group II. Crosslet. ℞. Varied £100

470   — — Group III. Tall cross with MERCIORŪ ℞.
Crosslet. SIGESTEF DOROBERNIA   ..   ..   *Unique*

468   476

471	— *Rochester*. Group I. Bust r. ℞. Varied	£100
472	— — Group IIA. As last but head r.	£125
473	— — Group IIB. Ecclesiastical issue by Bp. of Rochester. With mint name, DOROBREBIA, but no moneyer *Extr. rare*	
474	— *East Anglia*. Crude style and lettering with barbarous portrait. ℞. Varied	£100
475	**Beornwulf** (823-825). Bust r. ℞. Moneyer's name in three lines	£250
476	— ℞. Cross crosslet in centre	£225
477	Crude copy of 475 but moneyer's name in two lines with crosses between .. .. .. *Extr. rare*	

479	**Ludica** (825-827). Bust r. ℞. Moneyer's name in three lines as 475 .. .. *Extr. rare*	
480	— Similar. ℞. Moneyer's name around cross crosslet in centre, as 476 .. .. .. *Extr. rare*	
481	**Wiglaf,** first reign (827-829). Crude head r. ℞. Crosslet	£400

482	Second reign (830-840). Cross and pellets. ℞. Moneyer's name in and between lunettes of pellets	£500

| 483 | **Berhtwulf** (840-852). Various types with bust *from* | £125 |

484 — Cross potent over saltire. ℞. Cross potent .. £150

485 Berhtwulf with Aethelwulf of Wessex. As before. ℞. IAETHELWLF REX, cross pommée over cross pattée *Unique*

486 **Burgred** (852-874). *B.M.C.* type A. Bust r. ℞. Moneyer's name in and between lunettes £15

| Type A | B | C | D |

487 — — B. Similar but lunettes broken in centre of curve £18

488 — — C. Similar but lunettes broken in angles .. £16

489 — — D. Similar but legend divided by two lines with a crook at each end £15

489A — — E. As 489, but ᴑ above and below £45

490 **Ceolwulf II** (874-*c.* 880). Bust r. ℞. Two emperors seated, Victory above .. .. .. *Unique*

491 — ℞. Moneyer's name in angles of long cross with lozenge centre £450

KINGS OF EAST ANGLIA

Fine

492 **Beonna** (*c.* 760). Æ *sceat.* As illustration below .. £200

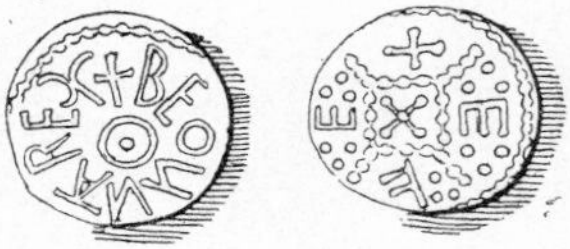

492    492A

492A **Aethelberht** (d. 794). As illustration .. *Only 3 known*

492B **Eadwald** (*c.* 798). King's name in three lines. ℞. Moneyer's name in quatrefoil or around cross *Extr. rare*

493 **Aethelstan I** (*c.* 825–*c.* 840). Bust r. or l. ℞. Crosslet or star £125

494 Bust r. ℞. Moneyer's name in three or four lines .. £125

495 Alpha or A. ℞. Varied £60

496 *O.* and *rev.* Cross with or without wedges or pellets in angles £60

497 Similar, with king's name both sides £80

498 **Aethelweard** (*c.* 840–*c.* 855). Alpha, A, Omega or cross and crescents. ℞. Cross with pellets or wedges .. £100

498    499

499 **Edmund** (855–870). Alpha or A. ℞. Cross with pellets or wedges £45

500 — *O.* Varied. ℞. Similar £50

For the St. Edmund coins and the Danish issues struck in East Anglia having on them the name of Aethelred I of Wessex and Alfred, see Danish East Anglia.

VIKING COINAGES

Danish East Anglia, c. 885–915

501 **Aethelstan II** (878–890), originally named Guthrum? Cross pattée. ℞. Moneyer's name in two lines .. £150

502 **Oswald** (unknown except from his coins). Alpha or A. ℞. Cross pattée .. .. *Extr. rare*

502A — Copy of Carolingian "temple" type. ℞. Cross and pellets .. .. *Unique*

502B **Aethelred I.** As last, with name of Aethelred I of Wessex. ℞. As last, or cross-crosslet .. *Extr. rare*

503 **St. Edmund,** memorial coinage, Æ *penny*, type as illus. below, various legends of good style £12

504 — Similar, but barbarous or semi-barbarous legends .. £10

505 *Halfpenny.* Similar £50

504   506

506 **St. Martin of Lincoln.** As illustration £400

507 **Alfred.** (Viking imitations, usually of very barbarous workmanship). Bust r. ℞. ' LONDONIA ' monogram .. £60

507A — Similar, but ' LINCOLLA ' monogram £200

508 — Small cross, as Alfred group II (*Br.* 6), various legends .. .. *from* £30

509 — Similar. ℞. ' St. Edmund,' A in centre £50

510 — Two emperors seated. ℞. As 507. (Previously attributed to Halfdene) .. .. *Unique*

511 *Halfpenny.* As 507 and 507A .. .. .. *from* £100

512 — As 508 .. .. £50

508   513

Danish Northumbria, c. 898-915

513 **Alfred** (Imitations). ELFRED between ORSNA and FORDA. ℞. Moneyer's name in two lines £75

514 — *Halfpenny.* Similar, of very crude appearance
                                     Extr. rare

514A **Alfred/Plegmund.** *Obv.* ELFRED REX PLEGN *Extr. rare*

514B **Plegmund.** Danish copy of 449 .. .. .. £50

514C **Earl Sihtric.** Type as 513. SCELDFOR between GVNDI BERTVS. ℞. SITRIC COMES in two lines £500

515	**Siefred.** c . SIEFREDIIS REX in two lines. ℞ . EBRAICE CIVITAS (or contractions), small cross	£25
516	— Cross on steps between. ℞ . As last	£50
517	— Long cross. ℞ . As last .. .. *Extr. rare*	
518	SIEFREDVS REX, cross crosslet within legend. ℞ . As last	£15
519	SIEVERT REX, cross crosslet to edge of coin. ℞ . As last	£15
520	— Cross on steps between. ℞ . As last	£50
521	— Patriarchal cross. ℞ . DNS DS REX, small cross ..	£15
522	— — ℞ . MIRABILIA FECIT, small cross	£20
523	REX, at ends of cross crosslet. ℞ . SIEFREDVS, small cross..	£12
524	— Long cross. ℞ . As last	£10
525	*Halfpenny.* Types as 516, 519 and 522 .. *Extr. rare*	
526	**Cnut.** CNVT REX, cross crosslet to edge of coin. ℞ . EBRAICE CIVITAS, small cross	£18
527	— — ℞ . CVNNETTI, small cross	£20
528	— Long cross. ℞ . EBRAICE CIVITAS, small cross ..	£12
529	— — ℞ . CVNNETTI, small cross	£12
530	— Patriarchal cross. ℞ . EBRAICE CIVITAS, small cross ..	£10
531	— — ℞ . — KAROLUS monogram in centre	£45

532   534

532	— — ℞ . CVNNETTI, small cross..	£8
533	*Halfpenny.* Types as 526, 528, 530, 531, 532 .. *from*	£40
534	As 531, but CVNNETTI around KAROLVS monogram ..	£35
535	**Cnut and/or Siefred.** CNVT REX, patriarchal cross. ℞ . SIEFREDVS, small cross	£15
536	— — ℞ . DNS DS REX, small cross	£20

537   539

537	— — ℞ . MIRABILIA FECIT	£16
538	EBRAICE C, patriarchal cross. ℞ DNS DS REX, small cross..	£16
539	— — ℞ . MIRABILIA FECIT	£15

Viking Coinage of York? Cnut and/or Siefred *Fine*

540 DNS DS REX in two lines. ℞. ALVALDVS, small cross *Extr. rare*

541 DNS DS O REX, similar. ℞. MIRABILIA FECIT £16

542 *Halfpenny.* As last .. .. .. *Extr. rare*

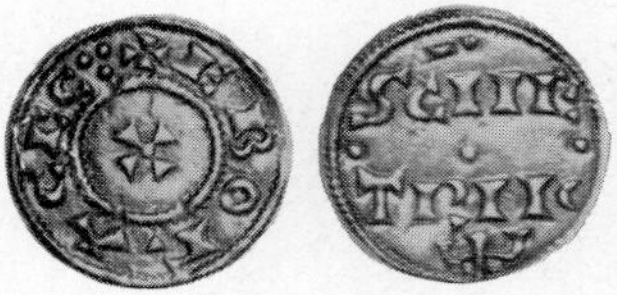

543 **St. Peter of York.** SCI PETRI MO in two lines. ℞. Cross pattée £35

544 Similar. ℞. 'Karolus' monogram .. *Extr. rare*

545 *Halfpenny.* Similar. ℞. Cross pattée £75

546 **Regnald** (Blundered types). RAIENALT, head to l. or r. ℞. EARICE CT, 'Karolus' monogram £250

547 — Open hand. ℞. Similar £150

548 — Hammer. ℞. Bow and arrow £200

548A — Similar. ℞. Sword .. .. .. *Extr. rare*

English Coins of the Hiberno-Norse Vikings

Early period, c. 919-925

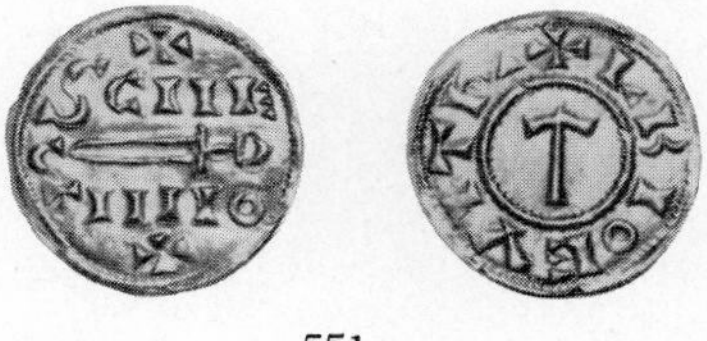

551

549 **Sihtric** (921-927). SITRIC REX, sword. ℞. Cross or T £300

550 **St. Peter of York.** SCI PETRI MO, sword and hammer. ℞. EBORACEI, cross and pellets £60

551 — Similar. ℞. Hammer £60

Coins of St. Peter of York with blundered legends are rather cheaper.

Later period, 939-954 (after the battle of Brunanburh).   All
struck at York except the first two which were struck at Derby.

553 **Anlaf Guthfrithsson,** 939-941. Flower type. Small
cross, ANLAF REX TO D. ℞. Flower above moneyer's name £300
554 — Circular type. Small cross each side, ANLAF VNVNC
MOT £400
555 — Raven type. As illustration, CVNVNC £200

555   556

556 **Anlaf Sihtricsson,** first reign, 941-944. Triquetra type.
As illus. CVNVNC. ℞. Danish standard £225
557 — Circular type (a). Small cross each side, CVNVNC ..   £300
558 — Cross moline type, CVNVNC. ℞. Small cross
Extr. rare
559 — Two line type. Small cross. ℞. ONLAF REX. ℞.
Name in two lines £200

560 **Regnald Guthfrithsson,** 943-944. Triquetra type. As
556. REGNALD CVNVNC £500
561 — Cross moline type. As 558, but REGNALD CVNVNC ..   £350

562 **Sihtric Sihtricsson,** *c.* 942. Triquetra type. As 556,
SITRIC CVNVNC   ..   ..   ..   *Unique*
563 — Circular type. Small cross each side. SITRIC CVNVNC
Unique

561   564

564 **Eric,** first reign, 948. Two line type. Small cross,
ERICVS REX A; ERIC REX AL; OR ERIC REX EFOR. ℞. Name
in two lines £175

565 **Anlaf Sihtricsson,** second reign, 948-952. Circular
type (b). Small cross each side. ONLAF REX £200

566 **Eric,** second reign, 952-954. Sword type. ERIC REX in
two lines, sword between. ℞. Small cross £225

KINGS OF WESSEX
Later, KINGS OF ALL ENGLAND
All are silver pennies unless otherwise stated.

BEORHTRIC, 786-802

Fine

567 As illustration .. .. *Extr. rare*
568 Alpha and omega in centre. ℞. Omega in centre
Extr. rare

ECGBERHT, 802-839

569 *Canterbury.* Group I. Diad. hd. r. within inner circle.
℞. Various.. .. .. .. *from* £225
569A — II. Non-portrait types. ℞. Various .. *from* £200
569B — III. Bust r. breaking inner circle. ℞. DORIB C. .. £180
569D *London.* Cross potent. ℞. LVN/DONIA/CIVIT *Unique*
569E — — ℞. REDꟽVND MONE around TA £300
569F *Rochester,* royal mint. Non-portrait types with king's
name ECGBEORHT .. .. *from* £200
569G — — Portrait types, ECGBEORHT .. .. *from* £200
570 *Rochester,* bishop's mint, Bust r. ℞. SCS ANDREAS
(APOSTOLVS) £300
570A *Winchester.* SAXON monogram or SAXONIORVM in three
lines. ℞. Cross £200

569B   571

AETHELWULF, 839-858

571 *Canterbury.* Phase I (839-*c.* 843). Head within inner
circle. ℞. Various. (*Br.* 3).. .. .. .. £70
572 — — Larger bust breaking inner circle. ℞. A. (*Br.*
1 & 2) £70

51

	Aethelwulf. *Canterbury*	*Fine*
573	— — Cross and wedges. ℞. SAXONIORVM in three lines in centre. (*Br.* 10)	£75
574	— — Similar. ℞. Similar, but OCCIDENTALIVM in place of moneyer. (*Br.* 11)	£100
575	— Phase II (*c.* 843-848 ?). Cross and wedges. ℞. Various, but chiefly a form of cross or a large A. (*Br.* 4)	£70
576	— — New portrait, somewhat as 572. ℞. As last (*Br.* 7)	£85
577	— — Smaller portrait. ℞. As last, but also with *Chi/Rho* monogram. (*Br.* 7)	£80
578	— Phase III (*c.* 848/51-*c.* 855). DORIB in centre. ℞. CANT monogram. (*Br.* 5)	£70
579	— — CANT mon. ℞. CAN M in angles of cross. (*Br.* 6)	£100

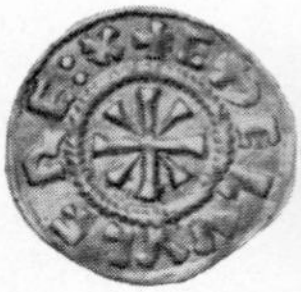

573

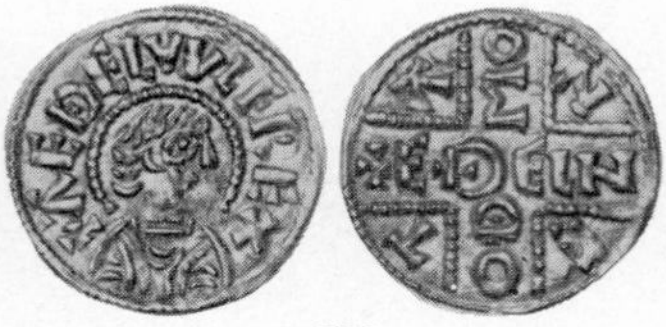

580

580	— Phase IV (*c.* 855-859). Type as Aethelberht. New neat style bust. ℞. Large voided long cross. (*Br.* 8) ..	£40
581	*Winchester*. SAXON mon. ℞. Cross and wedges. (*Br.* 9)	£80

AETHELBERHT, 858-865/6

582	As illustration below	£45
583	*O.* Similar. ℞. Cross fleury over quatrefoil	£175

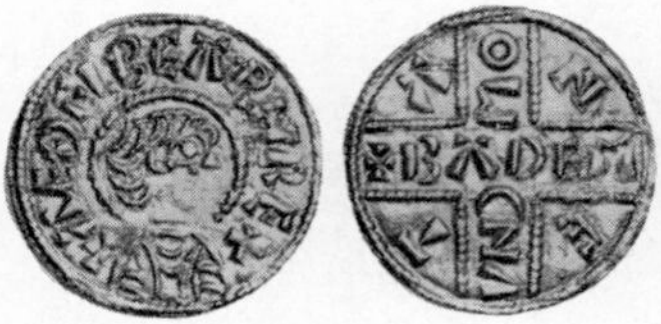

582

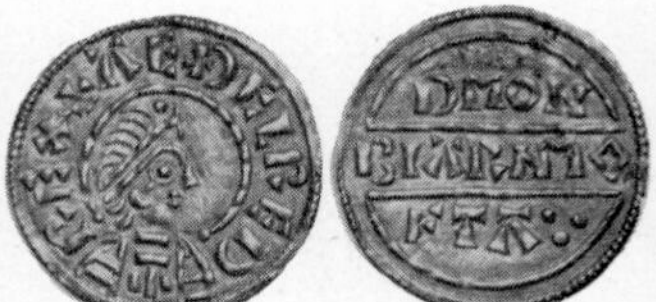

584

AETHELRED I, 865/6-871

584	As illustration	£60
584A	Similar, but moneyer's name in four lines	£85

For another coin with the name Aethelred see 502B under Viking coinages.

ALFRED THE GREAT, 871-899

Types with portraits.

		Fine
585	Bust r. ℞. As Aethelred I. (*Br.* 1)	£60
586	— ℞. Long cross with lozenge centre. (*Br.* 5) ..	£300
587	— ℞. Two seated figures. (*Br.* 2) .. *Unique*	
588	— ℞. As Archbp. Aethered; cross within large quatrefoil. (*Br.* 3) .. .. *Unique*	

590

589	*London.* Bust r. ℞. LONDONIA monogram	£85
590	— — ℞. Similar, but with moneyer's name added ..	£120
591	— *Halfpenny.* Bust r. ℞. LONDONIA monogram as 589	£120
592	*Gloucester.* ℞. ÆT GLEAPA in angles of three limbed cross .. .. *Unique*	

Types without portraits.

593	King's name on limbs of cross, trefoils in angles. ℞. Moneyer's name in quatrefoil. (*Br.* 4) .. .. *Unique*	

594	Cross pattée. ℞. Moneyer's name in two lines. (*Br.* 6)	£35
594A	— As last, but neater style, as Edw. the Elder	£40
595	*Halfpenny.* As 594	£60
596	*Canterbury.* As last but DORO added on *obv.* (*Br.* 6a) ..	£65

For other pieces bearing the name of Alfred see under the Viking coinages.

598	*Exeter ?* King's name in four lines. ℞. EXA vertically *Extr. rare*	
599	*Winchester ?* Similar to last, but PIN .. *Extr. rare*	
600	" Offering " penny. Very large and heavy. AELFRED REX SAXORVM in four lines. ℞. ELIMO in two lines *Extr. rare*	

Fine

601 **Rare types.** *Br.* 1. *Bath?* R. BA .. *Extr. rare*

602    612

602 — 2. *Canterbury.* As illustration	£150
603 — 3. *Chester?* Small cross. R. Minster	£175
604 — 4. — Small cross. R. Moneyer's name in single line	£125
605 — 5. — R. Two stars	£150
606 — 6. — R. Flower above central line, name below..	£150
607 — 7. — R. Floral design with name across field ..	£150
608 — 8. — R. Bird holding twig .. *Extr. rare*	
609 — 9. — R. Hand of Providence	£200
610 — 10. — R. City gate of Roman style *Extr. rare*	
611 — 11. — R. Anglo-Saxon burg	£165
612 **Ordinary types.** *Br.* 12. Bust l. R. Moneyer's name in two lines .. .. *from*	£65
612A — — As last, but in *gold* .. .. .. *Unique*	
613 — 12a. Similar, but bust r. of crude style	£50
614 — 13. Small cross. R. Similar	£20
615 *Halfpenny.* Similar to last	£140

614    616

AETHELSTAN, 924-939

616 **Main issues.** Small cross. R. Moneyer's name in two lines	£25
617 Diad. bust r. R. As last	£120

621 628

618	— ℞. Small cross	£85
619	Small cross both sides	£30
620	— Similar, but mint name added	£40
621	Crowned bust r. As illustration. ℞. Small cross ..	£70
622	— Similar, but mint name added	£85
624	**Local Issues.** *N.W. mints.* Star between two pellets. ℞. As 616	£150
625	— Small cross. ℞. Floral ornaments above and below moneyer's name	£150
626	— Rosette of pellets each side	£45
627	— Small cross one side, rosette on the other side ..	£50
628	*York.* Small cross. ℞. Tower over moneyer's name	£120
629	— Similar, but mint name added	£150
629A	— Bust in high relief r. or l. ℞. Small cross ..	£100
629B	— Bust r. in high relief. ℞. Cross-crosslet	£120
629C	*Lincoln?* Helmeted bust r. ℞. As last	£125

EADMUND, 939-946

631 633

631	Small cross or rosette. ℞. Moneyer's name in two lines with crosses or rosettes between .. .. .. *from*	£18
632	Crowned bust r. ℞. Small cross	£65
633	Similar, but with mint name	£80
634	Small cross either side, or rosette on one side	£50
635	Cross of five pellets. ℞. Moneyer's name in two lines	£50
636	Small cross. ℞. Flower above name	£175
636A	Helmeted bust r. ℞. Cross-crosslet	£125
636B	*Halfpenny.* As 631	£140

EADRED, 946-955

637

				Fine
637	As illustration. ℞. Moneyer's name in two lines		..	£20
638	Similar, but mint name after REX			£125
639	Crowned bust r. As illustration			£80

639

640	— ℞. Similar, with mint-name added	£90
641	Rosette. ℞. As 637	£30
642	Small cross. ℞. Rosette	£35
642A	— ℞. Flower enclosing moneyer's name	Extr. rare	
642B	Halfpenny. Similar to 637 .. .. .. from	£165

HOWEL DDA, d. 949/950 (King of Wales)

642C HOFEL REX, small cross or rosette. ℞. Moneyer's name in
two lines .. ..Unique

EADWIG, 955-959

643

643	Br. 1. Type as illustration	£28
644	— — Similar, but mint name in place of crosses ..	£45
645	— 2. As 643, but moneyer's name in one line	£125
646	— 3. Similar. ℞. Floral design.	£185
647	— 4. Similar. ℞. Rosette or small cross	£40
648	— 5. Bust r. ℞. Small cross.. .. Extr. rare	
648A	Halfpenny. Small cross. ℞. Flower above moneyer's name .. .. Unique	

56

EADGAR, 959-975

It is now possible on the basis of the lettering to divide up the majority of Eadgar's coins into issues from the following regions. N.E. England, N.W. England, York, East Anglia, Midlands, S.E. England, Southern England, and S.W. England. (*Vide* "Anglo-Saxon Coins," ed. R. H. M. Dolley).

Fine

649	*Br.* 1. Small cross. R. Moneyer's name in two lines, crosses between trefoils top and bottom	£18
650	— — R. Similar, but rosettes top and bottom (a N.W. variety)	£20
651	— — R. Similar, but annulets between	£20
652	— — R. Similar, but mint name between (a late N.W. type)	£25
653	— 2. — R. Floral design	£140

649   654

654	— 4. Small cross either side	£18
655	— — Similar, with mint name	£45
656	— — Rosette either side	£20
657	— — Similar, with mint name	£40
658	— 5. Large bust to r. R. Small cross	£75
659	— — Similar, with mint name	£90
660	— 6. Small bust l., as next illustration, with mint name	£70
661	*Halfpenny.* (8½ grains). *Br.* 3. Small cross. R. Flower above name .. .. .. *Extr. rare*	

N.B. From now onwards all Saxon and Norman regal pennies have a mint name on the reverse.

EDWARD THE MARTYR, 975-978

662	Type as illustration above	£75

AETHELRED II, 978-1016

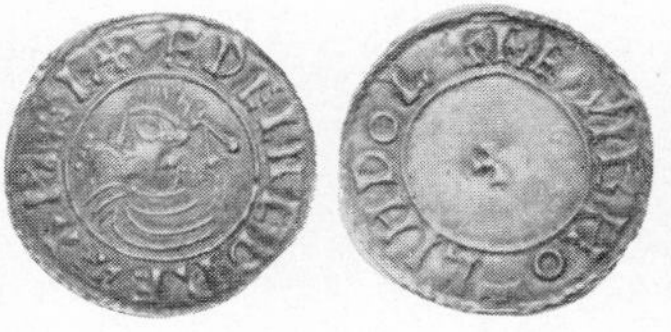

663

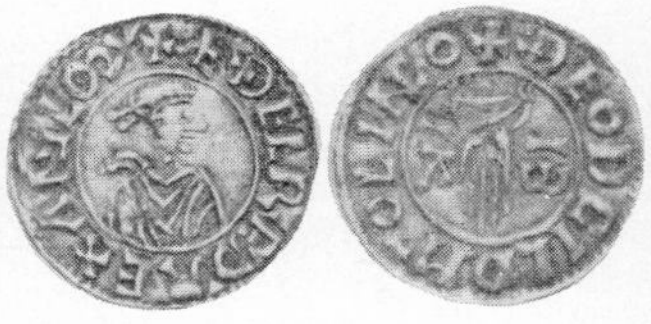

664

Fine

663 First small cross type. Style of 662. (*Br.* 1; *B.M.C.* I) £35

664 First Hand type. Bust r., no sceptre. ℞. Hand of Providence. (*Br.* 2; *B.M.C.* IIA) £12

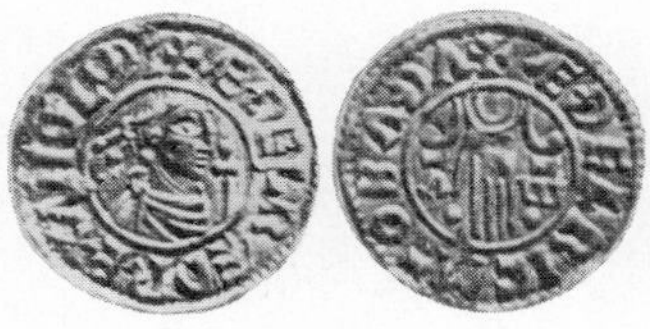

665

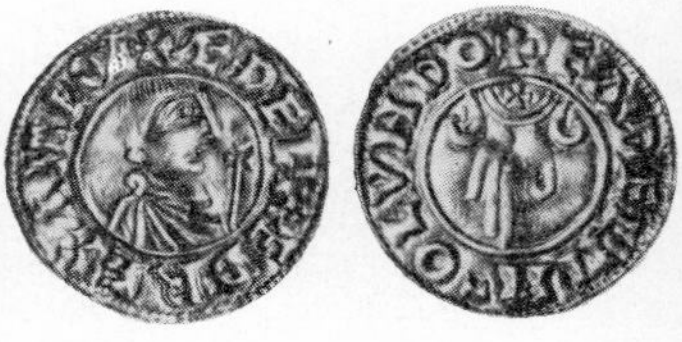

666

665 Second Hand type, with sceptre. (*B.M.C.* IID) .. £12

666 Benediction type. *O.* as last. ℞. Hand giving Benediction. (*B.M.C.* IIF) £60

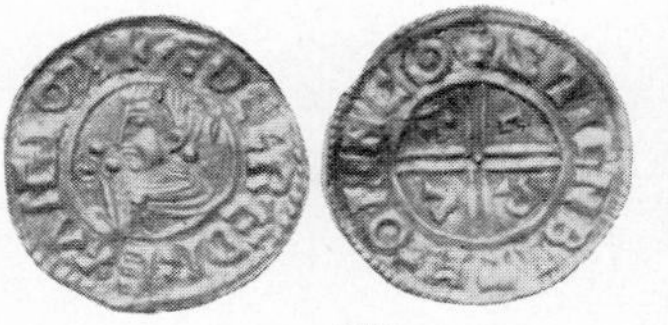

667

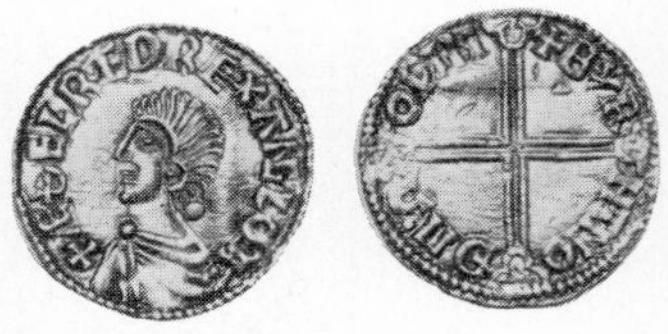

668

667 **CRVX type.** (*Br.* 3; *B.M.C.* IIIA) £9

667A **— Lightweight issue. Small flan** £24

668 **Long cross type.** (*Br.* 5; *B.M.C.* IVA) £6

669   670

669	Helmet type. (*Br.* 4; *B.M.C.* VIII)	£10
670	Last small cross type. As 663, but different style ..	£7
671	Agnus Dei type. (*Br.* 6; *B.M.C.* X) .. *Extr. rare*	
672	Gold *penny* of helmet type .. .. .. *Unique*	

N.B. *Prices in every case both in this and the following reigns are for London or the commonest mints, although the illustrations used may be of more expensive coins from scarcer mints.*

CNUT, 1016-1035

Transitional types (probably Scandinavian).

673	Small cross type, as Aethelred II. (*Br.* 1; *B.M.C.* 1) ..	£25
674	Long cross type, as Aethelred II. (*Br.* 1a)	£30

675   676

Main types.

675	Quatrefoil type. (*Br.* 2; *B.M.C.* VIII)	£12
676	Helmet type. (*Br.* 3; *B.M.C.* XIV)	£8

677	Short cross type. (*Br.* 4; *B.M.C.* XVI)	£10
678	Jewel cross type. as next illustration. (*Br.* 6; *B.M.C.* XX)	£80

HAROLD I, 1035-1040

679   681

HARTHACNUT, 1035-1042

685   686

EDWARD THE CONFESSOR, 1042-1066

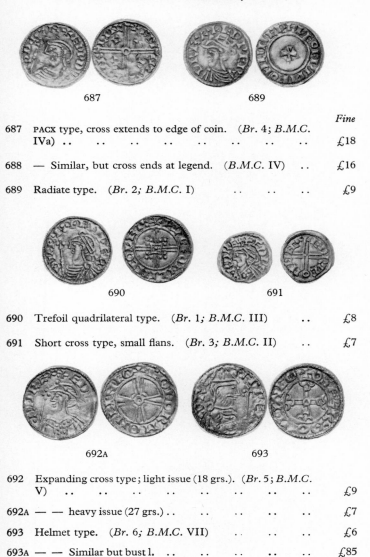

687   689

Fine

687   PACX type, cross extends to edge of coin. (*Br.* 4; *B.M.C.*
IVa) £18

688   — Similar, but cross ends at legend. (*B.M.C.* IV)   ..   £16

689   Radiate type. (*Br.* 2; *B.M.C.* I) £9

690   691

690   Trefoil quadrilateral type. (*Br.* 1; *B.M.C.* III)   ..   £8

691   Short cross type, small flans. (*Br.* 3; *B.M.C.* II)   ..   £7

692A   693

692   Expanding cross type; light issue (18 grs.). (*Br.* 5; *B.M.C.*
V) £9

692A   — — heavy issue (27 grs.)..   ..   ..   £7

693   Helmet type. (*Br.* 6; *B.M.C.* VII) £6

693A   — — Similar but bust l. £85

694   695

694   Sovereign type.   (*Br.* 7; *B.M.C.* IX) £10

695   Hammer cross type.   (*Br.* 8; *B.M.C.* XI) £5

696   697

696   Facing bust type.   (*Br.* 9; *B.M.C.* XIII) £6

697   Cross and piles type.   (*Br.* 10; *B.M.C.* XV) £8

697A Large facing bust with sceptre.   ℞.   Similar £150

698   Gold *penny* of expanding cross type   ..   .. *Unique*

       Most York coins of this reign have an annulet in one quarter of the reverse.

HAROLD II, 1066

699   Bust l. with sceptre.   ℞.   PAX across centre of *rev*.
       (*B.M.C.* I) £25

700   Similar, but without sceptre.   (*B.M.C.* Ia) £40

700A Bust r. with sceptre £100

ANGLO-SAXON AND NORMAN MINTS

In Anglo-Saxon times coins were struck at a large number of towns. The place of mintage was put on the coins, and, generally, the name of the person responsible (e.g. BRVNIC ON LVND). Below we give a list of the mints, showing the reigns, including the Norman kings, of which coins have been found. After the town names we give one or two of the spellings as found on the coins, although often they appear in an abbreviated or extended form. On the coins the Anglo-Saxon and Norman " W " is like a P or ғ and the " TH " is Ð. We have abbreviated the king's names etc.:—

Alf	— Alfred the Great	Hii	— Harold II.
EE	— Edward the Elder	Wi	— William I.
A'stan	— Aethelstan	Wii	— William II.
EM	— Edward the Martyr	He	— Henry I.
Ae	—Aethelred II.	St	— Stephen (regular issues)
Cn	— Cnut	T	— " Tealby " coinage
Hi	— Harold I.	sc	— " short cross " coinage
Ht	— Harthacnut	LC	— " long cross " coinage
ECfr	— Edward the Confessor		

Axbridge (ACXEPO, AGEPOR) Ae, Cn, Ht.
Aylesbury (AEGEL) Ae, Cn, ECfr.

Barnstaple (BEARDA, BARDI), Edwig, Ae-Hi, ECfr, Wi, He.
Bath (BAÐAN) EE-Edmund, Edwig-ECfr, Wi, He.
Bedford (BEDANF, BEDEF) Edwig-T.
Bedwyn (BEDEFIN) ECfr, Wi.
Berkeley (BEORC) ECfr
Bramber ? (BRAN) St.
Bridgnorth ? (BRIGIN) Ae.
Bridport (BRIPVT, BRIDI) A'stan, Ae, Cn, Ht, ECfr, Wi.
Bristol (BRICSTO) Ae-T, LC.
Bruton (BRIVT) Ae-Cn.
Buckingham (BVCIN) EM-Hi, ECfr.
Bury St. Edmunds (EDMVN, SEDM, SANTEA) A'stan ? ECfr, Wi, He-LC.

Cadbury (CADANB) Ae, Cn.
Caistor (CASTR) EM, Ae.
Cambridge (GRANTE) EM-Wii.
Canterbury (DORO, CAENT, CANTOR, CANTFAR) Alf, A'stan, Edgar-LC.
Cardiff (CAIRDI, CARDI, CARITI) Wi, He, St.
Carlisle (CAR, CARDI) Hi-LC.
Castle Gotha ? (GEOÐA, IOÐA) Ae-Ht.
Castle Rising (RISINGE) St.
Chester (LEIGECES, LEGECE, CESTRE) A'stan, Edgar-T.

Anglo-Saxon and Norman Mints

Chichester (CISSAN CIV, CICES, CICST) A'stan, Edgar-St., sc.
Christchurch, see Twynham.
Cissbury (SIÐEST) Ae, Cn.
Colchester (COLEAC, COLECES) Ae-Hi, ECfr-T.
Crewkerne (CRVCERN) Ae, Cn.
Cricklade (CROCGL, CRIC, CREC) Ae-Wii.

Derby (DEOR, DIORBI, DERBI) A'stan, Edgar-ECfr, Wi-St.
Dorchester (DORCE, DORECES) Ae-ECfr, Wi-He.
Dover (DOFER) A'stan, Edgar-St.
Durham (DVNE, DVRE, DVRHAN) Wi, St-Lc.

Exeter (EAXANC, EXEC, XECST) Alf, A'stan, Edwig-Lc.

Frome? (FRO) Cn-ECfr.

Gloucester (GLEAFEC, GLEF, GF) Alf, A'stan, Edgar-T, Lc.
Guildford (GILDEF) EM-Cn, Ht-Wii.

Hastings (HAESTIN) Ae-St.
Hedon, near Hull (HEDVN) St.
Hereford (HEREFOR) A'stan, Ae-T, Lc.
Hertford (HEORTF) A'stan, Edwig-Hi, ECfr, Wi, Wii.
Horncastle? (HORN) EM, Ae.
Horndon ? (HORNIDVNE) ECfr.
Huntingdon (HVNTEN) Edwig-St.
Hythe (HIÐEN) ECfr, Wi, Wii.

Ilchester (IVELCE, GIFELCST, GIVELC) Edgar, EM-He, T, Lc.
Ipswich (GIPESFIC) Edgar-sc.

Kings Lynn (LENN, LENE) sc.

Langport (LANCPOR) A'stan, Cn, Hi, ECfr.
Launceston (LANSTF, SANCTI STEFANI) Ae, Wi, Wii, St, T.
Leicester (LIGER, LIHER, LEHRE) A'stan, Edgar-T.
Lewes (LAEFES) A'stan, Edgar-T.
Lincoln (LINCOLNE, NICOLE) Edgar-Lc.
London (LVNDENE) Alf-Lc.
Louth ? (LVD) Ae.
Lydford (LYDAN) EM-Hi, ECfr.
Lympne (LIMEN) Edgar-Cn.

Maldon (MAELDVN, MAELI) A'stan, Ae-Hi, ECfr, Wii.
Malmesbury (MALD, MEALDMES) Ae-Wii.
Marlborough (MAERLEB) Wi, Wii.
Milborne Port (MYLE) Ae, Cn.

Newark (NEPIR, NIFOR) Edwig, Ae, Cn.
Newcastle (NEWEC, NIVCA) T, Lc.
Newport (NIFAN, NIFEP) Edgar, ECfr.

Anglo-Saxon and Norman Mints

Northampton (HAMTVN, NORHANT) Edgar-Wi, He-LC.
Norwich (NORFIC) A'stan-LC.
Nottingham (SNOTINC) A'stan, Ae-St.

Oxford (OXNAFOR, OXENEF) A'stan. Edmund, Edred, Edgar-I C.

Pembroke (PAN, PAIN) He-T.
Pershore (PERESC) ECfr.
Peterborough (MEÐE, BVR) Ae, Cn, Wi.
Petherton (PEÐR) ECfr.
Pevensey (PEFNESE, PEVEN) Wi, Wii, St.

Reading (READIN) ECfr.
Rhuddlan (RVDILI, RVLA) Wi, SC.
Rochester (ROFEC) A'stan, Edgar-He, sc.
Romney (RVME, RVMNE) Ae-Hi, ECfr-He.

Salisbury (SAEREB, SALEB) Ae-ECfr, Wi-He,T.
Sandwich (SANPIC) ECfr, Wi-St.
Shaftesbury (SCEFTESB, SCEFITI) A'stan, Ae-St.
Shrewsbury (SCROBES, SALOF) A'stan, Edgar-LC.
Southampton (HAMWIC, HAMTVN) A'stan, Edwig-Cn.
Southwark (SVÐGE, SVÐFEEORC) Ae-St.
Stafford (STAFF, STAEF) A'stan, Ae-Hi, ECfr, Wi, Wii, St., T
Stamford (STANFOR) Edgar-St.
Steyning (STAENIG) Cn-Wii.
Sudbury (SVÐBI, SVB) Ae, Cn, ECfr, Wi-St.

Tamworth (TOMFEARÐGE, TAMFRÐ,) A'stan, Edwig-Hi, ECfr, Wi-St
Taunton (TANTVNE) Ae, Cn, Ht-St.
Thetford (ÐEOTFOR, TETFOR) Edgar-T.
Torksey (TORC, TVRC) EM-Cn.
Totnes (DARENT VRB, TOTANES, TOTNESE) A'stan, Edwig-Cn, Wii.
Twynham, now Christchurch (TFIN, TVEHAM) Wi, He.

Wallingford (FELING, FALLIG) A'stan, Edgar-He, T, LC.
Wareham (FERHAM) A'stan, Ae, Cn, Ht-He.
Warminster (FORIME) Ae-Hi, ECfr.
Warwick (FAERING, FERFIC) A'stan, Edgar-St.
Watchet (FECEDPORT, FICEDI) Ae-ECfr, Wi-St.
Wilton (FILTVNE) Edgar-LC.
Winchcombe (FINCELE, FINCL) Edgar-Cn, Ht-Wi.
Winchester (FINTONIA, FINCEST) Alf-A'stan, Edwig-LC.
Worcester (FIHRAC, FIHREC) Ae-Hi, ECfr-sc.

York (EBORACI, EOFERFIC) A'stan, Edmund, Edgar-LC

The location of the following is uncertain.
DERNE, DYR, ECfr. (an East Anglian mint)
DEVITVN, Wi. (*? Cardiff*)
EANBYRIG, Cn.
ORSNAFORDA, Alf. (*? Horsforth Yorks.*)
WEARDBYRIG, A'stan, Edgar.

NORMAN KINGS AND THEIR SUCCESSORS

From William I to Edward II all are silver pennies unless
otherwise stated.

WILLIAM I, 1066-1087

701

702

Fine

701	Profile left type. (*Br.* I) ..	..	..	..	..		£15
702	Bonnet type. (*Br.* II) ..	..	..	..	..		£12

703

704

703	Canopy type. (*Br.* III) ..	..	..	..	..		£18
704	Two sceptres type. (*Br.* IV)	..	..	..	..		£18

705

706

705	Two stars type. (*Br.* V) ..	..	..	..	..		£10
706	Sword type. (*Br.* VI) ..	..	..	..	..		£30

707	Profile right type. (*Br.* VII)	..	..	..	£35
708	PAXS type. (*Br.* VIII)	..	..	..	£7

WILLIAM II, 1087-1100

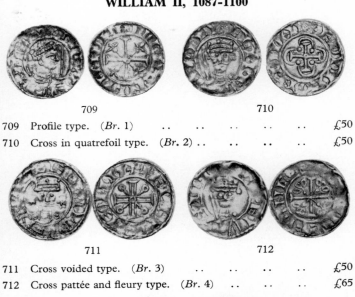

709	Profile type. (*Br.* 1)	..	..	..	£50
710	Cross in quatrefoil type. (*Br.* 2)	..	..	..	£50
711	Cross voided type. (*Br.* 3)	..	..	..	£50
712	Cross pattée and fleury type. (*Br.* 4)	..	..	..	£65

713	Cross fleury and piles type. (*Br.* 5)	..	..	..	£85

HENRY I, 1100-1135

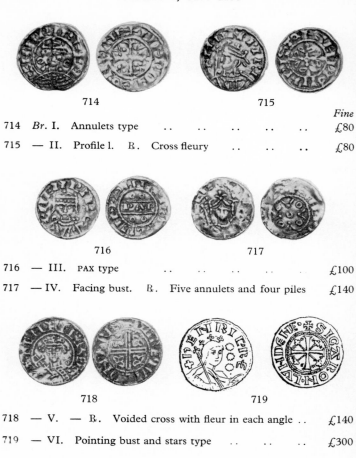

714

715

716

717

718

719

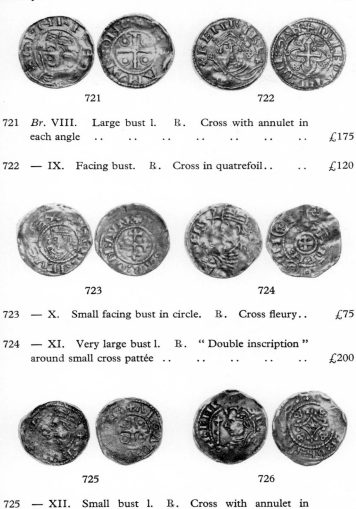

721

722

723

724

725

726

721 *Br.* VIII.   Large bust l.   ℞.   Cross with annulet in
each angle £175

722 — IX.   Facing bust.   ℞.   Cross in quatrefoil.. .. £120

723 — X.   Small facing bust in circle.   ℞.   Cross fleury.. £75

724 — XI.   Very large bust l.   ℞.   " Double inscription "
around small cross pattée £200

725 — XII.   Small bust l.   ℞.   Cross with annulet in
each angle £125

726 — XIII.   Star in lozenge fleury type £85

727   728

727   *Br*. XIV.   Pellets in quatrefoil type £18

728   — XV.   Quadrilateral on cross fleury type £16

729   *Halfpenny*. Facing head. ℞. Cross potent with
pellets in angles   ..   .. *Unique*

STEPHEN, 1135-1154

Regal issues.

730   *Br*. I. " Watford " type.   Bust r.   ℞.   Cross moline
with fleurs £20

731   — II.   Cross voided and mullets type £50

732   — III.   Facing bust.   ℞.   Cross with fleur in each
angle £175

733   — IV.   Facing bust.   ℞.   Lozenge fleury and annulets   £200

734   — V.   Bust three-quarter r. with sceptre.   ℞.   Voided
cross and fleurs £200

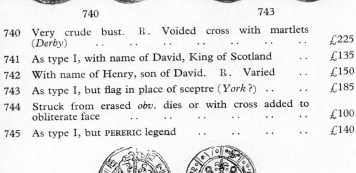

735   736

| 735 | *Br.* VI. Profile l. with sceptre. R. Cross fleury and trefoils .. .. | £150 |
| 736 | — VII. "Awbridge" type. Bust l. nearly facing, with sceptre. R. Short voided cross with lis in each angle.. | £65 |

Irregular issues. The coinage of the Civil War is a most interesting series; we only give here some of the more important pieces.

737	As type I, but coarse work and bust to l...	£125
738	Similar, but mace instead of sceptre ..	*Extr. rare*
739	Long cross fleury superimposed on *rev.*	£175

740   743

740	Very crude bust. R. Voided cross with martlets (*Derby*)	£225
741	As type I, with name of David, King of Scotland ..	£135
742	With name of Henry, son of David. R. Varied ..	£150
743	As type I, but flag in place of sceptre (*York?*)	£185
744	Struck from erased *obv.* dies or with cross added to obliterate face	£100
745	As type I, but PERERIC legend	£140

| 746 | Double-figure type   As illus.. .. .. | £225 |

747   748

747 **Eustace Fitzjohn?** Lion to r. £300
748 — Armed figure r. ..   ..   *Extr. rare*

749   750

749 **Bishop Henry.** Bust r., with crozier   ..   *Extr. rare*
750 **Robert de Stuteville.** Armed figure on horseback
                                                    Extr. rare

751   754

751 **The Empress Matilda.** Similar to Stephen type I but
reading IMPERATR or MATILDA IMP..   ..   ..   £400
752 **Henry of Anjou.** *Br.* 1. As Stephen type I £200
753 — 2. ℞. As type XV of Henry I, quadrilateral on
cross fleury £325
754 — 3. Facing bust between two stars. ℞. As last ..   £250
755 — 4. Bust r. ℞. Crosslet in quatrefoil £300
756 **Robert of Gloucester.** As Stephen type II but
ROBERTV   ..   ..   *Extr. rare*
757 **William of Gloucester.** As type 3 of Henry of Anjou
                                                    Extr. rare
758 **Brian Fitzcount** or **Baldwin de Redvers.** Similar
                                                    Unique ?
759 **Patrick, Earl of Salisbury.** As 753, but helmeted bust
r. with sword, star behind ..   ..   ..   *Extr. rare*

HENRY II, 1154-1189

	A	B	C

Cross-and-crosslets (" Tealby ") coinage, 1158-80

		Fair	Fine
760	Bust A. No hair	60/-	£8
761	— B. Similar but mantle varies	60/-	£8
762	— C. Decorated collar, curl of hair	60/-	£8

	D	E	F

763	— D. Decoration continues along shoulder ..	65/-	£9
764	— E. Similar bust, but shoulder not decorated	65/-	£9
765	— F. Hair in long ringlet to r. of bust	£5	£12

" Short cross " coinage.

This issue started in 1180 and continued with little variation, except in style and portraiture, right through the reigns of Richard I and John until it was changed in 1247 during the reign of Henry III. Throughout this period the king's name was kept as HENRICVS. *See " Notes on English Silver Coins, 1066-1648."*

	1a	1b	1c

766	Class 1a. Narrow face, square E and C	£16
767	— 1b. Curls usually two to l., five to r., round ᴇ and c	£5
768	— 1c. First evidence of degradation, more curls to r. than to l., no stop in *obv.* legend	80/-

RICHARD I, 1189-1199

2a   2b   3   4

" Short-cross " coinage (reading hЄNRICVS)   *Fine*

769   Class 2a. Face with no relief, mass of tiny curls either
side of head £15

770   — 2b. Three curls at each side, 7 pearls in crown,
colon often each side of ON..   ..   ..   ..   £8

771   — 3. Longer, narrower face, well defined beard   ..   £6

772   — 4. Degraded style, large coarse head, beard of pellets   £5

This last class continues into the reign of John. The only coins
bearing Richard's name are those struck for his territories in France.

JOHN, 1199-1216

5a   5b   5c

" Short-cross " coinage (reading hЄNRICVS)

773   Class 5a. New coinage of neat work, reversed S; *mm.*
cross pommée 70/-

774   — Similar, but with ornamental letters £6

775   — 5a/5b, or 5b/5a mules 85/-

776   Class 5b. Similar, but normal S; *mm.* cross pattée   ..   40/-

777   — 5c. As last but X of RЄX is a St. Andrew's cross   ..   40/-

Pennies, halfpennies and farthings bearing John's name were struck
in Ireland.

HENRY III, 1216-1272

The Short-cross money was replaced by a new coinage in 1247. Under the Angevin kings the number of mints had gradually been reduced, and during the later years of this reign the only royal mints were London and Canterbury working under the control of a single master moneyer. An attempt to introduce a gold currency was made in 1257 by the striking of a 20 penny piece.

6 ornamental   7   8

"Short-cross" coinage, 1216-1247.

Fine

778	Class 6. Thin pointed face, squinting eyes, x is a quatrefoil	35/-
779	— — With ornamental letters	£7
780	— 7. Face cut off at chin	25/-
781	— 8. Crude work; *mm.* frequently cross-pommée ..	£7

"Long-cross" coinage, 1247-1272.

In 1247 the type of the penny was changed and with variations this continued until 1278. Those struck during the early years of Edward I still bear the name hENRICVS. For further particulars on this series see the article by Patricia Seaby in "Notes on English Silver Coins, 1066-1648."

Ib   II   IIIb

Without sceptre.

782	Class Ia. hENRICVS: REX. R. ANGLIE TERCI	£10
783	— Ib. hENRICVS REX. ANG. R. LIE TERCI LON (*London*), CAN (*Canterbury*) or AED (*Bury St. Edmunds*)	80/-
784	— I/II mule..	60/-
785	— II. hENRICVS REX TERCI'. R. Moneyer and mint..	35/-
786	— IIIa. hENRICVS REX · III, thin face as class II ..	30/-
787	— IIIb. Smaller, rounder face	30/-
788	— IIIc. Face with pointed chin, neck indicated by two lines, usually REX: III	30/-

IVa   Vb   Vg

With sceptre.

789	Class IVa. Similar to last, but with sceptre	70/-
790	— IVb. Similar, but new crown with half-fleurs and large central fleur	90/-
791	— Va. With class IV bust, round eyes, from now on legend begins at 10 o'clock..	32/6
792	— Vb. Narrower face, wedge-tailed R, round eyes ..	30/-
793	— Vc. As last, but almond-shaped eyes..	30/-
794	— Vd. Portrait of quite different style; new crown with true-shaped fleur	70/-
795	— Ve. Similar, with jewelled or beaded crown	70/-
796	— Vf. New style larger face, double-banded crown ..	45/-
797	— Vg. Single band to crown, low central fleur, curule .. chair shaped x	30/-
798	— Vh. Crude copy of Vg, with pellets in lieu of fleur..	80/-

799	**Gold penny** of 20d. As illustration	£4000

EDWARD I, 1272-1307.

In 1279 a new style coinage set the pattern for the next two centuries. It included a fourpence or groat (Fr. *gros*) and halfpennies and farthings.

"Long-cross" coinage, 1272-78 (reading hЄNRICVS)

800	Class VI. Crude face with new realistic curls, Є and N ligate .. .. *Extr. rare*	
801	— VII. Similar, but of improved style, usually with Lombardic U. As illustration on next page	£9

801   802

New coinage, 1278-1307.

802 **Groat.** (=4d.; wt. 89 grs.). Type as illustration but
     several minor varieties £55

> Most extant specimens show traces of having been mounted on the
> obverse and gilded on the reverse; unmounted coins are worth more.

1c   2

803 **Penny.** *London.* Class 1a. Crown with plain band,
     ЄDW RЄX; Lombardic N 85/–
804 — 1b. — ЄD RЄX; no drapery on bust, Roman N   ..   £15
805 — 1c. — ЄDW RЄX; Roman N, normal or reversed;
     small lettering 30/–
806 — 1d. — ЄDW R; —; large lettering and face   ..   35/–
807 — — — — Annulet below bust (for the Abbot of
     Reading) £12
808 — 2. Crown with band shaped to ornaments; tall
     bust; long neck; N reversed 30/–

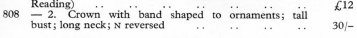

3a   3b   3c

809 — 3a. Crescent-shaped contraction marks; pearls in
     crown, drapery is foreshortened circle 37/6
810 — 3b. — — drapery is segment of a circle 35/–
811 — 3c. — normal crown: drapery in one piece, hollowed
     in centre 21/–

Edward I Pennies   *Fine*

812 — 3d. — — drapery in two pieces, broad face   ..   21/–

812A — 3e. — — long narrow face (mostly Northern mints)   27/6

813 — 3f. — — broad face, large nose, rougher work,
late S first used 30/–

814 — 3g. — — small neat bust, narrow face 20/–

815 — 4a. Comma-shaped contraction marks, late S always
used, C and ∈ open 30/–

4c   5a   5b

816 — 4b. Similar, but face and hair shorter 30/–

817 — 4c. Larger face with more copious hair; unbarred
A first used 35/–

818 — 4d. Pellet at beginning of *obv.* and/or *rev.* inscription   27/6

819 — 4e. Three pellets on breast; pellet in *rev.* legend   ..   32/6

820 — 5a. Well spread coins, pellet on breast, A normally
unbarred 65/–

821 — 5b. Coins more spread, tall lettering, long narrow
face, pellet on breast..   ..   ..   65/–

6b   7a   7b   9b

822 — 6a. Smaller coins, initial cross almost plain, crown
with wide fleurs 65/–

823 — 6b. Initial cross well pattée; lettering of good style;
closed ∈ (from now on) 65/–

824 — 7a. Rose on breast; almond-shaped eyes; double
barred N 65/–

825 — 7b. — — longer hair, new crown 30/–

826 — 8a. Smaller crown; top-tilted S; longer neck   ..   27/6

827 — 8b. Not unlike 9a, but top-tilted S 32/6

828 — 9a. Narrow face, flatter crown, star on breast   ..   25/–

829 — 9b. Small coins; Roman N, normal, un-barred, or
usually of pot-hook form; often star or pellet on breast   ..   20/–

10a 10d 10f

830	— 10a. Bi-foliate crown (from now on), long narrow face, narrow-waisted lettering, ЄDWARD R..	22/6
831	— 10b. — — — ЄDWAR R	27/6
832	— 10c. — — — ЄDWA R	17/6
833	— 10d. Broader face and larger crown, more ornate lettering	25/-
834	— 10e. Square face with short neck; thin initial cross	27/6
835	— 10f. Thicker and more dumpy initial cross.. ..	27/6

The prices for the above types are for London. We can sometimes supply coins of the following mints; types struck in brackets.

836	*Berwick-on-Tweed.* (Blunt types I-IV) .. .. *from*		20/-
837	*Bristol.* (2; 3b, c, d; 3f, g; 9b) .. .. .. *from*		22/6
838	*Bury St. Edmunds.* Robert de Hadelie (3c, d, g; 4a, b, c) *from*		45/-
839	— Villa Sci Edmundi (4e; 5b; 6b; 7a; 8a-10f) .. *from*		25/-
840	*Canterbury.* (2; 3b-g; 4; 5; 7a; 9; 10) .. .. *from*		20/-
841	*Chester.* (3g; 9b) .. .. *from*		35/-
842	*Durham.* King's Receiver (9b; 10a, b, e, f) .. *from*		40/-
843	— Bishop de Insula (2; 3b, c, e, g; 4a) .. .. *from*		27/6
844	— Bishop Bec. (4b, c, d; 5b; 6b; 7a; 8b; 9; 10b-f) mostly with *mm.* cross moline .. .. .. *from*		32/6
844A	— — (4b) cross moline in one angle of *rev.*		£10
845	*Exeter.* (9b)		37/6
846	*Kingston-upon-Hull.* (9b)		45/-
847	*Lincoln.* (3c, d, f, g) .. .. *from*		30/-
848	*Newcastle-on-Tyne.* (3e; 9b; 10) .. .. .. *from*		21/-
849	*York.* Royal mint (2; 3b, c, d, f; 9b) .. .. *from*		25/-
850	— Archbishop's mint (3e, g; 9b). ℞. Quatrefoil in centre *from*		37/6

855

851	**Halfpenny.** Class IIIb. Drapery segment of circle ..	65/-
852	— IIIc. Normal drapery	40/-
853	— IVe. Usually three pellets on breast, one on *rev.* ..	£5
854	— VII. Double barred N	90/-
855	— IX. Pot-hook N, usually no star on breast	50/-
856	— X. ЄDWAR R ANGL DNS hYB	50/-

The above prices are for London; halfpence of the mints given below were also struck.

857	*Berwick-on-Tweed.* (Blunt types II and III) .. *from*	£8
858	*Bristol.* (IIIc)	90/-
859	*Lincoln.* (IIIc)	£11
860	*Newcastle.* (IIIe). With single pellet in each angle of rev.	£10
861	*York.* (IIIb)	£10

865   866

863	**Farthing.** Class I. Heavy weight (6.85 grains), ЄDWARDVS REX. Ŗ. LONDONIЄNSIS	95/-
864	— II. Similar, but reversed N's	60/-
865	— IIIc. As class I, but different bust	50/-
866	— IIIg. Lighter weight (5.5 grs.), Є R ANGLIЄ.. ..	50/-
867	— VII. Similar	70/-
868	— VIII. Є R ANGL DN	55/-
869	— IX. — pot-hook N	50/-
870	— X. ЄDWARDVS REX A or AN	40/-

The above prices are for London; farthings of the mints given below were also struck.

871	*Berwick-on-Tweed.* (Blunt type III)	£20
872	*Bristol.* (II; III) .. .. *from*	£5
873	*Lincoln.* (III)	£18
874	*York.* (II; III) .. .. *from*	£13

For further information on the pennies of Edward I and II see the articles by K. A. Jacob in " Notes on English Silver Coins, 1066-1648," and for the mint of Berwick on Tweed, see the article by C. E. Blunt, in the Num. Chron., 1931.

EDWARD II, 1307-27

The coinage of this reign differs only in minor details from that of Edward I. No groats were issued in the years *c.* 1282-1351.

11a   12

Fine

875 **Penny.** Class 11a. Broken spear-head or pearl on l. side of crown; long narrow face, straight-sided N .. 32/6
876 — 11b. — Є with angular back (till 15b), N with well-marked serifs 30/–
877 — 11c. — — A of special form 40/–
878 — 12. Central fleur of crown formed of three wedges 45/–
879 — 13. Central fleur of crown as Greek double axe .. 35/–

14   15c

880 — 14. Crown with tall central fleur; large smiling face with leering eyes 30/–
881 — 15a. Small flat crown with both spear-heads usually bent to l.; face of 14 .. .. 35/–
882 — 15b. — very similar, but smaller face 35/–
883 — 15c. — large face, large Є 45/–

The prices of the above types are for London. We can sometimes supply coins of the following mints; types struck in brackets.

884 *Berwick-on-Tweed.* (Blunt types V, VI and VII) .. *from* 50/–
885 *Bury St. Edmunds.* (11; 12; 13; 14; 15) .. *from* 45/–
886 *Canterbury.* (11; 12; 13; 14; 15) .. .. *from* 45/–
887 *Durham.* King's Receiver (11a; 14); *mm.* plain cross *from* 50/–
888 — Bishop Bek. (11a), *mm.* cross moline 55/–
889 — Bishop Kellawe (11; 13), crozier on *rev.* .. *from* 50/–
890 — Bishop Beaumont (13; 14; 15), *mm.* lion with lis *from* 60/–
890A — Sede Vacante (15c); *mm.* plain cross £12
891 **Halfpenny** of *London.* ЄDWARDVS REX A(NG) .. £6
892 — *Berwick-on-Tweed.* (Blunt type V) £14
893 **Farthing** of *London.* ЄDWARDVS REX A(NG) .. 80/–
893A — *Berwick-on-Tweed.* (Blunt type V) .. *Extr. rare*

EDWARD III, 1327-77

During the early years of this reign the coinage followed the pattern of the previous two reigns. In 1344 a second attempt was made to introduce a gold coinage, but this was not very successful owing to the incorrect ratio of value established for the two metals. In 1351 there was a reform of the coinage, the weight of both gold and silver coins being reduced and the value of the two metals adjusted at a proportion of 12 to 1. At the same time the groat (4 pence) was reintroduced and the halfgroat was added to the silver coinage.

During the remainder of the reign a vast quantity of coins was minted, and a mint was opened at the port of Calais for recoining continental currency into English money. With the signing of the Treaty of Brétigni the title " King of France," previously used by Edward, was omitted from the coinage, but in 1369 the treaty was broken and the French title was used again.

Mintmarks

1334-51	Cross pattée (6)	1356	Crown (74)
1351-2	Cross 1 (1)	1356-61	Cross 3 (4)
1351-7	Crozier on cross end	1361-9	Cross potent (5)
	(76a, *Durham*)	1369-77	Cross pattée (6)
1352-3	Cross 1 broken (2)		Plain cross (7a)
1354-5	Cross 2 (3)		Cross potent and four pellets

The figures in brackets refer to the plate of mintmarks on page 10.

GOLD

Third coinage, 1344-51
First period, 1344

Fine

894 **Florin** (=6s.; wt. 108 grs.). King enthroned beneath canopy; fleured field. ℞. Royal cross in quat., etc. .. £4000

895 **Half-florin** or **Leopard.** Leopard sejant with banner l. ℞. Somewhat as last £3000

896 **Quarter-florin** or **Helm.** Helmet on fleured field. ℞. Floriate cross £2000

Edward III   Third Coinage Gold   *Fine*
Second period, 1344-6

897 **Noble** (=6s. 8d., wt. 138$\frac{6}{13}$ grs.).   King stg. facing in
    ship with sword and shield.   ℞. L in centre of royal
    cross in tressure £1500

898 **Quarter-noble.**   Shield in tressure.   ℞. As last   ..   £225

Third period, 1346-51

899 **Noble** (wt. 128$\frac{4}{7}$ grs.).   As 897, but Є in centre;
    large letters £175

900 **Half-noble.**   Similar £300

901 **Quarter-noble.**   As 898, but Є in centre £35

Fourth coinage, 1351-77
Pre-treaty period, 1351-61.   With French title.

    906   916

902 **Noble** (wt. 120 grs.), series B (1351).   Open Є and C.
    Roman M; *mm.* cross 1 (1) £65

903 — — *rev.* of series A (1351).   Round lettering,
    Lombardic M and N; closed inverted Є in centre   ..   £120

904 C (1351-2).   Closed Є and C, Lomb. M; *mm.* cross 1 (1) £47/10/-

905 D (1352-3).   *O.* of series C. ℞. *Mm.* cross 1 broken (2) £67/10/-

906 E (1354-5).   Broken letters, V often has a nick in r. limb;
    mm. cross 2 (3) £45

907 F (1356).   *Mm.* crown (74) £100

908 G (1356-61).   *Mm.* cross 3 (4).   Many varieties   ..   £40

909 **Half-noble,** B.   As noble with *rev.* of series A, but
    closed Є in centre not inverted £47/10/-

910 C.   *O.* as noble.   *Rev.* as last £40

911 E.   As noble £80

912 G.   As noble.   Many varieties £32/10/-

913 **Quarter-noble,** B.   Pellet below shield.   ℞. Closed
    Є in centre £25

914 C.   *O.* of series B.   *Rev.* details as noble £21

915 E.   *O.* as last.   *Rev.* details as noble, pellet in centre ..   £18

916 G.   *Mm.* cross 3 (4).   Many varieties £16

Transitional treaty period, 1361. Omits French title, irregular sized letters; *mm.* cross potent (5).

917   **Noble.** ℞. Pellets or annulets at corners of central panel   £80

918   **Half-noble.** Similar £32/10/-
919   **Quarter-noble.** Similar. Many varieties £15

Treaty period, 1361-9. Omits French title, new letters, usually curule-shaped x; *mm.* cross potent (5).

920   **Noble.** *London.* Saltire before ЄDWARD £42/10/-
921   — Annulet before ЄDWARD £40
923   *Calais.* c in centre of *rev.*, flag at stern of ship   .. £60
923A — — without flag £55

924   926

924   **Half-noble.** *London.* Saltire before ЄDWARD £27/10/-
925   — Annulet before ЄDWARD £30
926   *Calais.* c in centre of *rev.*, flag at stern of ship..   .. £52/10/-
927   — — without flag £45
928   **Quarter-noble.** *London.* As 916.   ℞.   Lis in centre   £14
929   — — annulet before ЄDWARD £15
930   *Calais.*   ℞.   Annulet in centre £17
931   — — cross in circle over shield £18
932   — ℞.   Quatrefoil in centre; cross over shield £25
933   — — crescent over shield £30

Post-treaty period, 1369-77. French title resumed.

934	**Noble.** *London.* Annulet before ЄD. Ŗ. Treaty period die	£57/10/–
935	— — — crescent on forecastle	£70
936	— — post-treaty letters. Ŗ. Є and pellet in centre ..	£48
937	— — — — Ŗ. Є and saltire in centre	£67/10/–
938	*Calais.* Flag at stern. Ŗ. C in centre	£48

939	— — *Rev.* as 936 (i.e., London die)	£52/10/–
940	— As 938, but without flag (i.e., London *obv.* die) ..	£52/10/–
941	**Half-noble.** *London.* O. Treaty die. *Rev.* as 936..	£75
942	*Calais.* Without AQT, flag at stern. Ŗ. Є in centre ..	£45
943	— — Ŗ. Treaty die with C in centre	£50

SILVER

First coinage, 1327-35

944	**Penny.** *London.* As Edw. II; class XVd with Lombardic n's	£30
945	*Bury St. Edmunds.* Similar .. .. *Extr. rare*	
946	*Canterbury; mm.* cross pattée with pellet centre	£20
947	— — three extra pellets in one qtr.	£20

	948 958	
948	*Durham.* Ŗ. Small crown in centre	£20
949	*York.* As 944, but quatrefoil in centre of *rev.*	£16
950	— — — pellet in each qtr. of *mm.*	£16
951	— — — three extra pellets in one qtr.	£16
952	— — — Roman N on *obv.*	£16
953	*Berwick* (1333-42, Blunt type VIII). Bear's head in one qtr. of *rev.*	£40

Edward III First Coinage Silver *Fine*

954 **Halfpenny.** *London.* ЄDWARDVS RЄX AII*, neat work, flat crown £25

955

955	*Berwick* (Bl. VIII). Bear's head in one or two qtrs ..	£12
956	**Farthing.** *London.* ЄDWARDVS RЄX A*, flat crown ..	£40
957	*Berwick* (Bl. VIII). As 955	£35

Second coinage, 1335-43

958 **Halfpenny.** *London.* ЄDWARDVS RЄX A(NG)*, rough work, tall crown 40/-
959 *Reading.* Escallop in one qtr. £30
960 **Farthing.** *London.* As halfpenny £7

Third or florin coinage, 1344-51. Bust with bushy hair.

961*   973

961 **Penny.** *London.* Class 1, ЄDW, Lombardic n's .. 75/-
962 — 2, ЄDWA, n's, but sometimes N's on *rev.* 40/-
963 — 3, ЄDW, N's, sometimes reversed or n's on *rev.* .. 50/-
964 — 4, ЄDW, no stops, reversed N's, but on *rev.* sometimes n's, N's or double-barred N's 65/-
  *There are also five unusual varieties of *obv.*

965 *Canterbury.* ЄDWA, n's £20
966 — ЄDW, reversed N's £15
967 *Durham*, Sede Vacante (1345). A, ЄDW R. ℞. No marks £5
968 — — B, similar, ЄDWAR R £10
969 — Bp. Hatfield. C, similar, but pellet in centre of *rev.*... £10
970 — — — Crozier on *rev.* £10
971 — — — — with pellet in centre of *rev.* £10
972 — — D, ЄDWARDVS RЄX AIn, crozier on *rev.* £20
973 *Reading.* *O.* as 964. ℞. Escallop in one quarter .. £24
974 *York.* *O.* as 964. ℞. Quatrefoil in centre .. £5
975 **Halfpenny.** *London.* ЄDWARDVS RЄX(An).. .. 40/-
975A — — pellet either side of crown 80/-
975B — — saltire either side of crown and in one quarter of *rev.* 90/-
976 *Reading.* *O.* similar. ℞. Escallop in one qtr. .. £35
976A *Continental type* 25/-
977 **Farthing.** *London.* ЄDWARDVS RЄX £15

Fourth coinage, 1351-77

> *Reference:* L. A. Lawrence, *The Coinage of Edward III from 1351.*

Pre-treaty period, 1351-61.   With French title.

| | Series E | G |

<table>
<tr><td>978</td><td>Groat (=4d., 72 grs.).   London, series B (1351).   Roman M, open C and E; mm. cross 1   ..   ..</td><td>£10</td></tr>
<tr><td>979</td><td>— — — crown in each qtr.   ..   ..   Unique</td><td></td></tr>
<tr><td>980</td><td>— C (1351-2).   Lomb. m, closed C and E, R with wedge-shaped tail; mm. cross 1   ..   ..</td><td>60/-</td></tr>
<tr><td>981</td><td>— D (1352-3).   R with normal tail; mm. cross 1 or cross 1 broken (2)   ..   ..</td><td>65/-</td></tr>
<tr><td>982</td><td>— E (1354-5).   Broken letters, V often with nick in r. limb; mm. cross 2 (3)   ..   ..</td><td>60/-</td></tr>
<tr><td>983</td><td>— — — lis on breast   ..   ..</td><td>60/-</td></tr>
<tr><td>984</td><td>— F (1356).   Mm. crown (74)   ..   ..</td><td>80/-</td></tr>
<tr><td>985</td><td>— G (1356-61).   Usually with annulet in one qtr. and sometimes under bust, mm. cross 3 (4).   Many varieties</td><td>60/-</td></tr>
<tr><td>986</td><td>York, series D.   As London   ..   ..</td><td>95/-</td></tr>
<tr><td>987</td><td>— E.   As London ..   ..</td><td>65/-</td></tr>
</table>

Series B

<table>
<tr><td>988</td><td>Halfgroat.   London, series B.   As groat ..   ..   ..</td><td>£9</td></tr>
<tr><td>989</td><td>— C.   As groat   ..   ..</td><td>32/6</td></tr>
<tr><td>990</td><td>— D.   As groat   ..   ..</td><td>37/6</td></tr>
<tr><td>991</td><td>— E.   As groat   ..   ..</td><td>37/6</td></tr>
<tr><td>992</td><td>— F.   As groat   ..   ..</td><td>65/-</td></tr>
<tr><td>993</td><td>— G.   As groat   ..   ..</td><td>55/-</td></tr>
<tr><td>994</td><td>— — — annulet below bust   ..   ..</td><td>80/-</td></tr>
<tr><td>995</td><td>York, series D.   As groat ..   ..</td><td>80/-</td></tr>
<tr><td>996</td><td>— E.   As groat   ..   ..</td><td>60/-</td></tr>
<tr><td>997</td><td>— — — lis on breast   ..   ..</td><td>85/-</td></tr>
</table>

Series A   C   F
Durham   London

998	**Penny** *London*. Series A (1351). Round letters, Lomb. m and n, ann. in each qtr.; *mm.* cross pattée	£5
999	— C. Details as groat, but ann. in each qtr.	40/-
1000	— D. Details as groat, but ann. in each qtr.	30/-
1001	— E. Sometimes annulet in each qtr.	30/-
1002	— F. Details as groat	50/-
1003	— G. Details as groat	30/-
1004	— — — annulet below bust	45/-
1005	— — — saltire in one quarter	60/-
1006	*Durham*, Bp. Hatfield. Series A. As 998, but extra pellet in each qtr., VIL LA crozier DVRReM	£12
1007	— C. Details as groat. ℞. Crozier, CIVITAS DVNELMIE	60/-
1008	— D — — —	65/-
1009	— E — — —	35/-
1010	— F — ℞. Crozier, CIVITAS DVReME	65/-
1011	— G — — —	40/-
1012	— — — — — annulet below bust	45/-
1013	— — — — — saltire in one qtr.	65/-
1013A	— — — — — annulet on each shoulder	60/-
1014	— — — — — trefoil of pellets on breast	85/-
1015	— — — ℞. Crozier, CIVITAS DVReLMIE	£5
1016	*York*, Royal Mint. Series D	80/-
1017	— — E	30/-
1018	— Archb. Thorsby. Series D. ℞. Quatrefoil in centre	75/-
1019	— — G —	30/-
1020	— — — annulet or saltire on breast	45/-
1021	**Halfpenny**, *London*. Series E. EDWARDVS REX An	£6
1022	— G, but with *obv.* of F (*mm.* crown). Ann. in one qtr. *Extr. rare*	
1023	**Farthing**, *London*. Series E. EDWARDVS REX *Extr. rare*	

Transitional treaty period, 1361. French title omitted, irregular sized letters; *mm.* cross potent (5).

1024	**Groat**, *London*. Annulet each side of crown	£20

1025	**Halfgroat.** Similar, but only seven arches to tressure	£20

1026	**Penny,** *London.* Omits REX, annulet in two upper qtrs. of *mm.*	£15
1027	*York,* Archb. Thoresby. Similar, but quatrefoil enclosing pellet in centre of *rev.*	£9
1028	*Durham,* Bp. Hatfield. Similar. ℞. Crozier, CIVITAS DORELME	£10
1029	**Halfpenny.** Two pellets over *mm.*, EDWARDVS REX An	£30

Treaty period, 1361-9. French title omitted, new letters, usually " Treaty " X; *mm.* cross potent (5).

1030	**Groat,** *London.* Many varieties	80/-
1031	— Annulet before EDWARD	£5
1032	— Annulet on breast	£10
1033	*Calais.* As last	£8

1035   1049

1034	**Halfgroat,** *London.* As groat	45/-
1035	— — Annulet before EDWARDVS..	40/-
1036	— — Annulet on breast	£5
1037	*Calais.* As last	£10
1038	**Penny,** *London.* EDWARD AnGL R, etc.	50/-
1039	— — — pellet before EDWARD	70/-
1040	*Calais.* ℞. VILLA CALESIE	£10
1041	*Durham.* ℞. CIVITAS DVNELMIS	£5
1042	— ℞. Crozier, CIVITAS DVREME	70/-
1043	*York,* Archb. Thoresby. Quatrefoil in centre of *rev.,* EDWARDVS DEI G REX An	£10
1044	— — — EDWARDVS REX ANGLI	55/-
1045	— — — — quatrefoil before ED and on breast ..	65/-
1046	— — — — annulet before ED	£5
1047	— — — EDWARD AnGL R DnS HYB	85/-
1048	**Halfpenny.** EDWARDVS REX An, pellet stops	95/-
1049	— Pellet before ED, annulet stops	£6
1050	**Farthing.** EDWARDVS REX, pellet stops..	£15

Post-treaty period, 1369-77. French title resumed, x
like St. Andrew's cross; *mm.* 5, 6, 7a.

1051   1053

1051	**Groat.** Various readings, *mm.* cross pattée	£6
1052	— — row of pellets across breast (chain mail).. ..	£28
1053	— row of annulets below bust (chain mail); *mm.* cross potent with four pellets	£35
1054	**Halfgroat.** Various readings	£7
1055	— row of pellets one side of breast (chain mail) ..	£35
1056	**Penny,** *London.* No marks on breast	60/-
1057	— Pellet or annulet on breast	95/-
1058	— Cross or quatrefoil on breast	65/-
1059	*Durham,* Bp. Hatfield. *Mm.* 7a, CIVITAS DVnOLM, crozier	55/-
1060	— — — — annulet on breast	65/-
1061	— — — — lis on breast	£5
1062	*York,* Archb. Thoresby or Neville. R. Quatrefoil in centre	45/-
1063	— — — lis on breast	80/-
1064	— — — annulet on breast	60/-
1065	— — — cross on breast	60/-
1066	**Farthing.** EDWARD REX ANGL, large head without neck..	£30

RICHARD II, 1377-99

There was no significant change in the coinage during this reign. Noteworthy is the first appearance of symbols on the ship's rudder on some of the gold coins. The earlier silver coins have a portrait like that on the coins of Edward III, but the king's head and the style of lettering was altered on the later issues.

Mintmark: cross pattée (6)

GOLD   *Fine*

1067	**Noble,** *London.* With altered *obv.* and/or *rev.* die of Edw. III	£180
1068	— Lettering as Edw. III, lis over sail	£120
1069	— Straight-sided letters, annulet over sail	£100
1070	— Late issue, fish-tail lettering; no marks, or trefoil by shield	£100
1070A	— — — lion or lis on rudder	£180
1071	— — small dumpy lettering; escallop or crescent on rudder and/or trefoil over sail or by shield	£150

1076   1074A   1084/5

1072	*Calais.* Flag at stern; as 1067	£175
1073	— — as 1069, but quatrefoil over sail	£120
1074	— — as 1070; no marks	£120
1074A	— — — lion on rudder	£175
1075	— — as 1071	£120
1076	**Half-noble,** *London.* As 1067	£100
1077	— as 1069	£70
1078	— as 1070; lion on rudder	£100
1079	— as 1071; crescent on rudder	£125
1080	*Calais.* Flag at stern; as 1067	£125
1081	— — as 1069; quatrefoil over sail	£125
1082	— — as 1070; lion on rudder	£100
1083	— — as 1071, but one var. has saltire behind rudder ..	£150
1084	**Quarter-noble,** *London.* R in centre of *rev.*	£50
1085	— Lis or pellet in centre of *rev*	£37/10/-
1086	— — *obv.* die of Edw. III altered	£55
1087	— — escalop over shield	£57/10/-
1088	— — trefoil of annulets over shield	£57/10/-
1089	— — quatrefoil, cross or slipped trefoil over shield ..	£42/10/-

SILVER

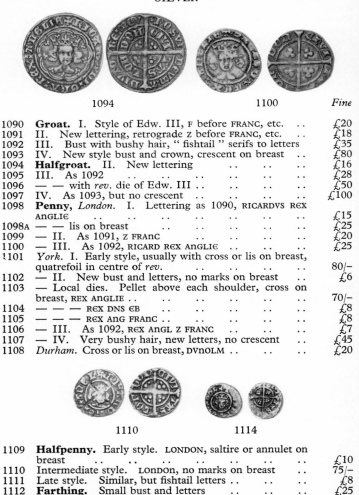

1094   1100   *Fine*

1090	**Groat.** I. Style of Edw. III, F before FRANC, etc. ..	£20
1091	II. New lettering, retrograde Z before FRANC, etc. ..	£18
1092	III. Bust with bushy hair, "fishtail" serifs to letters	£35
1093	IV. New style bust and crown, crescent on breast ..	£80
1094	**Halfgroat.** II. New lettering	£16
1095	III. As 1092	£28
1096	— — with *rev.* die of Edw. III	£50
1097	IV. As 1093, but no crescent	£100
1098	**Penny,** *London*. I. Lettering as 1090, RICARDVS REX ANGLIE	£15
1098A	— — lis on breast	£25
1099	— II. As 1091, Z FRANC	£20
1100	— III. As 1092, RICARD REX ANGLIE	£25
1101	*York*. I. Early style, usually with cross or lis on breast, quatrefoil in centre of *rev.*	80/-
1102	— II. New bust and letters, no marks on breast ..	£6
1103	— Local dies. Pellet above each shoulder, cross on breast, REX ANGLIE	70/-
1104	— — — REX DNS EB	£8
1105	— — — REX ANG FRANC	£8
1106	— III. As 1092, REX ANGL Z FRANC	£7
1107	— IV. Very bushy hair, new letters, no crescent ..	£45
1108	*Durham*. Cross or lis on breast, DVNOLM	£20

1110   1114

1109	**Halfpenny.** Early style. LONDON, saltire or annulet on breast	£10
1110	Intermediate style. LONDON, no marks on breast ..	75/-
1111	Late style. Similar, but fishtail letters	£8
1112	**Farthing.** Small bust and letters	£25
1112A	— — rose after REX	£35
1113	Large head, no bust	£30
1114	Rose in each angle of *rev.* instead of pellets	£70

HENRY IV, 1399-1413

In 1412 the standard weights of the coinage were reduced, the noble by 12 grains and the penny by 3 grains, partly because there was a scarcity of bullion and partly to provide revenue for the king, as Parliament had not renewed the royal subsidies. As in France, the royal arms was altered, three fleur-de-lis taking the place of the four or more lis previously displayed.

Mintmark: cross pattée (6)

GOLD

1116   1124

		Fine
Heavy coinage, 1399-1412		
1115	**Noble** (120 grs.), *London.* Old arms with four lis in French qtrs.; crescent or annulet on rudder ⸱⸱ ⸱⸱	£1750
1116	— New arms with three lis; crescent, pellet or no marks on rudder ⸱⸱ ⸱⸱ ⸱⸱ ⸱⸱ ⸱⸱ ⸱⸱	£2000
1117	*Calais.* Flag at stern, old arms; crown on or to l. of rudder ⸱⸱ ⸱⸱ ⸱⸱ ⸱⸱ ⸱⸱ *Extr. rare*	
1118	— — new arms; crown or star on rudder *Extr. rare*	
1119	**Half-noble,** *London.* Old arms ⸱⸱ *Extr. rare*	
1120	— new arms ⸱⸱ ⸱⸱ ⸱⸱ ⸱⸱ *Extr. rare*	
1121	**Quarter-noble,** *London.* Crescent over old arms ⸱⸱	£175
1122	— — — new arms ⸱⸱ ⸱⸱ ⸱⸱ ⸱⸱ ⸱⸱	£200
1123	*Calais.* New arms. ℞. *Mm.* crown ⸱⸱ ⸱⸱ ⸱⸱	£250
Light coinage, 1412-13		
1124	**Noble** (108 grs.). Trefoil, or also with annulet, on side of ship. ℞. Trefoil in one qtr. ⸱⸱ ⸱⸱ ⸱⸱	£750
1125	**Half-noble.** Similar, but always with annulet *Extr. rare*	
1126	**Quarter-noble.** Trefoils, or trefoils and annulets beside shield, lis above. ℞. Lis in centre ⸱⸱ ⸱⸱	£150

Henry IV

SILVER

    1131   1140   1137

Heavy coinage, 1399-1412	*Fine*

1127 **Halfgroat** (36 grs.). Star on breast £110

1128 **Penny,** *London.* Similar, early bust with long neck .. £80

1129 — later bust with shorter neck, no star £80

1130 *York.* Early bust with long neck £35

1131 — later bust with broad face, round chin £35

1132 **Halfpenny.** Early small bust £30

1133 Later large bust, with rounded shoulders £25

1134 **Farthing.** Face without neck £70

Light coinage, 1412-13

1135 **Groat** (60 grs.). I. Pellet to l., annulet to r. of crown; altered die of Richard II £130

1136 New dies; II. Annulet to l., pellet to r. of crown, 8 or 10 arches to tressure £110

1137 — III. Similar but 9 arches to tressure.. .. .. £110

1138 **Halfgroat.** Pellet to l., annulet to r. of crown .. £110

1139 Annulet to l., pellet to r. of crown £90

1140 **Penny,** *London.* Annulet and pellet by crown; trefoil on breast and before CIVI £55

1141 — — annulet or slipped trefoil before LON £55

1142 — Pellet and annulet by crown .. .. *Unique*

1143 *York.* Annulet on breast. ℞. Quatrefoil in centre .. £45

1144 *Durham.* Trefoil on breast, DVnOLM £45

1145 **Halfpenny.** Struck from heavy dies £30

1146 New dies; annulet either side of head £30

1147 **Farthing.** Face, no bust; slipped trefoil after REX .. £70

HENRY V, 1413-22

There was no change of importance in the coinage of this reign. There was, however, a considerable development in the use of privy marks which distinguished various issues, except for the last issue of the reign when most marks were removed. The Calais mint, which had closed in 1411, did not re-open until early in the next reign.

Mintmarks

Cross pattée (4, but with pellet centre). Pierced cross (18).

GOLD

1153   1163

Fine

1148	**Noble.** Quatrefoil over sail and in second qtr. of *rev.*		
	A. Short broad letters, no other marks	*Extr. rare*	
1149	— B. Ordinary letters; similar, or with annulet on rudder		£110
1150	— C. Mullet by sword arm, annulet on rudder		£85
1151	— — — broken annulet on side of ship		£67/10/-
1152	— D. Mullet and annulet by sword arm, trefoil by shield, broken annulet on ship		£85
1153	— E. Mullet, or mullet and annulet by sword arm, trefoil by shield, pellet by sword point and in one qtr., annulet on side of ship		£100
1153A	— — Similar, but trefoil on ship instead of by shield		£120
1154	— F. Similar, but no pellet at sword point, trefoil in one qtr.		£100
1155	G. No marks; annulet stops, except for mullet after first word		£200
1156	**Half-noble.** B. As noble; Hen. IV *rev.* die	*Extr. rare*	
1157	C. Broken annulet on ship, quatrefoil below sail		£75
1158	— — Mullet over shield, broken annulet on *rev.*		£60
1159	F. Similar, but no annulet on ship, usually trefoil by shield		£80
1160	F/E. As last, but pellet in 1st and annulet in 2nd qtr.		£100
1161	G. As noble, but quatrefoil over sail, mullet sometimes omitted after first word of *rev.*		£140

1162   **Quarter-noble.** Lis over shield and in centre of *rev*.
       A.   Short broad letters; quatrefoil and annulet beside
       shield, stars at corners of centre on *rev*...   ..   ..   £65
1163   — C.   Ordinary letters; quatrefoil to l., quat. and
       mullet to r. of shield £40
1164   — — annulet to l., mullet to r. of shield £40
1165   — F — trefoil to l., mullet to r. of shield £70
1166   — G — no marks, except mullet after first word   ..   £60

SILVER

1167   1170

1167   **Groat.** A.   Short broad letters; " emaciated " bust   ..   £35
1168   — — muled with Hen. IV *obv.* or *rev.* £65
1169   — — muled with later *rev.* of Hen. V £45
1170   B.   Ordinary letters; " scowling " bust £20
1171   — — muled with Hen. IV or later Hen. V £30
1172   C.   Normal bust £15
1173   — — mullet on r. shoulder £8
1174   — — mullet in centre of breast £11
1175   G.   Normal bust; no marks £14
1176   **Halfgroat.** A.   As groat, but sometimes with annulet
       and pellet by crown £30
1177   B.   Ordinary letters; no marks £12
1178   — — muled with Hen. IV or class C £15
1179   C.   Tall neck, broken annulet to l. of crown £15
1180   — — — mullet on r. shoulder £10

1181   — — — mullet in centre of breast £10
1182   F.   Annulet and trefoil by crown, mullet on breast   ..   £12
1183   G.   New neat bust; no marks £9

1186   1199

1184	**Penny,** *London.* A. Letters, bust and marks as 1176..			£20
1185	— B. Altered A *obv.*, with mullet and broken annulet added by crown. R. Ordinary letters			£35
1186	— C. Tall neck, mullet and broken annulet by crown			80/–
1187	— D. Similar, but whole annulet			85/–
1188	— F. Mullet and trefoil by crown			£8
1189	— G. New neat bust, no marks, DI GRA			85/–
1190	*Durham.* C. As 1186 but quatrefoil at end of legend ..			£5
1191	— D. As 1187			80/–
1192	— G. Similar, but new bust. R. annulet in one qtr...			£8
1193	*York.* C. As 1186, but quat. in centre of *rev.*			65/–
1194	— D. Similar, but whole annulet by crown			75/–
1195	— E. As last, but pellet above mullet			£8
1196	— F. Mullet and trefoil by crown			£5
1197	— — Trefoil over mullet to l., annulet to r. of crown			60/–
1198	— G. Mullet and trefoil by crown (London dies)			55/–
1199	— — Mullet and lis by crown, annulet in one qtr. (usually local dies)			55/–

1203   1206

1200	**Halfpenny.** A. Emaciated bust, annulets by crown..			£8
1201	— altered dies of Hen. IV			£10
1202	C. Ordinary bust, broken annulets by crown ..			50/–
1203	D. Annulets, sometimes broken, by hair			60/–
1204	F. Annulet and trefoil by crown			70/–
1205	G. New bust; no marks			80/–
1206	**Farthing.** G. Small face with neck ..			£40

HENRY VI, 1422-61

The supply of gold began to dwindle early in the reign, which accounts for the rarity of gold after 1426. The Calais mint was re-opened in 1424 and for some years a large amount of coin was struck there. It soon stopped minting gold; the mint was finally closed in 1440. A royal mint at York was opened for a short time in 1423/4.

Marks used to denote various issues become more prominent in this reign and can be used to date coins to within a year or so.

Reference: *Heavy Coinage of Henry VI*, by C. A. Whitton (B.N.J., 1938-41).

Mintmarks

1422-60	Plain cross (7a, intermittently)
	Lis (105, on gold)
1422-27	Pierced cross (18)
1422-34	Cross pommée
1427-34	Cross patonce (8)
	Cross fleurée (9)

1434-35	Voided cross (15)
1435-60	Cross fleury (9)
1460	Lis (105, on *rev.* of some groats)
	For Restoration marks see p. 104.

GOLD

Annulet issue, 1422-7

Fine

1207	**Noble,** *London.* Annulet by sword arm, and in one spandril on *rev.*; trefoil stops on *obv.* with lis after hENRIC, annulets on *rev.*, with mullet after IHC	£47/10/-
1207A	— Similar, but *obv.* from Henry V die	£150
1207B	— As 1207, but a Flemish copy	£42/10/-
1208	*Calais.* As 1207, but flag at stern and c in centre of *rev.*	£80
1209	— — with h in centre of *rev.*	£65
1210	*York.* As London, but with lis over stern	£75
1211	**Half-noble,** *London.* As 1207	£45
1211A	— Similar, but *obv.* from Henry V die	£80
1212	*Calais.* As noble, with c in centre of *rev.*	£90
1213	— — with h in centre of *rev.*	£70
1214	*York.* As noble	£82/10/-

Henry VI Gold. Annulet issue

		Fine
1215	**Quarter-noble**, *London*. Lis over shield; *mm.* large lis	£25
1216	— — — trefoil below shield	£45
1217	— — — pellet below shield .. .. *Extr. rare*	
1218	*Calais*. Three lis over shield; *mm.* large lis £32/10/-	
1218A	— Similar but three lis around shield £37/10/-	
1219	— As 1215, but much smaller *mm.* £30	
1220	*York*. Two lis over shield £40	

Rosette-mascle issue, 1427-30

1221	**Noble**, *London*. Lis by sword arm and in *rev.* field; stops, rosettes, or rosettes and mascles	£135
1222	*Calais*. Similar, with flag at stern	£185
1223	**Half-noble**, *London*. Lis in *rev.* field; stops, rosettes and mascles	£140
1224	*Calais*. Similar, flag at stern; stops, rosettes	£200
1225	**Quarter-noble**, *London*. As 1215; stops, as noble ..	£65
1226	— without lis over shield..	£65
1227	*Calais*. Lis over shield, rosettes r. and l., and as stops	£100

Pinecone-mascle issue, 1430-4

1228	**Noble**, *London*. Stops, pinecones and mascles ..	£125
1229	**Half-noble**, *London*. *O.* Rosette-mascle die. R. As last .. .. *Extr. rare*	
1230	**Quarter-noble**. As 1215, but pinecone and mascle stops .. .. *Unique*	

Leaf-mascle issue, 1434-5

1231	**Noble**. Leaf in waves; stops, saltires with two mascles and one leaf	£300
1232	**Quarter-noble**. As 1215; stops, saltire and mascle; leaf on inner circle of *rev.* .. .. *Extr. rare*	

Leaf-trefoil issue, 1435-8

1233	**Noble**. Stops, leaves and trefoils .. *Extr. rare*	
1234	**Quarter-noble**. Similar .. .. *Unique*	

Trefoil issue, 1438-43

1235	**Noble**. Trefoil below shield and in *rev.* legend ..	£375

Leaf-pellet issue, 1445-54

1236	**Noble**. Annulet, lis and leaf below shield	£275

SILVER

Annulet issue, 1422-7

1237   1242

1237	**Groat,** *London.* Annulet in two quarters of *rev.*	..	70/-
1238	*Calais.* Annulets at neck. ℞. Similar	.. ..	40/-
1239	— — no annulets on *rev.*	.. .. ..	70/-
1240	*York.* Lis either side of neck. ℞. As 1237 ..	..	£75
1241	**Halfgroat,** *London.* As groat	..	60/-
1242	*Calais.* As 1238	..	40/-
1243	— — no annulets on *rev.*	..	80/-
1244	— — only one annulet on *rev.*	..	90/-
1245	*York.* As groat	..	£100
1246	**Penny,** *London.* Annulets in two qtrs.	..	45/-
1247	*Calais.* Annulets at neck. ℞. As above	..	40/-
1248	— — only one annulet on *rev.*	..	55/-
1249	*York.* As London, but lis at neck ..	..	£100
1250	**Halfpenny,** *London.* As penny ..	..	45/-
1251	*Calais.* Similar, but annulets at neck ..	..	35/-
1252	*York.* Similar, but lis at neck	..	£65
1253	**Farthing,** *London.* As penny, but *mm.* cross pommée ..		£25

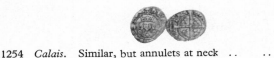

1254	*Calais.* Similar, but annulets at neck ..	.. ..	£50

Annulet-trefoil sub-issue

1255	**Groat,** *London.* As 1237, but trefoil of pellets to l. of crown (*North*)		
1256	*Calais.* Similar, but annulets by neck also ..	..	90/-
1257	**Halfgroat,** *Calais.* Similar	..	85/-
1258	**Penny,** *Calais.* Similar	..	85/-
1259	— — only one annulet on *rev.*	..	90/-

Rosette-mascle issue, 1427-30. All with rosettes (early) or rosettes and mascles somewhere in the legends.

1260	**Groat,** *London*	..	75/-
1261	*Calais*	..	45/-
1262	— mascle in two spandrils (as illus. 1265) ..	..	£8

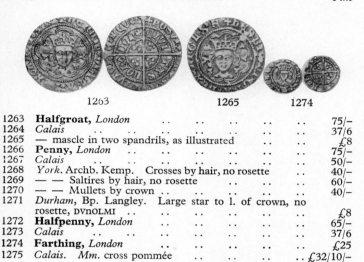

1263   1265   1274

1263	**Halfgroat,** *London*	..	..	..	..	..	75/-
1264	*Calais*	..	..	..	..	..	37/6
1265	— mascle in two spandrils, as illustrated		..	..	£8
1266	**Penny,** *London*	..	..	..	..	..	75/-
1267	*Calais*	..	..	..	..	..	50/-
1268	*York.* Archb. Kemp. Crosses by hair, no rosette		..	40/-
1269	— — Saltires by hair, no rosette		..	..	60/-
1270	— — Mullets by crown	..	..	..	..	40/-
1271	*Durham,* Bp. Langley. Large star to l. of crown, no rosette, DVnOLMI	..	..	..	..	..	£8
1272	**Halfpenny,** *London*	..	..	..	..	65/-
1273	*Calais*	..	..	..	..	..	37/6
1274	**Farthing,** *London*	..	..	..	..	£25
1275	*Calais. Mm.* cross pommée	..	..	..	£32/10/-

1281

Pinecone-mascle issue, 1430-4. All with pinecones and mascles in legends.

1276	**Groat,** *London*	..	..	..	..	..	..	60/-
1277	*Calais*	..	..	..	..	..	..	50/-
1278	**Halfgroat,** *London*	..	..	..	..	..	60/-
1279	*Calais*	..	..	..	..	..	..	45/-
1280	**Penny,** *London*	..	..	..	..	..	85/-
1281	*Calais*	..	..	..	..	..	..	55/-
1282	*York,* Archb. Kemp. Mullet by crown, quatrefoil in centre of *rev.*	..	..	..	65/-
1283	— — rosette on breast, no quatrefoil	..	..	55/-
1283A	— — mullet on breast, no quatrefoil	..	..	£6
1284	*Durham,* Bp. Langley. DVnOLMI	..	..	£6
1285	**Halfpenny,** *London*	..	..	..	..	60/-
1286	*Calais*	..	..	..	..	..	60/-
1287	**Farthing,** *London*	..	..	..	..	£20
1288	*Calais. Mm.* cross pommée	..	..	..	£40

1293   1298

Leaf-mascle issue, 1434-5. Usually with a mascle in the legend and a leaf somewhere in the design.

1289	**Groat,** *London.* Leaf below bust	£9
1290	— — *rev.* of last or next coinage	£5
1291	*Calais.* Leaf below bust, and usually below MƐVM ..	65/-
1292	**Halfgroat,** *London.* No leaf, pellet under TAS and DON	85/-
1293	*Calais.* Leaf below bust, and sometimes on *rev.* ..	£6
1294	**Penny,** *London.* Leaf on breast, no stops on *rev.* ..	85/-
1295	*Calais.* Leaf on breast and below SIƐ	75/-
1296	**Halfpenny,** *London.* Leaf on breast and on *rev.* ..	65/-
1297	*Calais.* Leaf on breast and below SIƐ	£8

Leaf-trefoil issue, 1435-8. Mostly with leaves and trefoil of pellets in the legends.

1298	**Groat,** *London.* Leaf on breast	80/-
1299	— without leaf on breast	65/-
1300	*Calais.* Leaf on breast	£12
1301	**Halfgroat,** *London.* Leaf on breast; *mm.* plain cross	80/-
1302	— *O. mm.* cross fleury; leaf on breast	80/-
1303	— — without leaf on breast	80/-
1304	**Penny,** *London.* Leaf on breast	70/-
1305	*Durham,* Bp. Neville. Leaf on breast. ℞. Rings in centre, no stops, DVNOLM	£6
1306	**Halfpenny,** *London.* Leaf on breast	50/-
1307	— without leaf on breast	65/-
1308	**Farthing,** *London.* Leaf on breast; stops, trefoil and saltire on *obv.*	£30

Trefoil issue, 1438-43. Trefoil of pellets either side of neck and in legend, leaf on breast.

1309	**Groat,** *London.* Sometimes a leaf before LON ..	60/-
1310	— Fleurs in spandrils, sometimes extra pellet in two qtrs.	85/-
1311	— Trefoils in place of fleurs at shoulders, none by neck, sometimes extra pellets	60/-
1312	*Calais*	£10

1313	**Halfpenny,** *London*	65/-

Henry VI   Silver

Fine

Trefoil-pellet issue, 1443-5.

1314	**Groat.** Trefoils by neck, pellets by crown, small leaf on breast; sometimes extra pellet in two qtrs.	85/–

Leaf-pellet issue, 1445-54. Leaf on breast, pellet each side of crown, except where stated.

1315	**Groat.** ᴀɴɢʟ; extra pellet in two qtrs...	60/–
1316	Similar, but ᴀɴɢʟɪ	50/–
1317	— — trefoil in *obv.* legend	65/–
1318	Leaf on neck, fleur on breast, often extra pellet in two qtrs.	45/–
1319	As last, but two extra pellets by hair	£12
1320	**Halfgroat.** As 1315	85/–
1321	Similar, but *mm.* plain cross; sometimes no leaf on breast and no stops on *rev.*	80/–
1322	**Penny,** *London.* Usually extra pellets in two qtrs. ..	80/–
1323	— — pellets by crown omitted	£5
1324	— — trefoil in legend	£5
1325	*York,* Archb. Booth. ℟. Quatrefoil and pellet in centre	70/–
1326	— — two extra pellets by hair (local dies)	50/–

1328

1327	*Durham,* Bp. Neville. Trefoil in *obv.* legend. ℟. Two rings in centre of cross	£6
1328	— — Similar, but without trefoil	£6
1329	**Halfpenny.** Usually extra pellet in two qtrs. ..	50/–
1330	— *mm.* plain cross	55/–
1331	**Farthing.** As last	£25

Unmarked issue, 1453-54.

1332	**Groat.** No marks on *obv.*; two extra pellets on *rev.* ...	£10
1333	— four extra pellets on *rev.*	£12/10/–
1334	**Halfgroat.** As 1332	£15

Cross-pellet issue, 1454-60.

1335	**Groat.** Saltire either side of neck, pellets by crown, leaf and fleur on breast, extra pellets on *rev.*	£10
1336	Saltire on neck, no leaf, pellets by crown, usually mullets in legend; extra pellets on *rev.*	70/–
1337	— Similar, but mascles in place of mullets on *obv.* ..	80/–
1338	— — pellets by hair instead of by crown	£6
1339	**Halfgroat.** Saltire on neck, pellets by crown and on *rev.,* mullets in legend	£10

1340 **Penny,** *London.* Saltire on neck, pellets by crown and on *rev.,* mascle(s), or mullet and mascle in legend .. £10

1341 *York,* Archb. Wm. Booth. Saltires by neck, usually leaf on breast, pellets by crown. ℞. Cross in quatrefoil in centre. Illustrated below. 85/-

1342 *Durham,* Bp. Laurence Booth. Saltire and B at neck, pellets by crown. ℞. Rings in centre £12

1343 **Halfpenny.** Saltires by neck, usually two extra pellets on *rev.* £7

1344 Similar, but saltire on neck, sometimes mullet after hꞬnRIC 65/-

1345 **Farthing.** Saltire on neck, pellets by crown and on *rev.* £30

1341   1346

Lis-pellet issue, 1456-60.

1346 **Groat.** Lis on neck; pellets by crown. ℞. Extra pellets £9

EDWARD IV, First Reign, 1461-70

In order to increase the supply of bullion to the mint the weight of the penny was reduced to 12 grains in 1464, and the current value of the noble was raised to 8s. 4d. Later, in 1465, a new gold coin was issued, the Ryal or "Rose Noble," weighing 120 grains and having a value of 10s. However, as 6s. 8d. had become the standard professional fee the old noble was missed, and a new coin was issued to take its place, the Angel of 80 grains.

Royal mints were opened at Canterbury and York to help with the re-coinage, and other mints were set up at Bristol, Coventry and Norwich, though they were not open for long.

Reference: C. E. Blunt and C. A. Whitton, *The Coinage of Edward IV and Henry VI (Restored),* B.N.J. 1945-7.

Mintmarks

1461-4	Lis (105)	1467-70 Lis (105, *York*)
	Cross fleury (9)	1467-8 Crown (74) ⎱ often
	Plain cross (7a)	Sun (28) ⎰ combined
1464-5	Rose (33 and 34)	1468-9 Crown (74) sometimes
1464-7	Pall (99, *Canterbury*)	Rose (33) combined
1465-6	Sun (28)	1469-70 Long cross
1466-7	Crown (74)	fitchee (11) often
		Sun (28) combined

GOLD

Heavy coinage, 1461–64.

1347 **Noble** (=6s. 8d., wt. 108 grs). Normal type, but *obv.* legend commences at top left, lis below shield; *mm.* –/lis
Extr. rare

Light coinage, 1464–70.

1348 **Noble** (=8s. 4d., wt. 108 grs.). Normal type; quatrefoil below sword arm; *mm.* rose/lis *Unique*

1349 **Ryal** or rose-noble (=10s., wt. 120 grs.), *London.* Type as next illus. Large fleurs in spandrils; *mm.* 33–74 £42/10/–

1350 — — Small trefoils in spandrils; *mm.* 74–11 .. .. £45

1351 — — Flemish copy, mostly struck *c.* Elizabeth I .. £30

1352 *Bristol.* B in waves, large fleurs; *mm.* 28, 74 .. .. £60

1353 — — small fleurs in spandrils; *mm.* 74, 28 .. .. £60

1354 *Coventry.* C in waves; *mm.* sun £150

1355 *Norwich.* N in waves; *mm.* sun, rose? £180

1356 *York.* Є in waves, large fleurs in spandrils, *mm.* 28, 105 £67/10/–

1357 — — small fleurs, *mm.* 105, 28 .. ..£67/10/–

1358 **Half-ryal,** *London.* As 1349 .. ..£42/10/–

1359 *Bristol.* B in waves; *mm.* 28–28/74 .. .. .. £55

1360 *Coventry.* C in waves; *mm.* sun £300

1361 *Norwich.* N in waves; *mm.* rose £250

1362 *York.* Є in waves; *mm.* 28, 105, 33/105 .. ..£47/10/–

1363 **Quarter-ryal.** Shield in tressure of eight arcs, rose above. ℞. Somewhat as half ryal; *mm.* 28/33 *Unique?*

1364 Shield in quatrefoil, Є above, rose on l., sun on r.; *mm.* 33/28–74/33 .. .. £30

1365 — — sun on l., rose on r.; *mm.* 74–11 .. .. £30

1366 **Angel** (=6s. 8d., wt. 80 grs.). St. Michael spearing dragon. ℞. Ship, rays of sun at masthead, large rose and sun beside mast; *mm.* –/34 .. .. £650

1367 — — small rose and sun at mast; *mm.* –/74 *Extr. rare*

SILVER

1371   1384

Heavy coinage, 1461-64.

1368	**Groat** (60 grs.). Group I, lis on neck, pellets by crown; *mm.* 9, 7a, 105, 9/105	70/-
1369	— Lis on breast, no pellets; *mm.* plain cross, 7a/105 ..	90/-
1370	— — with pellets at crown; *mm.* plain cross	90/-
1371	II, quatrefoils by neck, crescent on breast; *mm.* rose ..	80/-
1372	III, similar, but trefoil on breast; *mm.* rose	85/-
1373	— — — eye in *rev.* inner legend, *mm.* rose	65/-
1374	— Similar, but no quatrefoils by bust	£7
1375	— — Similar, but no trefoil on breast	£6
1376	IV, annulets by neck, eye after TAS; *mm.* rose	90/-
1377	**Halfgroat.** I, lis on breast, pellets by crown and extra pellets in two qtrs.; *mm.* 9, 7a	£18
1378	II, quatrefoils at neck, crescent on breast; *mm.* rose ..	£24
1379	III, similar, but trefoil on breast, eye on *rev.*; *mm.* rose	£24
1380	— Similar, but no mark on breast £27/10/-	
1381	IV, annulets by neck, sometimes eye on *rev.*; *mm.* rose ..£22/10/-	
1382	**Penny** (15 grs.), *London.* I, marks as 1377, but mascle after REX; *mm.* plain cross	£28
1383	— II, quatrefoils by neck; *mm.* rose £22/10/-	
1384	— III, similar, but eye after TAS; *mm.* rose	£18
1385	— IV, annulets by neck; *mm.* rose £22/10/-	
1386	*York*, Archb. Booth. Quatrefoils by bust, voided quatrefoil in centre of *rev.*; *mm.* rose	£16
1387	*Durham.* O. of Hen. VI. ℞. DVnOLIn	£25
	Some of the Durham pennies from local dies may belong to the heavy coinage period, but if so they are indistinguishable from the light coins.	
1388	**Halfpenny.** I, as 1382, but no mascle	£16
1389	II, quatrefoils by bust; *mm.* rose..	£8
1390	— saltires by bust; *mm.* rose	£12
1391	III, no marks by bust; *mm.* rose	£10
1392	IV, annulets by bust; *mm.* rose	£9
1393	**Farthing.** I, as 1388 .. .. .. 2 *known*	

Light coinage, 1464–70.   There is a great variety of groats and we give only a selection.   Some have pellets in one quarter of the reverse, or trefoils over the crown; early coins have fleurs on the cusps of the tressure, then trefoils or no marks on the cusps, while the late coins have only trefoils.

1399   1401

1394	**Groat** (48 grs.), *London*. Annulets at neck, eye after TAS; *mm.* 33 (struck from heavy dies, IV)	65/-
1395	— — Similar, but new dies, eye after TAS or DON ..	55/-
1396	— Quatrefoils at neck, eye; *mm.* 33 (heavy dies, III))..	65/-
1397	— — Similar, but new dies	50/-
1398	— No marks at neck, eye; *mm.* 33	90/-
1399	— Quatrefoils at neck, no eye; *mm.* 33, 74, 28, 74/28, 74/33, 11/28	50/-
1400	— — rose or quatrefoil on breast; *mm.* 33, 74/78 ..	75/-
1401	— No marks at neck; *mm.* 28, 74, 11/28, 11	70/-
1402	— Trefoils at neck; *mm.* 11/33, 11/28, 11	80/-
1403	*Bristol.* B on breast, quatrefoils at neck; *mm.* 28/33, 28, 28/74, 74, 74/28	50/-
1404	— — trefoils at neck; *mm.* 28	£5
1405	— — no marks at neck; *mm.* 28	£6
1406	— Without B, quatrefoils at neck; *mm.* 28	85/-
	Bristol is variously rendered as BRESTOLL, BRISTOLL, BRESTOW, BRISTOW.	
1407	*Coventry.* C on breast, quatrefoils at neck, COVETRE; *mm.* 28/33, 28	£5
1408	— — Local dies, similar; *mm.* rose	£7
1409	— — — as last, but no C or quatrefoils	£10
1410	*Norwich.* n on breast, quatrefoils at neck, NORWIC or NORVIC, *mm.* 28/33, 28	£5
1411	*York.* є on breast, quatrefoils at neck, єBORACI; *mm.* 28, 105/74, 105, 105/28	50/-
1412	— Similar, but without є on breast, *mm.* 105	90/-
1413	— є on breast, trefoils at neck; *mm.* 105/28, 105 ..	60/-

1414 **Halfgroat,** *London.* Annulets by neck (heavy dies);
mm 33 .. .. £20
1415 — Quatrefoils by neck; *mm.* 33/–, 28/–, 74, 74/28 .. 70/–
1416 — Saltires by neck; *mm.* 74, 74/28 .. .. .. 90/–
1417 — Trefoils by neck; *mm.* 74, 74/28, 11/28 .. .. 80/–
1418 — No marks by neck; *mm.* 11/28 .. .. .. £9
1419 *Bristol.* Saltires or crosses by neck; *mm.* 33/28, 28, 74, 74/– £14
1420 — Quatrefoils by neck; *mm.* 28/–, 74, 74/– £12/10/–
1421 — Trefoils by neck; *mm.* 74 .. .. .. £20
1422 — No marks by neck; *mm.* 74/28 .. .. .. £20
1423 *Canterbury,* Archb. Bourchier (1464-7). Knot below bust; quatrefoils by neck; *mm.* 99/–, 99, 99/33, 99/28 .. 40/–
1424 — — — quatrefoils omitted 50/–
1425 — — — saltires by neck; *mm.* 99/–, 99/28 .. .. 60/–
1426 — — — wedges by hair and/or neck; *mm.* 99, 99/33, 99/28 .. .. 85/–
1427 — — As 1423 or 1424, but no knot £5

1429   1426

1428 — Royal mint (1467-69). Quats. by neck; *mm.* 74, 74/– 50/–
1429 — — Saltires by neck; *mm.* 74/–, 74 .. .. .. 80/–
1430 — — Trefoils by neck; *mm.* 74, 74/–, 74/28, 33 .. 70/–
1430A — No marks by neck; *mm.* 28 .. .. £15
1431 *Coventry.* Crosses by neck; *mm.* sun .. *Unique*
1432 *Norwich.* Saltires by neck; *mm.* sun .. *Extr. rare*
1433 *York.* Quatrefoils by neck; *mm.* sun, lis, lis/– £6
1434 — Saltires by neck; *mm.* lis £9
1435 — Trefoils by neck; *mm.* lis, lis/– £7
1436 — є on breast, quatrefoils by neck; *mm.* lis/– £12
1437 **Penny** (12 grs.), *London.* Annulets by neck (heavy dies); *mm.* 33 .. .. £18
1438 — Quatrefoils by neck; *mm.* 28, 74 .. .. .. 80/–
1439 — Trefoil and quatrefoil by neck; *mm.* 74 .. .. £6
1440 — Saltires by neck; *mm.* 74 .. .. £6
1441 — Trefoils by neck; *mm.* 74, 11 .. .. .. 80/–
1442 — No marks by neck; *mm.* 11 .. .. *Extr. rare*
1443 *Bristol.* Crosses, quatrefoils or saltires by neck, BRISTOW; *mm.* crown £14
1444 — Quatrefoils by neck, BRI(trefoil)STOLL £16
1445 — Trefoil to r. of neck, BRISTOLL .. *Unique?*

1446	**Penny,** *Canterbury*, Archb. Bourchier. Quatrefoils or saltires by neck, knot on breast; *mm.* pall..		£7
1447	— — Similar, but no marks by neck		£13
1448	— — As 1446, but no knot		£10
1449	— — Crosses by neck, no knot ..		£10
1450	— Royal mint. Quatrefoils by neck; *mm.* crown		£30
1451	*Durham*, King's Receiver (1462-4). Local dies, mostly with rose in centre of *rev.; mm.* 7a, 33 ..		35/–
1452	— Bp. Lawrence Booth (1465-70). B and D by neck, B on *rev.; mm.* 33 ..		55/–
1453	— — Quatrefoil and B by neck; *mm.* 28		65/–
1454	— — B and quatrefoil by neck; *mm.* 74 ..	*Extr. rare*	
1455	— — D and quatrefoil by neck; *mm.* 74 ..		85/–
1456	— — Quatrefoils by neck; *mm.* crown ..		£5
1457	— — Trefoils by neck; *mm.* crown		£5
1458	— — Lis by neck; *mm.* crown ..		£5
1459	*York*, Sede Vacante (1464-5). Quatrefoils at neck, no quatrefoil in centre of *rev.; mm.* 28, 33 ..		£18
1460	— Archb. Neville (1465-70). Local dies, G and key by neck, quatrefoil on *rev.; mm.* 33, 7a		35/–

1461	— — London-made dies, similar; *mm.* 28, 105, 11 ..		40/–
1462	— — Similar, but no marks by neck; *mm.* large lis	*Extr. rare*	
1463	— — — Quatrefoils by neck; *mm.* large lis ..		70/–
1464	— — — Trefoils by neck; *mm.* large lis ..		£5
1465	**Halfpenny,** *London*. Saltires by neck; *mm.* 34, 28, 74..		95/–
1466	— Trefoils by neck; *mm.* 28, 74, 11 ..		75/–
1467	— No marks by neck; *mm.* 11 ..	*Unique?*	
1468	*Bristol*. Crosses by neck; *mm.* 74		£25
1469	— Trefoils by neck; *mm.* 74		£20
1470	*Canterbury*, Archb. Bourchier. No marks; *mm.* pall ..		£30
1471	— Royal mint. Saltires by neck; *mm.* crown ..		£18
1472	— — Trefoils by neck; *mm.* crown		£15
1473	*York*, Royal mint. Saltires by neck; *mm.* lis/–		£18
1474	— — Trefoils by neck; *mm.* lis/–		£10
1475	**Farthing.** ЄDWARD DI GRA RЄX ..	*Unique*	

HENRY VI RESTORED, Oct. 1470-Apr. 1471

The coinage of this short restoration follows closely that of the previous reign. Only angel gold was issued, the ryal being discontinued. Many of the coins have the king's name reading hɛnʀɪcᴠ—a distinguishing feature.

Mintmarks

Cross pattée (6) Rose (33, Bristol)
Restoration cross (13) Lis (105)
Trefoil (44 and 45) Short cross fitchée (12)

GOLD

1477 *Fine*

1476	**Angel,** *London,* As illus. but no ʙ; *mm.*–/6, 13, –/105, none	£100
1477	*Bristol.* ʙ in waves; *mm.* –/13, none	£200
1478	**Half-angel,** *London.* As 1476; *mm.* –/6, –/13, –/105 ..	£200
1479	*Bristol.* ʙ in waves; *mm.* –/13	*Unique*

SILVER

1480 1482

1480	**Groat,** *London.* Usual type; *mm.* 6, 6/13, 6/105, 13, 13/6, 13/105, 13/12	£9
1481	*Bristol.* ʙ on breast; *mm.* 13, 13/33, 13/44, 44, 44/13, 44/33, 44/12	£10
1482	*York.* ɛ on breast; *mm.* lis, lis/sun	£10

Henry VI restored Silver *Fine*

1483	**Halfgroat,** *London.* As 1480; *mm.* 13, 13/-	..	..	£20
1484	*York.* ε on breast; *mm.* lis	..	*Extr. rare*	
1485	**Penny,** *London.* Usual type; *mm.* 6, 13, 12	..	..	£28
1486	*York.* G and key by neck; *mm.* lis	..	..	£18
1487	**Halfpenny,** *London.* As 1485; *mm.* 12	..	..	£25
1488	*Bristol.* Similar; *mm.* cross	..	*Unique?*	

EDWARD IV, Second Reign, 1471-83

The Angel and its half were the only gold denominations issued during this reign. The main types and weight standards remained the same as those of Edward's first reign light coinage. The use of the " initial mark " as a mint mark to denote the date of issue was now firmly established.

Mintmarks

1471-83	Rose (33, *York* & *Durham*)	1473-7	Cross pattée (6)
			Pierced cross 1 (18)
1471	Short cross fitchée (12)	1477-80	Pierced cross and pellet (19)
1471-2	Annulet (large, 55)		Pierced cross 2 (18)
	Trefoil (44)		Pierced cross, central pellet (20)
	Rose (33, *Bristol*)		Rose (33, *Canterbury*)
1471-3	Pansy (20, *Durham*)	1480-3	Heraldic cinquefoil (31)
1472-3	Annulet (small, 55)		Long cross fitchée (11, *Canterbury*)
	Sun (28, *Bristol*)		Halved sun and rose (38) ?
1473-7	Pellet in annulet (56)		
	Cross and four pellets (17)		
	Cross in circle		

GOLD

1491 *Fine*

1489	**Angel,** *London.* Type as illus.; *mm.* 12, 55, 56, 17, 18, 19, 31		£42/10/-
1490	*Bristol.* B in waves; *mm.* 55		£200
1491	**Half-angel.** As illus.; *mm.* 55, cross in circle, 19, 20/19, 31		£50
1492	King's name and title on *rev.; mm.* 12/-		£90
1493	King's name and title both sides; *mm.* 55/-		£75

SILVER

1499   1504

1494	**Groat,** *London.* Trefoils on cusps no marks by bust; *mm.* 12 to cross-in-circle	75/-
1495	— — roses by bust; *mm.* 56	£5
1496	— Fleurs on cusps, no marks by bust; *mm.* 18–20 ..	70/-
1497	— — pellets by bust; *mm.* 18(2)	90/-
1498	— — rose on breast; *mm.* 31	75/-
1499	*Bristol.* B on breast; *mm.* 33, 33/55, 28/55, 55, 55/-, 28 ..	90/-
1500	*York.* E on breast; *mm.* lis	£5
1501	**Halfgroat,** *London.* As 1494; *mm.* 12–31	85/-
1502	*Bristol.* B on breast; *mm.* 33/12 .. *Extr. rare*	
1503	*Canterbury* (Royal mint). As 1501; *mm.* 31, 11 ..	50/-
1504	— c on breast; *mm.* rose	45/-
1505	— — R. c in centre; *mm.* rose	40/-
1506	— — R. Rose in centre; *mm.* rose	45/-
1507	*York.* E on breast; *mm.* lis	£18
1508	**Penny,** *London.* No marks by bust; *mm.* 12–31 ..	85/-
1509	*Bristol.* Similar; *mm.* rose .. .. *Unique?*	
1510	*Canterbury* (Royal). Similar; *mm.* 33, 11	£16
1511	— c on breast; *mm.* 33	£25

1513   1514   1520

1512	*Durham,* Bp. Booth (1471-6). No marks by neck; *mm.* 12, 44	65/-
1513	— — D in centre of *rev.;* B and trefoil by neck; *mm.* 44, 33, 56	45/-
1514	— — — two lis at neck; *mm.* 33	60/-
1515	— — — crosses over crown, and on breast; *mm.* 33 ..	50/-
1516	— — — crosses over crown, V under CIVI; *mm.* 33, 30..	55/-
1517	— — — B to l. of crown, V on breast and under CIVI ..	50/-
1517A	— — — As last but crosses at shoulders	42/-
1518	— Sede Vacante (1476). R. D in centre; *mm.* 33 ..	£10
1519	— Bp. Dudley, (1476-83). V to r. of neck; as last ..	60/-
1520	— — D and V by neck; as last, but *mm.* 31	45/-

Nos. 1515-1520 are from locally-made dies.

1522   1531

1521	*York*, Archb. Neville (1471-2). Quatrefoils by neck. R. Quatrefoil; *mm.* 12 (over lis) *Extr. rare*	
1522	— — Similar, but G and key by neck; *mm.* 12	50/–
1523	— Neville suspended (1472-5). As last, but no quatrefoil in centre of *rev.*	70/–
1524	— — No marks by neck, quatrefoil on *rev.; mm.* 55, cross in circle, 33 ..	60/–
1525	— — Similar but Є and rose by neck; *mm.* 33	60/–
1526	— Archb. Neville restored (1475-6). As last, but G and rose	95/–
1527	— — Similar, but G and key by bust ..	45/–
1528	— Sede Vacante (1476). As 1524, but rose on breast; *mm.* 33	95/–
1529	— Archb. Lawrence Booth (1476-80). B and key by bust, quatrefoil on *rev.; mm.* 33, 31	42/–
1530	— Sede Vacante (1480). Similar, but no quatrefoil on *rev.; mm.* 33	55/–
1531	— Archb. Rotherham (1480-83). T and slanting key by neck, quatrefoil on *rev.; mm.* 33 ..	45/–
1532	— — — Similar, but star on breast *Extr. rare*	
1533	— — — Star on breast and to r. of crown	£20
1534	**Halfpenny,** *London.* No marks by neck; *mm.* 12–31 ..	55/–
1535	— Pellets at neck; *mm.* 18	85/–
1536	*Canterbury* (Royal). C on breast and in centre of *rev.; mm.* rose	£20
1537	— C on breast only; *mm.* rose	£15
1538	— Without C either side; *mm.* 11(?)	£23
1539	*Durham*, Bp. Booth. No marks by neck. R. DERAM, D in centre; *mm.* rose	£30
1540	— — — Similar, but V to l. of neck ..	£30

EDWARD IV or V

Mintmark: Halved sun and rose.

Learned numismatists have been arguing about the attribution of this mintmark for many years. The consensus of opinion now favours the last year of Edward IV. Even if that is the case the first pieces struck under the new young king may have been from these Edw. IV dies. In any case, the coins are very rare.

GOLD

								Fine
1541	**Angel.** As 1489 ..	..	..	..	..	..		£135
1542	**Half-angel.** As 1491.	..	..	..	*Extr. rare*			

SILVER

1543	**Groat.** As 1496 ..	..	..	..	..	..		£50
1544	**Penny.** As 1508 ..	..	..	..	..	..		£80
1545	**Halfpenny.** As 1534	..	..	..	..	..		£50

EDWARD V, 1483

On the death of Edward IV, 9th April, 1483, the 12-year-old Prince Edward was placed under the guardianship of his uncle, Richard, Duke of Gloucester, but within eleven weeks Richard usurped the throne, and Edward and his younger brother were confined to the Tower and were later murdered there. Very few coins of this reign have survived. The boar's head was a personal badge of Richard, Edward's " Protector."

Mintmarks: Boar's head on *obv.*, halved sun and rose on *rev.*

GOLD

1546	**Angel.** As 1489 ..	..	..	..	..	..		£2000
1546A	**Half-angel.** Similar	..	..	..	*Unique*			

SILVER

1547	**Groat.** As 1496	..	..	..	..	..		£300
1548	**Halfgroat.** As 1501	..	..	..	*Unknown ?*			
1549	**Penny.** As 1508 ..	..	..	..	*Unknown ?*			

RICHARD III, 1483-5

Richard's brief and violent reign was brought to an end on the field of Bosworth. His coinage follows the pattern of the previous reigns. The smaller denominations of the London mint are all rare.

Mintmarks
Halved sun and rose, 3 styles (38, 39 and another with the sun more solid, see *North*).
Boar's head, narrow (62) wide (63).
Lis (105, *Durham*).
Rose only (33).

GOLD   *Fine*

1550 **Angel.** Reading ЄDWARD but with R (over Є) and rose by
       mast; *mm.* sun and rose .. .. .. *Unique*
1551 — Similar, but boar's head *mm.* on *obv.* £350

1552 Reading RICARD or RICAD.   R   R and rose by mast; *mm.*
       various combinations £175
1553 — Similar, but R by mast over Є (?) £185
1554 **Half-angel.** R and rose by mast; *mm.* boar's head .. £1000

SILVER

1555   1556

1555 **Groat.** *London.* Mm. various combinations £18
1556 — Pellet below bust — £15
1557 *York.* Mm. sun and rose (*obv.*) £50

Richard III, Silver.   *Fine*

1558 **Halfgroat.** *Mm.* sun and rose or on *obv.* only .. £100

1559 Pellet below bust; *mm.* sun and rose £120

1560 — *mm.* boar's head (*obv.*).. .. .. £150

1561 **Penny.** London. *Mm.* boar's head (*obv.*) *Unique*
        The only known specimen was stolen from our premises Feb. 1962.

1562 *York*, Archb. Rotherham. R. Quatrefoil in centre;
        mm. sun and rose £30

1563 — — T and upright key at neck; *mm.* rose £30

1564 — — — *mm.* boar's head £30

1565 *Durham*, Bp. Sherwood. s on breast. R. D in centre;
        mm. lis.. .. .. £15

1566 **Halfpenny,** London. *Mm.* sun and rose £60

1567 — *Mm.* boar's head .. .. .. *Extr. rare*

HENRY VII, 1485-1509

This reign is most interesting from a numismatic point of view. New denominations were issued both in gold and silver and there is a change from late medieval to Tudor-Renaissance style. The gold sovereign and the testoon or shilling made their first appearance. A German die-sinker, Alexander Bruchsal, was responsible for the very fine royal portraits that replaced the representational king's head on the testoons and later groats and halfgroats.

Mintmarks

1485-90	Halved sun and rose (39)	1490-1504	Escallop (78)
	Lis upon sun and rose (41)		Pansy (30)
	Lis upon half-rose (40)		Leopard's head (91)
	Lis-rose dimidiated (42)		Lis issuant from rose (43)
	Rose (33)		Anchor (57 but vertical)
	Cross fitchée (11)	1500-7	Lis (105)
	Cross, plain (7a, *Durham*)		Greyhound's head (85)
1486-1500	Tun (123, *Canterbury*)	1501-9	Martlet (94, *York, Canterbury*)
	Lis (105)		
	Crozier (76b, *Durham*)	1504-7	Dragon (118, gold only)
1490-1504	Heraldic cinquefoil (31)		Crosslet (21)
			Rose (33)
		1507-9	Pheon (53)

The coins are placed in groups, as in Brooke, to correspond to the classification of the groats.

GOLD

1568 **Sovereign** (20s; wt. ∠40 grs.). Group I. Large figure of king sitting on throne with low back. ℞. *Mm.* 11. Large Tudor rose bearing small shield   ..   ..   *Extr. rare*

1569 II. *O.* Somewhat similar but no lis as background. ℞. Large shield crowned on large Tudor rose; *mm.* 31
Unique

1570 III. King on high-backed very ornamental throne, with greyhound and dragon on side pillars. ℞. Shield on Tudor rose; *mm.* 118 ..   ..   £1200

1571 IV. Similar but throne with high canopy breaking legend and broad seat, *mm.* 105/118 ..   ..   ..   £1000

1572 — Similar but narrow throne with a portcullis below the king's feet (like Henry VIII); *mm.* 105/21, 105/53 ..   ..   £1100

1573 **Double-sovereign** and **Treble-sovereign** from sovereign dies. *Probably* patterns or presentation pieces
Unique

1574 **Ryal** (10s). As illustration: *mm.* 11   ..   *Extr. rare*

1580   1578

Fine

1575 **Angel** (6s 8d). I. Angel of old type with one foot on
dragon. ℞. PER CRVCEM, etc.; *mm.* 39, 41, 40, 33 .. £80
1576 II. Similar *but mm.* none, 31/–, 31/78 .. .. .. £60
1577 — — ℞. IHC AVTE TRANSIEnS etc.; *mm.* none £75
1578 III. New dies, angel with both feet on dragon; *mm.* 78,
30, 43, 57, 85 (large straight lettering) £40
1579 — — ℞. IHC AVT TRANSIEnS, etc.; *mm.* 78 .. .. £70
1580 IV. Small square lettering; *mm.* 85 .. .. .. £40
1581 — Tall thin lettering; *mm.* 21 .. .. £38
1582 V. Large crook-shaped abbreviation after HEnRIC; *mm.*
21, 21 and 53, 53 .. .. £35
1583 **Half-angel or angelet.** I. *Mm.* 39 (old dies altered),
41 .. .. £150
1584 III. Angel with both feet on dragon: *mm.* 30, 57/30, 57/
85 .. .. £50
1585 IV. Small square lettering; *mm.* 33 .. .. .. £50
1586 — Tall thin lettering; *mm.* 33/21 .. .. .. £50
1587 V. As angel; *mm.* pheon.. .. .. £42

SILVER

Facing bust issues. Including " Sovereign " type pennies.

1589   1590

1588 **Groat.** I. Open crown; *mm.* 39, 40, 40/41, 41, 42 .. 95/–
1589 — — crosses by neck, 33, 11, 105 .. .. .. 95/–
1590 II. Crown with two unjewelled arches; *mm.* none, 31 50/–
1590A — — similar but crosses by neck; *mm.* none, –/105 .. 60/–
1591 — — ℞. Portcullis over long cross; *mm.* –/lis
Extr. rare

Henry VII, Silver.

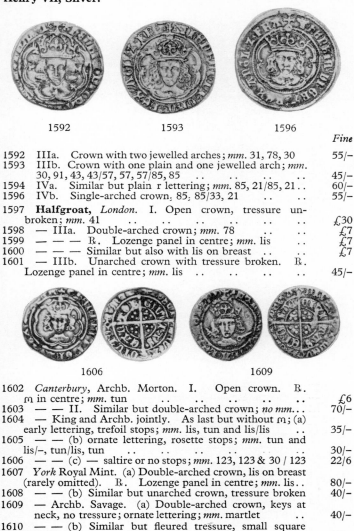

| | 1592 | 1593 | 1596 |

Fine

		Fine
1592	IIIa. Crown with two jewelled arches; *mm.* 31, 78, 30	55/–
1593	IIIb. Crown with one plain and one jewelled arch; *mm.* 30, 91, 43, 43/57, 57, 57/85, 85	45/–
1594	IVa. Similar but plain r lettering; *mm.* 85, 21/85, 21 ..	60/–
1596	IVb. Single-arched crown; 85; 85/33, 21	55/–
1597	**Halfgroat,** *London.* I. Open crown, tressure unbroken; *mm.* 41	£30
1598	— IIIa. Double-arched crown; *mm.* 78	£7
1599	— — — ℞. Lozenge panel in centre; *mm.* lis ..	£7
1600	— — — Similar but also with lis on breast ..	£7
1601	— IIIb. Unarched crown with tressure broken. ℞. Lozenge panel in centre; *mm.* lis	45/–

| | 1606 | 1609 |

1602	*Canterbury,* Archb. Morton. I. Open crown. ℞. ꭑ in centre; *mm.* tun	£6
1603	— — II. Similar but double-arched crown; *no mm.*..	70/–
1604	— King and Archb. jointly. As last but without ꭑ; (a) early lettering, trefoil stops; *mm.* lis, tun and lis/lis	35/–
1605	— — (b) ornate lettering, rosette stops; *mm.* tun and lis/–, tun/lis, tun	30/–
1606	— — (c) saltire or no stops; *mm.* 123, 123 & 30 / 123	22/6
1607	*York* Royal Mint. (a) Double-arched crown, lis on breast (rarely omitted). ℞. Lozenge panel in centre; *mm.* lis..	80/–
1608	— — (b) Similar but unarched crown, tressure broken	40/–
1609	— Archb. Savage. (a) Double-arched crown, keys at neck, no tressure; ornate lettering; *mm.* martlet	40/–
1610	— — (b) Similar but fleured tressure, small square lettering	40/–
1611	— — (c) As last but tall thin lettering	45/–
1612	— Sede Vacante, 1507/8. As last but no keys ..	55/–

119

1616   1619

1613	**Penny.** Old type. *London; mm.* 41	£30
1614	— — — crosses by bust, *mm.* uncertain *Extr. rare*	
1615	— *Canterbury*, Archb. Morton. Open crown, *mm.* tun. ℞. m in centre	£45
1616	— — King and Archb. jointly, arched crown; *mm.* tun	£10
1617	— *Durham*, Bp. Sherwood. s on breast. ℞. D in centre; *mm.* 7a	£7
1618	— *York*, Archb. Rotherham. With or without cross on breast, *mm.* 41; T and cross at neck. ℞. h in centre ..	80/-
1619	— — — T and trefoil at neck. ℞. Quatrefoil in centre and two extra pellets	70/-

1621   1626-7

1620	" Sovereign " type. *London*. Early lettering, trefoil stops, no pillars to throne; no *mm.*	£8
1621	— — — single pillar; no *mm.* or 31	70/-
1622	— — Ornate letters, rosette stops, single pillar; *mm.* lis	85/-
1623	— — — saltire stops, two pillars; *mm.* none, 30 ..	70/-
1624	— — Similar but small square lettering; no *mm.* ..	70/-
1625	— — Similar but lettering as profile groats; *mm.* 21, 53	90/-
1626	— *Durham*, Bp. Sherwood. Crozier to r. of king, throne with one pillar. ℞. D and s beside shield..	65/-
1627	— — Throne with two pillars, no crozier. ℞. As last	70/-
1628	— — Bp. Fox. Throne with one pillar. ℞. Mitre above shield, RD or DR at sides	52/6
1629	— — Similar but two pillars	65/-
1630	*York*, Archb. Rotherham. Keys below shield; early lettering, trefoil stops, no pillars to throne	50/-
1631	— — — single pillar	50/-
1632	— — — ornate lettering, rosette or no stops, single pillar	50/-
1633	— — — — — — two pillars	50/-

1640   1643

1634	**Halfpenny,** *London.* I. Open crown; *mm.* 41, 42 ..	£14
1635	— — — trefoils at neck; no *mm.*	£14
1636	— — — crosses at neck; *mm.* 33, 11 ..	£8
1637	— II. Arched crown; *mm.* cinquefoil, none ?..	65/-
1638	— — — saltires at neck; no *mm.*	75/-
1639	— III. Crown with lower arch, ornate lettering; no *mm.*	70/-
1640	— V. Much smaller portrait; *mm.* pheon	90/-
1641	*Canterbury,* Archb. Morton. I. Open crown. ℞. ʍ in centre	£35
1642	— — II. Similar but arched crown, saltires by bust; *mm.* profile eye (82) ?	£50
1643	— King and Archb. III. Arched crown; *mm.* none, 105	£15
1644	*York,* Archb. Savage. Arched crown, key below bust ..	£17
1645	**Farthing,** henRIC DI GRA REX (A) ..	£30

Profile issue

1646	**Testoon** (1s.) Type as groat. henRIC(VS); *mm.* lis ..	£125
1647	— henRIC VII; *mm.* lis. ..	£150
1648	— henRIC SEPTIM; *mm.* lis.	£200

1649   1653

1649	**Groat,** *Tentative issue* (contemporary with full-face groats). Double band to crown henRIC VII; *mm.* none, 105/-, -/105, 105/85, 105, 85, 21 ..	£20
1650	— — — tressure on *obv.; mm.* 21 ..	£150
1651	— — henRIC (VS); *mm.* 105, -/105, 105/85 ..	£32
1652	— — henRIC SEPTIM; *mm.* -/105..	£185
1653	*Regular issue.* Triple band to crown; *mm.* 21, 21 and 53/21, 21/21 and 53, 53 ..	80/-
1654	**Halfgroat,** *London.* As last; *mm.* 105, 53/105, 53 ..	60/-
1655	— — no numeral after king's name, no *mm.* ..	£40
1656	*Canterbury,* King and Archb. As London, but *mm.* 94, 33	40/-
1657	*York,* Archb. Bainbridge. As London, but two keys below shield; *mm.* 94, 33 ..	40/-
1658	— — XB beside shield; *mm.* 33/94 ..	£40

HENRY VIII, 1509-1547

On the silver coins Henry VIII kept his father's portrait for the first sixteen years of his reign. His reign is noted for the lowering of the fineness of the coinage. In 1526 some coins started to be made in 22 carat gold owing to the wholesale exportation of English money; later on it became the normal standard. The debasement of the silver started in 1543 at first 5 parts fine to 1 of alloy, then it fell to half and half and at the end only one-third silver; this was done to make money for the king, whose treasury was exhausted. Gold was further reduced to 20 carat. New types include the George noble. His later coins bear his old portrait. The Wolsey coinage brings to an end the ecclesiastical issues. Additional mints were set up at Southwark and Bristol to speed the production of the vast quantities of base money needed to provide revenue for the king.

Mintmarks

1509-26 Pheon (53)
Castle (69)
Castle with H (70, gold)
Portcullis crowned (108)
Rose (33, *Canterbury*)
Martlet (94, *Canterbury*)
Pomegranate (73, but broader, *Cant.*)
Cross fitchée (11, *Cant.*)
Lis (105, *Canterbury, Durham*)

1509-14 Martlet (94, *York*)

1509-23 Radiant star (22, *Durham*)

1514-26 Star (23, *York*)
Pansy (30, *York*)
Escallop (78, *York*)
Voided cross (*York*)

1523-6 Spur rowel (24)

1526-44 Rose (33)
Lis (105)
Sunburst (110)
Arrow (52)
Pheon (53)

1526-44 Lis (106)
Star (23, *Durham*)

1526-9 Crescent (72a, *Durham*)
Trefoil (44 variety, *Durham*)
Flower of eight petals and circle centre (*Durham*)

1526-30 Cross (7a, sometimes slightly voided, *York*)
Acorn (65a, *York*)

1526-32 Cross patonce (8, *Cant.*)
T (114, *Canterbury*)
Uncertain mark (121, *Canterbury*)

1529-44 Radiant star (22, *Durham*)

1530-44 Key (90, *York*)

1533-44 Catherine wheel (36, *Canterbury*)

1544-47 Lis (105 and 106)
Pellet in annulet (56)
S
Є or E

1546-7 WS monogram (116, *Bristol*)

GOLD

First coinage, 1509-26

1659   **Sovereign** (20s.). As last sov. of Hen. VII; *mm.* 108   £650

1660   **Angel** (6s. 8d.). As Hen. VII, but hⱸɴʀɪᴄ ? ᴠɪɪɪ ᴅɪ ɢʀᴀ
ʀⱸx, etc.; *mm.* 53, 69, 70, 108   ..   .. £37/10/-

1661   **Half-angel.** Similar; *mm.* 69, 70, 108   ..   ..£42/10/-

Second coinage, 1526-44

1662   **Sovereign** (22s. 6d.).   As 1659 but *mm.* 110, 105,
105/52   ..   ..   £500

1663   **Angel** (7s. 6d.).   As 1660 but hⱸɴʀɪᴄ ᴠɪɪɪ ᴅ ɢ ʀ etc.;
mm. 110, 105   ..   ..   £57

1664   **Half-angel.** Similar; *mm.* 105 ..   ..   £100

1665   **George-noble** (6s. 8d.). As illustration; *mm.* rose   ..   £1500

1666   **Half-George-noble.** Similar ..   ..   ..*Unique*

1667   **Crown of the rose** (4s. 6d.). As illustration; *mm.* rose
Extr. rare

Henry VIII, Gold.

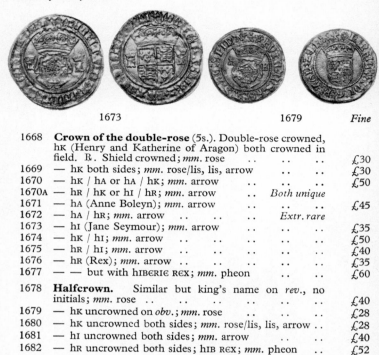

1673   1679   *Fine*

1668	**Crown of the double-rose** (5s.). Double-rose crowned, hK (Henry and Katherine of Aragon) both crowned in field. ℞. Shield crowned; *mm.* rose	£30
1669	— hK both sides; *mm.* rose/lis, lis, arrow	£30
1670	— hK / hA or hA / hK; *mm.* arrow	£50
1670A	— hR / hK or hI / hR; *mm.* arrow .. *Both unique*	
1671	— hA (Anne Boleyn); *mm.* arrow	£45
1672	— hA / hR; *mm.* arrow .. .. *Extr. rare*	
1673	— hI (Jane Seymour); *mm.* arrow	£35
1674	— hK / hI; *mm.* arrow	£50
1675	— hR / hI; *mm.* arrow	£40
1676	— hR (Rex); *mm.* arrow ..	£35
1677	— — but with hIBERIE REX; *mm.* pheon	£60
1678	**Halfcrown.** Similar but king's name on *rev.*, no initials; *mm.* rose	£40
1679	— hK uncrowned on *obv.*; *mm.* rose	£28
1680	— hK uncrowned both sides; *mm.* rose/lis, lis, arrow ..	£28
1681	— hI uncrowned both sides; *mm.* arrow	£40
1682	— hR uncrowned both sides; hIB REX; *mm.* pheon ..	£52

Third coinage, 1544-7

1685

Henry VIII, Gold.   *Fine*

1683 **Sovereign,** I (20s., wt. 200 grs., 23 ct.). As illustration
      but king with larger face and larger design; *mm.* lis   ..   £1500

1684 II (20s., wt. 200 or 192 grs., 23, 22 or 20 ct.). *London.* As
      illustration; *mm.* lis, pellet in annulet/lis £475

1685 — *Southwark.* Similar; *mm.* s, є/s £450

1686 — — Similar but є below shield; *mm.* s/є £500

1687 — *Bristol.* As London but *mm.* ws/– £500

1688 **Half-sovereign** (wt. 96 grs.), *London.* As illus.; *mm.*
      lis, pellet in annulet £35

1689 — Similar but with annulet on inner circle £40

1690 *Southwark.* Mm. s £35

1691 — є below shield; *mm.* s, є £40

1692 *Bristol.* Lombardic lettering; *mm.* ws, ws/– £60

        1697   1696

1693 **Angel.** Annulet by angel's head and on ship, hєnRIC' 8;
      mm. lis £37/10/–

1694 — Similar but annulet one side only £42/10/–

1695 **Half-angel.** Annulet on ship; *mm.* lis..   ..   ..   £40

1695A — No annulet in ship £45

1696 — Three annulets on ship; *mm.* lis £57/10/–

1697 **Quarter-angel.** *Mm.* lis £40

1698 **Crown,** *London.* As 1677 but hєnRIC'8; Lombardic
      lettering; *mm.* 56   ..   ..   £30

1699 — without RVTILAnS; *mm.* 56   ..   ..   £30

1700 — — — with annulet on inner circle £32/10/–

1701 *Southwark.* As 1698; *mm.* s, є, E/s, s/є..   ..   ..£32/10/–

1702 *Bristol.* hєnRIC VIII. ℞. DєI GRA, etc.; *mm.* ws,
      –/ws £37/10/–

1703 — Similar but hєnRIC(vs) 8   ..   ..   £30

1704 **Halfcrown,** *London.* As 1682 but hєnRIC'8; *mm.* 56 ..£27/10/–

1705 — — with annulet on inner circle £30

1706 *Southwark.* As 1704; *mm.* s £30

1707 — *O.* hєnRIC 8 ROSA SInє SPIn. ℞. DєI GRA, etc.; *mm.* є £37/10/–

1708 *Bristol. O.* RVTILAnS, etc. ℞. hєnRIC 8; *mm.* ws/–..   £50

For other gold coins in Henry's name, see page 130

1709   1719

1709	**Groat.** Portrait of Hen. VII; *mm.* 53, 69, 108	£5
1710	**Halfgroat.** Portrait of Hen. VII. *London*; *mm.* 108	80/-
1711	— *Canterbury*, Archb. Warham. POSVI *rev.*; *mm.* rose	£12
1712	— — — WA above shield; *mm.* martlet	60/-
1713	— — — WA beside shield; *mm.* cross fitchée	£5
1714	— — CIVITAS CANTOR *rev.*, similar; *mm.* 73, 105, 11/105	50/-
1715	— *York*, POSVI *rev.*, Archb. Bainbridge (1508-14). Keys below shield, *mm.* martlet	55/-
1716	— — — — XB beside shield; *mm.* martlet	£6
1717	— — — Archb. Wolsey (1514-30). Keys and cardinal's hat below shield; *mm.* 94, 22	£12
1718	— — CIVITAS EBORACI *rev.* Similar; *mm.* 22, 23, 30, 78, voided cross	45/-
1719	— — As last with TW beside shield; *mm.* voided cross	50/-

1720

1720	**Penny,** " Sovereign " type, *London*; *mm.* 69, 108	70/-
1721	— *Canterbury.* WA above shield; *mm.* martlet	£30
1722	— — — WA beside shield; *mm.* 73	£6
1723	— *Durham*, Bp. Ruthall (1509-23). TD above shield; *mm.* lis	45/-
1724	— — — TD beside shield; *mm.* lis, radiant star	55/-
1725	— — Bp. Wolsey (1523-9). DW beside shield, cardinal's hat below; *mm.* spur rowel	£12
1726	**Halfpenny.** Facing bust, HENRIC DI GRA REX (AGL). *London*; *mm.* 69, 108	60/-
1727	— *Canterbury.* WA beside bust; *mm.* 73	£9
1728	**Farthing.** O. *Mm.* portcullis HENRIC DI GRA REX, a portcullis as type. R. CIVITAS LONDON, rose in centre of long cross *Extr. rare*	

1729	**Groat.** His own young portrait. *London*; *mm.* rose (with three different portraits) to pheon, sometimes muled ..	60/-
1730	— — with Irish title HIB; *mm.* 53, 53/105, 105/53 ..	£30
1731	— *York*, Archb. Wolsey. TW beside shield, cardinal's hat below; *mm.* voided cross, acorn, sometimes muled ..	£6
1732	— — — omits TW; *mm.* voided cross	£10

1735   1740

1733	**Halfgroat.** Similar *London*; *mm.* rose to arrow ..	80/-
1734	— — with Irish title HIB; *mm.* pheon	£50
1735	— *Canterbury*, Archb. Warham (—1532). ℞. CIVITAS CANTOR, WA beside shield; *mm.* 121, 121/33, 8, 8/T, T	40/-
1736	— — nothing by shield; *mm.* 121, 121/-	£6
1737	— — Archb. Cranmer (1533—). TC beside shield; *mm.* 36, 36/-	50/-
1738	— *York*, Archb. Wolsey (—1530). ℞. CIVITAS EBORACI, TW beside shield, hat below; *mm.* voided cross	55/-
1739	— — Sede Vacante (1530/1). No marks; *mm.* key ..	60/-
1740	— — Archb. Lee (1531-44). EL or LE beside shield; *mm.* key	50/-

Henry VIII, Silver. Second Coinage. *Fine*

1741 **Penny,** " Sovereign " type, h . D . G . ROSA SInЄ SPInA, *London*; *mm.* rose to arrow 80/–

1742 — *Canterbury.* WA beside shield; *mm.* 121, 8, T £18

1743 — — TC beside shield; *mm.* 36 .. .. £15

1744 — *Durham*, Bp. Wolsey (—1529). TW beside shield, hat below; *mm.* 23, 72a, 44 .. .. 45/–

1745 — — Sede Vacante (1529-30). No marks; *mm. obv.* only, 23/–, 22/– 65/–

1746 — — Bp. Tunstall (1530—). CD beside shield; *mm.* 23, 23/–, 22/– 45/–

1747 — *York.* EL beside shield; *mm.* key £20

1746   1751

1748 **Halfpenny.** Facing bust, h D G ROSA SIЄ SPIA. *London*; *mm.* rose to sunburst 50/–

1749 — *Canterbury.* WA beside bust; *mm.* 8 ?, T £18

1750 — — TC beside bust; *mm.* 36 .. .. £12

1751 — *York.* TW beside bust; *mm.* cross voided £15

1752 — — Sede Vacante. Key below bust; *mm.* cross voided £12

1753 — — EL or LE beside bust; *mm.* key £9

1754 **Farthing.** *O.* RVTILANS ROSA, portcullis; *mm.* lis ? ℞. H D . . . . ., long cross with pellet in each angle *Extr. rare*

1755 — — *mm.* arrow. ℞. hЄ . .D G . .AC, rose on long cross *Extr. rare*

Third coinage, 1544-7. Old head, bearded. *Fair*

1756 **Testoon.** *Tower* mint. hЄnRIC'. VIII, etc. ℞. Crowned rose between hR, POSVI, etc.; *mm.* lis, two lis, lis and pellet in annulet £9

1757 — hЄnRIC' 8, similar; *mm.* lis, pellet in annulet .. £7

1758 — — annulet on inner circle of *rev.; mm.* pellet in annulet £12

1759 *Southwark.* As 1757. ℞. CIVITAS LOnDOn; *mm.* S, Є.. £9

1760 *Bristol.* Mm. –/WS monogram £12

Henry VIII, Silver.　Third Coinage.

Bust 1　　　　　2　　　　　3

Fine

1761	**Groat.** *Tower.* As 1757, busts 1, 2, 3; *mm.* lis	65/–
1762	— — annulet on inner circle	£6
1763	*Southwark.* As 1759, busts 1, 2, 3, 4; no *mm.* or lis; s or s and ϵ in forks	55/–
1764	*Bristol. Mm.* –/ws monogram	75/–
1765	*Canterbury.* Busts 1 var., 2; no *mm.*, 105/–	75/–
1766	*York.* Busts 1 var., 2, 3; no *mm.*	70/–
1767	**Halfgroat.** *Tower.* As 1757, bust 1; *mm.* lis, none ..	£10
1768	*Southwark.* As 1759, bust 1; no *mm.*; s or ϵ in forks ..	£6
1769	*Bristol. Mm.* –/ws monogram	70/–
1770	*Canterbury.* Bust 1; no *mm.*	45/–
1771	*York.* Bust 1; no *mm.*	60/–
1772	**Penny.** *Tower.* Facing bust; no *mm.* or lis	£5
1773	*Southwark.* Facing bust; *mm.* s, ϵ	£7
1774	*Bristol.* Facing bust; no *mm.*	70/–
1775	*Canterbury.* Facing bust; no *mm.*	£5
1776	*York.* Facing bust; no *mm.*	70/–
1777	**Halfpenny.** *Tower.* Facing bust; no *mm.* or lis ..	£10
1778	*Bristol.* Facing bust; no *mm.*	£24
1779	*Canterbury.* Facing bust; no *mm.*	£10
1780	*York.* Facing bust; no *mm.*	£10

HENRY VIII POSTHUMOUS COINAGE, 1547-51

Coins struck during the reign of Edward VI but bearing the name of Henry VIII and, except in the case of the half-sovereigns, his figure or bust.　Most of these coins have Roman lettering.

Mintmarks

1547	Annulet and pellet (56)	1548-9　Bow (66, *Durham House*)
1547-8	Lis (105)	1549　　TC monogram (115,
1547-9	Arrow (52)	*Bristol*)
	κ	Lis (105, *Canterbury*)
	Roman E (*Southwark*)	Rose (33, *Canterbury*)
	ws monogram (116,	Grapple (122)
	Bristol)	1549/50　t (*Canterbury*)
		1550/51　Martlet (94)

129

GOLD

1781 **Sovereign,** *London.* As no. 1684, but Roman lettering;
      mm. lis £450

1782 — *Bristol.* Similar but *mm.* ws £600

1784

1783 **Half-sovereign.** As no. 1688, but with youthful port-
      rait. *London*; *mm.* 52, 105, 122, 94   ..   ..   ..   £28

1784 — — — ᴋ below shield; *mm.* –/ᴋ, none £30

1785 — — — grapple below shield; *mm.* grapple, none   ..   £40

1786 — *Southwark.* *Mm.* ᴇ, and usually ᴇ below shield   ..   £25

1787 **Crown.** As no. 1698. *London*; *mm.* 52, –/ᴋ, 122, 94   ..   £27

1788 — Similar but king's name on *rev.* without numeral;
      mm. arrow/– £35

1789 — *Southwark.* Similar; *mm.* ᴇ ..   ..   *Extr. rare*

1790 — — King's name on *obv.*; *mm.* ᴇ/–   ..   *Extr. rare*

1791 **Halfcrown.** As no. 1704. *London*; *mm.* 52, ᴋ/–, 122/–, 94   £24

1792 — *Southwark.* *Mm.* ᴇ, ᴇ/–, –/ᴇ £32/10/–

SILVER   *Fair*

1793 **Testoon.** *Tower.* As 1757 with sleeve stops one side;
      no *mm.* or 56   ..   ..   £20

1794 *Southwark.* As 1759; *mm.* s/ᴇ £32/10/–

Some of the Bristol testoons, groats and halfgroats with WS
monogram were struck after the death of Henry VIII but cannot be
distinguished from those struck during his reign.

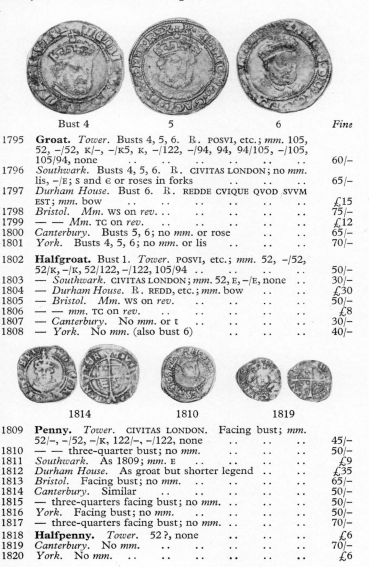

Bust 4   5   6   *Fine*

1795	**Groat.** *Tower.* Busts 4, 5, 6. ℞. POSVI, etc.; *mm.* 105, 52, –/52, K/–, –/K5, K, –/122, –/94, 94, 94/105, –/105, 105/94, none	60/–
1796	*Southwark.* Busts 4, 5, 6. ℞. CIVITAS LONDON; no *mm.* lis, –/E; S and Є or roses in forks	65/–
1797	*Durham House.* Bust 6. ℞. REDDE CVIQUE QVOD SVVM EST; *mm.* bow	£15
1798	*Bristol. Mm.* WS on *rev.*	75/–
1799	— — *Mm.* TC on *rev.*	£12
1800	*Canterbury.* Busts 5, 6; no *mm.* or rose	65/–
1801	*York.* Busts 4, 5, 6; no *mm.* or lis	70/–
1802	**Halfgroat.** Bust 1. *Tower.* POSVI, etc.; *mm.* 52, –/52, 52/K, –/K, 52/122, –/122, 105/94	50/–
1803	— *Southwark.* CIVITAS LONDON; *mm.* 52, E, –/E, none	30/–
1804	— *Durham House.* ℞. REDD, etc.; *mm.* bow	£30
1805	— *Bristol. Mm.* WS on *rev.*	50/–
1806	— — *mm.* TC on *rev.*	£8
1807	— *Canterbury.* No *mm.* or t	30/–
1808	— *York.* No *mm.* (also bust 6)	40/–

1814   1810   1819

1809	**Penny.** *Tower.* CIVITAS LONDON. Facing bust; *mm.* 52/–, –/52, –/K, 122/–, –/122, none	45/–
1810	— — three-quarter bust; no *mm.*	50/–
1811	*Southwark.* As 1809; *mm.* E	£9
1812	*Durham House.* As groat but shorter legend	£35
1813	*Bristol.* Facing bust; no *mm.*	65/–
1814	*Canterbury.* Similar	50/–
1815	— three-quarters facing bust; no *mm.*	50/–
1816	*York.* Facing bust; no *mm.*	50/–
1817	— three-quarters facing bust; no *mm.*	70/–
1818	**Halfpenny.** *Tower.* 52 ?, none	£6
1819	*Canterbury.* No *mm.*	70/–
1820	*York.* No *mm.*	£6

EDWARD VI, 1547-53

Coinage in his own name.

While base coins continued to be issued bearing the name of Henry VIII, plans were made early in Edward's reign to reform the coinage. As a first step, in 1549, the standard of the gold was raised to 22 carat and "silver" was increased to 50% silver content. Baser shillings were issued in 1550, but finally, in 1551, it was decided to resume the coinage of some "fine" gold and a new silver coinage was ordered of 11 oz. 1 dwt. fineness, i.e. almost up to the ancient standard. At the same time four new denominations were added to the coinage—the silver crown, halfcrown, sixpence and threepence. Pennies continued to be struck in base silver.

Mintmarks

1548-9	Bow (66, *Durham House*)	1549-50	Roman y
1549	Arrow (52)		**6** (126, gold only)
	Rose (35)	1550	Martlet (94)
	TC monogram (115, *Bristol*)	1550-1	Lion (92)
			Lis (105)
	Roman E (*Southwark*)		Rose (33)
	Pheon (53)	1552	y (117)
	Grapple (122)		Ostrich's head (97, gold only)
	Trefoil (44 variety)	1551-3	Tun (123)
	t or T (*Canterbury*)		Escallop (78)
1549-50	Swan (111)	1552-3	Pierced mullet (26, *York*)

GOLD

Fine

First period, Apr. 1547-Jan. 1549.

1821   1823

1821	**Half-sovereign.** As 1783 but reading EDWARD 6. *Tower; mm.* arrow	£120
1822	— *Southwark* (Usually with E or ϵ below shield; *mm.* E	£85
1823	**Crown.** RVTILANS, etc, crowned rose between E R both crowned. R. EDWARD 6 etc., crowned shield between ER both crowned; *mm.* arrow .. .. *Unique*	
1824	**Halfcrown.** Similar, but initials not crowned *Extr. rare*	

132

Edward VI, Gold.   *Fine*
  Second period, Jan. 1549–Apr. 1550.

1825 **Sovereign.**   As illustration ; *mm.* arrow, Y £350

1827   1830

1826 **Half-sovereign.**   Uncrowned bust.   *London.*   TIMOR
        etc., MDXLIX on *obv.; mm.* arrow ..   ..   *Extr. rare*
1827 — — SCVTVM, etc. as illustration; *mm.* arrow, **6**, Y   ..   £55
1828 — *Durham House.* Similar with MDXLVIII at end of *obv.*
        legend; *mm.* bow ..   ..   *Extr. rare*
1829 — — LVCERNA, etc. on *obv.; mm.* bow ..   *Extr. rare*
1830 Crowned bust. *London.* EDWARD VI etc. ℞ SCVTVM,
        etc.; *mm.* 52, 122, 111, Y, 94   ..   .. £45
1831 — *Durham House.* Half-length bust; *mm.* bow *Unique*
1832 — — King's name on *obv.* and *rev.; mm.* bow *Extr. rare*
1833 **Crown.** Uncrowned bust, as 1827; *mm.* arrow, **6**, Y .. £80
1834 Crowned bust, as 1830; *mm.* 52, 122, 111, Y £60

1836

Edward VI, Gold.   *Fine*

1835 **Halfcrown.** Uncrowned bust; *mm.* arrow, y £67/10/–
1836 Crowned bust as illus. above; *mm.* 52, 52/111, 122, y .. £67/10/–
1837 Similar, but king's name on *rev.; mm.* 52, 122 ..   ..   £85

Third period, 1550-3.

1838 " Fine " sovereign (=30s.).   King on throne; *mm.*
      97, 123 ..   ..   £2000
1839 **Double sovereign.** From the same dies   *Extr. rare*

1840    1843

1840 **Angel** (=10s.). As illustration; *mm.* 97, 123 ..   ..   £500
1841 **Half-angel.** Similar, *mm.* 97 ..   ..   *Unique*
1842 **Sovereign.** (=20s.)   Half-length figure of king r.,
      crowned and holding sword and orb.   ℞.   Crowned
      shield with supporters; *mm.* y, tun £125
1843 **Half-sovereign.** As illustration above; *mm.* y, tun ..   £70
1844 **Crown.** Similar, but for *rev.* legend; *mm.* y, tun   ..   £75
1845 **Halfcrown.** Similar £85

SILVER

First period, Apr. 1547-Jan. 1549.

1851    1852

1846 **Shilling.** *Durham House.* Crowned bust r.   ℞.
      TIMOR, etc. MDXLVIII, crowned garnished shield, ER at
      sides; *mm.* bow £100
1847 **Groat.** Similar. *Tower.* ℞. Shield over cross, POSVI,
      etc.; *mm.* arrow £20
1848 — *Southwark.* ℞. CIVITAS LONDON; *mm.* E or none..   £25
1849 **Halfgroat.** *Tower.* As groat £20
1850 *Southwark.* As groat; *mm.* arrow, E £15
1851 *Canterbury.* Similar, no *mm.* £18

Edward VI, Silver. *Fine*

1852 **Penny.** *Tower.* As halfgroat, but E.D.G. etc. ℞.
 CIVITAS LONDON; *mm.* arrow £32
1853 — *Southwark.* As last, but *mm.* E £32
1854 *Bristol.* Similar, but no *mm.* £25

1855 **Halfpenny.** *Tower.* As 1852, but *mm.* uncertain
 Extr. rare
1856 — *Bristol.* Similar, but no *mm.* £60

Second period, Jan. 1549–Apr. 1550.

1857 **Shilling.** As illus. *London.* MDXLIX or MDL; *mm.* 52-94 £5/10/–
1858 — — Similar, but legends transposed, MDXLIX; *mm.*
 52, 35, Y or none £8
1859 — *Bristol.* MDXLIX; *mm.* TC £25
1860 — *Canterbury.* MDXLIX; *mm.* T or t £7
1861 — *Durham House.* MDXLIX; *mm.* bow £27
1862 — — Similar, but legends transposed £30
1863 — — No date. ℞. INIMICOS etc. £14
1864 — — Similar, but legends transposed £18

Third period, 1550-3.
Base issue.

1865	1867

1865 **Shilling.** As 1857, MDL, MDLI; *mm.* lis, lion, rose .. £7
For coins of Edward VI countermarked, see p. 135.

1866 **Penny.** *O.* rose. *London; mm.* escallop £5
1867 — — *York. Mm.* mullet, as illus. 75/–
1868 **Halfpenny.** As penny, but single rose £60
1869 **Farthing.** *O.* Portcullis. ℞. Cross and pellets
 Extr. rare

Edward VI third period. *Fine*

Fine silver issue.

1870 **Crown.** King on horseback with date below horse.
℞. Shield on cross; *mm.* y, 1551; tun, 1551-3 .. £52/10/-

1871 **Halfcrown.** Walking horse with plume; *mm.* y, 1551 £24
1872 Galloping horse without plume; *mm.* tun, 1551-2 .. £35
1873 Large walking horse without plume; *mm.* tun, 1553 .. £60

1874 **Shilling.** As illus. below; but XII; *mm.* y, tun £5

1875   1878

1875 **Sixpence.** *London.* As illustration £8
1876 *York.* As last, but CIVITAS EBORACI; *mm.* mullet .. £15

1877 **Threepence.** *London.* As sixpence, but III; *mm.* tun .. £13
1878 *York.* As 1876, but III by bust £17

1879 **Penny.** " Sovereign " type; *mm.* tun .. *Extr. rare*

MARY, 1553-4

All Mary's gold coin was struck in 23 carat 3½ grain gold, the "crown" gold denominations being temporarily discontinued. The mintmarks appear at the end of the first word of the legends.

Mintmarks

Pomegranate (73)   Half rose

GOLD

Fine

1880 **"Fine" Sovereign** (=30s.). Queen enthroned. ℞. Shield on rose, MDLIII, MDLIIII and undated £350

1881 **Ryal** (=15s.). Queen in ship, MDLIII .. *Extr. rare*

1882 **Angel** (=10s.). Usual type; *mm.* pomegranate, half-rose £160

1883 **Half-angel.** Similar; *mm.* pomegranate *Extr. rare*

1881   1884

SILVER

1884 **Groat.** Crowned bust l. ℞. VERITAS, etc. 80/-

1885 **Halfgroat.** Similar £50

1886 **Penny.** Similar, but M . D . G . ROSA, etc. .. £40

1887 — As last. ℞. CIVITAS LONDON £35

PHILIP AND MARY, 1554-58

The groats of this period have Mary's portrait only, but the shillings and sixpences show the bust of the queen's husband, Philip of Spain.

GOLD

							Fine
1889	**Angel.** As illustration; *mm.* lis ..		..	..		..	£275
1890	**Half-angel.** Similar	..	..	..	*Extr. rare*		

SILVER

1898   1903

1891	**Shilling.** Busts face-to-face, full titles, undated		..	£10/10/-
1892	— — — also without mark of value	..	..	£38
1893	— — 1554	..	..	£7
1894	— English titles only, 1554, 1555	..	..	£8/10/-
1895	— — without mark of value, 1554	..	..	£50
1896A	— — date below bust, 1554, 1555	..	*fair* £50	
1896	— — As last, but without ANG., 1555	..	*fair* £60	
1897	**Sixpence.** Similar. Full titles, undated	..	..	£15
1898	— — 1554	..	..	£12
1899	— English titles only, 1555, 1557	..	..	£10
1900	— — date below bust, 1554, 1557	..	*fair* £50	
1901	**Groat.** Crowned bust of Mary l. ℞. POSVIMVS etc. *mm.* lis	..	..	£5
1902	**Halfgroat.** Similar, but POSVIM	..	..	£55
1903	**Penny.** Similar to 1887, but P . Z . M . etc.; *mm.* lis..		..	£40
1904	**Base penny.** Similar to 1888, but P . Z . M. etc.; *mm.* halved rose and H ..	..	..	80/-

ELIZABETH I, 1558-1603

Gold money was again struck in two standards of fineness—23 carat 3½ grains (standard gold) and 22 carat (crown gold). In 1559 Edward VI base shillings were countermarked and allowed to circulate at reduced values prior to being recalled. In 1601 the silver was restored to the standard it had been before Henry's debasement, i.e., 11 oz. 2 dwt. silver to 18 dwt. of alloy. Two more denominations were added to the silver, the three-halfpence and the three-farthings; and it will be seen that the number of silver denominations reached its maximum during this reign.

Coins manufactured by the screw-press and other machinery powered by a horse-drawn mill were produced by a French engraver, Eloye Mestrelle, in the years 1561-71. These became known as " milled money."

Mintmarks

1558-60	Lis (106)	1578-79	Greek cross (7)
1560-61	Cross crosslet (21)	1580-81	Latin cross (14)
	Martlet (94)	1582	Sword (113)
1560-66	Star (23, milled)	1582-83	Bell (60)
1561-65	Pheon (53)	1582-84	A (54)
1565	Rose (33)	1584-86	Escallop (79)
1566	Portcullis (107)	1587-89	Crescent (72b)
1566-67	Lion (92)	1590-92	Hand (86)
1567-70	Coronet (74)	1592-95	Tun (123)
	Lis (105, milled)	1594-96	Woolpack (124)
1569-71	Castle (71)	1595-98	Key (90)
1570	Pierced mullet (26, milled)	1597-1600	Anchor (57)
1572-73	Ermine (77)	1600	O
1573-74	Acorn (65b)	1601	1
1573-77	Eglantine (27)	1602	2

1906

Hammered coinage

1905   **"Fine" sovereign** (30s.) or **double-noble.**   Early issue (1558-61). As illus. on previous page, but tressure is broken by the back of the throne; *mm.* 106, 21   ..   £350

1906   — Late issue (1583-95). As illus.; *mm.* 54-123   ..   £180

1907   **Ryal** or **noble** (15s.).   Queen in ship; *mm.* 54-86   ..   £450

1908   **Angel.**   Usual type; wire-line inner circle; *mm.* lis   ..   £70

1909   — beaded inner circle; *mm.* 106, 21, 74, 77-123, 90-2 ..   £45

1910   — — ship to l. instead of to r.; *mm.* 77-27   ..   ..   £50

1911   **Half-angel;** *mm.* 106, 21, 74, 77-57   ..   ..   ..   £50

1911A   — without E and rose above ship; *mm.* 14   ..   ..   £75

1912   **Quarter-angel;** *mm.* 106, 74, 77-57   ..   ..   ..   £40

1912   1914A

1913   **Pound** (20s.).   Crowned profile portrait; *mm.* tun and lion/tun, tun, woolpack, key, anchor, **O, 1, 2** £100

1914   **Half-pound.**   Early issue, wire-line inner circles; *mm.* lis £75

1914A   — beaded inner circle; *mm.* crosslet, rose to castle   ..   £50

1915   Late issue, dress more decorated and with greater profusion of hair; *mm.* tun to **2** £75

1916   **Crown.**   Early issue, wire-line inner circle; *mm.* lis   ..   £90

1916A   — As 1914A £50

1917   Late issue; *mm.* tun to key, **O** to **2** £75

1918   **Halfcrown.**   Early issue, wire-line inner circles; *mm.* lis   £75

1918A   — As 1914A £45

1919   Late issue; *mm.* tun to **2** £60

Elizabeth I, Gold.   *Very Fine*

Milled coinage

1920 **Half-pound.** Crowned bust l.; *mm.* star, lis £300

1921 **Crown.** Similar £450

1922 **Halfcrown.** Similar £600

SILVER

1922A    1922B   Fair

Countermarked coins (1559). Devalued Edward VI base shillings.

1922A Portcullis cmk. on Edw. VI 2nd period shilling (devalued to 4½d.); *mm.* 66, 52, 122, t, 111, Y £52/10/-

1922B Greyhound cmk. on Edw. VI 3rd period base shilling (devalued to 2¼d.); *mm.* 92, 105, 33   ..   ..   ..   £55

Hammered coinage   *Fine*

1923 **Crown.** As illustration below; *mm.* **1, 2** £115

1924 **Halfcrown.** As illus.; *mm.* **1, 2** £27/10/-

1925 **Shilling.** Without rose or date, ELIZABET(H), wire-line inner circles; *mm.* lis £30

1926 — — beaded circles; *mm.* lis £20

1927 — — — ET instead of Z; *mm.* 21, 94 ..   ..   ..£7/10/-

1928 — ELIZAB; *mm.* bell to **2** £6

Elizabeth I, Silver. Hammered.

| | | 1929 | | | 1932 | *Fine* |

1929   **Sixpence.** With rose and date, ELIZABETH; 1561-1582;
     mm. pheon to sword 60/-

1930   — — without date; *mm.* lion, crown   ..   *Extr. rare*

1931   — — without rose; 1561, *mm.* pheon   ..   *Extr. rare*

1932   — ELIZAB; 1582-1602; *mm.* bell to **2** 75/-

1933   **Groat.** Without rose or date; wire line inner circles;
     mm. lis £10

1934   — beaded circles; *mm.* lis £8

1935   — — ET instead of Z; *mm.* 21, 94   ..   ..   80/-

1936   **Threepence.** With rose and date; 1561-1582; *mm.*
     53-113   ..   ..   35/-

1937   — without rose; 1568, *mm.* coronet   ..   *Extr. rare*

1938   **Halfgroat.** Without rose or date; ELIZABETH, wire line
     inner circles; *mm.* lis £10

1939   — — beaded circles; ET instead of Z; *mm.* 21, 53, 107-71   80/-

1940   — — E . D . G . ROSA, etc., two pellets behind bust.
     R. CIVITAS LONDON; *mm.* bell to **2** 35/-

1941   **Threehalfpence.** With rose and date, legends as last;
     1561-2, 64-70, 72-79, 81, 82; *mm.* pheon to sword   ..   85/-

| 1943 | | 1944 | | 1945 | |

1942   **Penny.** Without rose or date, legends as last, wire-line
     inner circles; *mm.* lis £18

1943   — beaded circles; *mm.* 21-94, 33-2   ..   ..   ..   50/-

1944   **Threefarthings.** With rose and date, legends as last;
     1561-2, 1568, 1572-8, 1581-2; *mm.* 53, 74, 77-113 *fair* £5   £15

1945   **Halfpenny.** Portcullis. R. Cross and pellets; *mm.*
     cross-crosslet, A-2, none 75/-

Elizabeth I, Silver. *Fine*

Milled coinage

1946 **Shilling.** Without rose or date; *mm.* star. Plain dress, large size £22/10/–

1947 — decorated dress, large size (over 31 mm.) £12

1948 — — intermediate size (30-31 mm.) £8

1949 — — small size (under 30 mm.) £10

1951   1958

Very fine

1950 **Sixpence.** Small bust, large rose, 1561; *mm.* star .. £6/10/–

1951 Tall narrow bust with plain dress, large rose, 1561-2, *mm.* star £6

1952 — similar, but decorated dress, 1562 .. .. .. £5

1953 Large broad bust, elaborately decorated dress, small rose, 1562; *mm.* star £5

1954 — — cross pattée on *rev.*, 1562-4; *mm.* star £7

1955 — similar, but with low ruff, pellet border, 1563-64, 1566 £7/10/–

1956 Small bust, 1567-8; *mm.* lis £7

1957 Large crude bust breaking legend; 1570, *mm.* lis; 1571, *mm.* castle £14

Fine

1958 **Groat.** As illustration £12

1959 **Threepence.** With rose, small bust with plain dress, 1561 .. .. £15

1960 Tall narrow bust with large rose, 1562 .. .. .. £7

1961 Short bust with small rose, 1562 .. .. .. £8

1962 Cross pattée on *rev.*, 1563-4 .. .. £12

1963 **Halfgroat.** As groat £10

1964 **Threefarthings.** E . D . G . ROSA, etc., with rose. ℞. CIVITAS LONDON, shield with 1563 above *Extr. rare*

JAMES I, 1603-25

With the accession of James VI of Scotland to the English throne, the royal titles and coat of arms are altered on the coinage; on the latter the Scottish rampant lion and the Irish harp now appear in the second and third quarters. In 1604 the weight of the gold pound was reduced and the new coin became known as the "Unite." Standard gold coins of 23½ carat and crown gold of 22 carat were both issued, and a gold four-shilling piece was struck 1604-1619. In 1612 all the gold coins had their values raised by 10%, but in 1619 the Unite was replaced by a new, lighter 20s. piece—the "Laurel."

In 1613 the King granted Lord Harrington a licence to coin farthings of copper as a result of repeated public demands for a low value coinage. Towards the end of the reign coins made from silver sent to the mint from the Welsh mines had the Prince of Wales's plumes inserted over the royal arms.

Mintmarks

1603-4	Thistle (125)	1613-5	Cinquefoil (32)
1604-5	Lis (105)	1615-6	Tun (123)
1605-6	Rose (33)	1616-7	Book on lectern (61 variety)
1606-7	Escallop (79)		
1607	Grapes (84)	1617-8	Crescent (72b, gold)
1607-9	Coronet (74)	1618-9	Plain cross (7a)
1609-10	Key (90)	1619	Saltire cross (16)
1610-1	Bell (60)	1619-20	Spur rowel (24)
1611-2	Mullet (25)	1620-1	Rose (33)
1612-3	Tower (71)	1621-3	Thistle (125)
1613	Trefoil (45)	1623-4	Lis (105)
		1624	Trefoil (46)

GOLD

Fine

First coinage, 1603-4

1965 **Sovereign** (=20s.). King crowned r. half-length, first bust with plain armour. ℞. EXVRGAT, etc.; *mm.* thistle .. — £300

1966 — second bust with decorated armour; *mm.* 125, 105 .. — £325

1967 **Half-sovereign.** Crowned bust r. ℞. EXVRGAT, etc.; *mm.* thistle .. .. *Extr. rare*

1968 **Crown.** Similar. ℞. TVEATVR, etc.; *mm.* 125, 105/125 — *Extr. rare*

1969 **Halfcrown.** Similar; *mm.* thistle, lis .. *Extr. rare*

Second coinage, 1604-19

1970 **Rose-ryal** (=30s.). King enthroned. ℞. Shield on rose; *mm.* 33-90, 25-61 var. £150

1971 **Spur-ryal** (=15s.). King in ship; *mm.* 33, 79, 74, 25-32, 61 var £375

1971   1972

| 1972 | **Angel** (=10s.). Old type; *mm.* 33-74, 60-16 .. | .. | £110 |
| 1973 | — pierced for use as touch-piece | .. .. .. | £50 |

| 1974 | **Half-angel** (=5s. 6d.). Similar; *mm.* 71-61 var., 7a, 16 | .. .. .. | *Extr. rare* |

1977

1975	**Unite** (=20s.). Half-length second bust r. ℞. FACIAM etc.; *mm.* lis or rose	.. .. ..	£30
1976	— fourth bust; *mm.* rose to cinquefoil	.. ..	..£27/10/-
1977	— fifth bust; *mm.* cinquefoil to saltire ..	..	..£27/10/-

1978	**Double-crown.** Third bust r. ℞. HENRICVS, etc.; *mm.* lis or rose	.. .. ..	£18
1979	Fourth bust; *mm.* rose to bell ..	.. .. ..	£18
1980	Fifth bust; *mm.* mullet to saltire	.. .. ..	£24

1981	**Britain crown.** First bust r.; *mm.* lis to coronet	..	£14
1982	Third bust; *mm.* key to cinquefoil	.. ..	£14
1983	Fifth bust; *mm.* cinquefoil to saltire	.. ..	£14

James I Second Coinage. Gold *Fine*

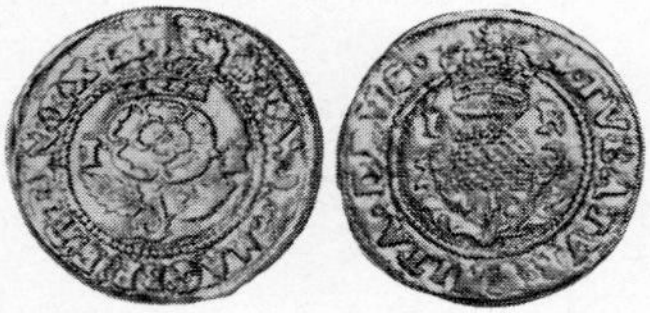

1984 **Thistle crown** (=4s.). As illus.; *mm.* lis to cross .. £21
1984A — IR only on one side £25
1985 **Halfcrown.** First bust; *mm.* lis to coronet £13
1986 Third bust; *mm.* key to trefoil £15
1987 Fifth bust; *mm.* cinquefoil to cross £13

Third coinage, 1619-25

1988 **Rose-ryal.** King enthroned. ℞. XXX above shield; *mm.* 24-105 .. .. £200
1989 Similar but plain back to throne; *mm.* 46 .. .. £225

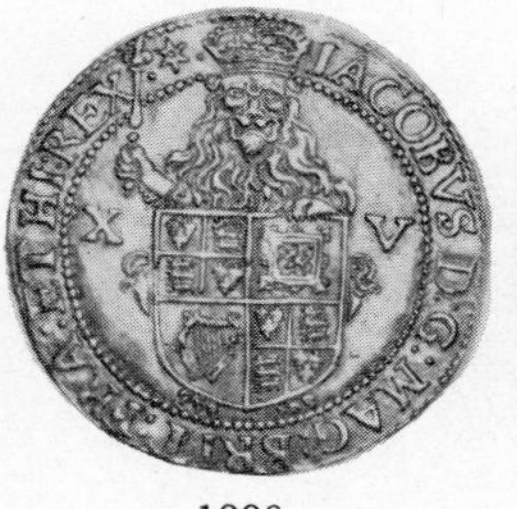

1990

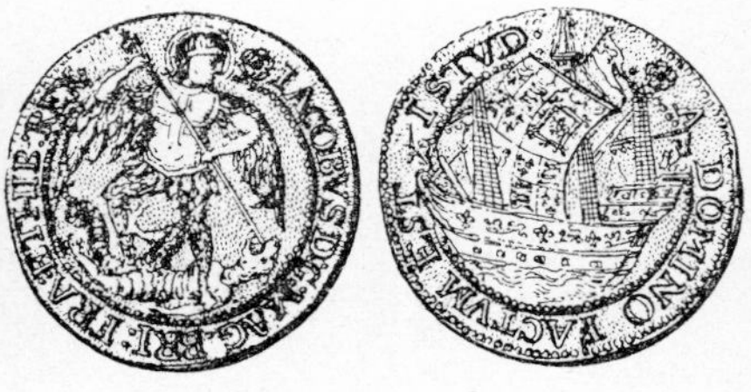

1991

1990 **Spur-ryal.** As illus.; *mm.* 24-125, 46 .. .. .. £375
1991 **Angel** of new type; *mm.* 24-46 .. .. £150
1991A — pierced for use as touch-piece £75

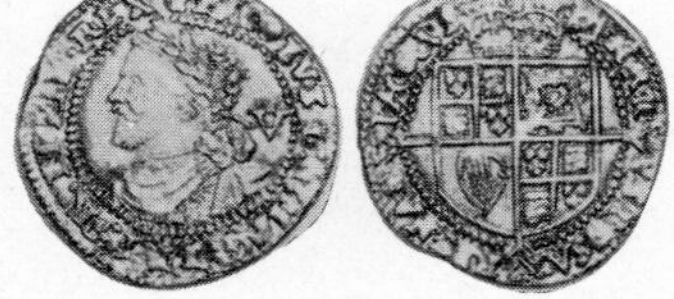

1995

1992 **Laurel** (=20s.). First (large) laur. bust l.; *mm.* 24 .. £35
1992A Second to fourth busts; *mm.* 24-46 .. .. .. £25
1992B Fifth, small rather crude, bust; *mm.* trefoil *Extr. rare*
1993 **Half-laurel.** First bust; *mm.* spur rowel £21
1994 Fourth bust; *mm.* 24-46 .. .. £18
1995 **Quarter-laurel.** Second or fourth bust; *mm.* 24-46 .. £15

For busts on the laurels, see North.

SILVER

First coinage, 1603-4

1996   **Crown.** King on horseback. ℞. EXVRGAT, etc., shield;
mm. thistle, lis £125

1997   **Halfcrown.** Similar £110

1998   **Shilling.** First bust, square-cut beard. ℞. EXVRGAT,
etc.; *mm.* thistle   ..   ..   ..   *fair* 45/–   £7

1999   — Second bust, pointed beard; *mm.* thistle, lis
fair 40/–   £6

            2000   2001

2000   **Sixpence.** First bust; 1603; *mm.* thistle   *fair* 45/–   £6

2001   Second bust; 1603-4; *mm.* thistle, lis   ..   *fair* 40/– £5/10/–

          2003   2004

2002   **Halfgroat.** As illustration but II; *mm.* thistle, lis   ..   90/–

2003   **Penny.** Similar, but I behind head; *mm.* thistle, lis ..   90/–

2004   **Halfpenny.** As illustration; *mm.* thistle, lis 60/–

Second coinage, 1604-19

2005   **Crown.** King on horseback. ℞. QVAE DEVS, etc.;
mm. 105-84   ..   ..   £105

2006   **Halfcrown.** Similar; *mm.* 105, 79, 123   ..   ..   £95

2007   **Shilling.** Third bust, beard cut square and stands out
(*cf.* illus. 2010); *mm.* lis, rose £5/10/–

2008   — Fourth bust, armour plainer (*cf.* illus. 2011); *mm.*
33-74 ..   ..   75/–

2009   — Fifth bust, similar but hair longer; *mm.* 74-7a   ..   85/–

2010   2011

2010 **Sixpence.** Third bust; 1604-5; *mm.* lis, rose   .. £5/5/–

2011 — Fourth bust; 1605-15; *mm.* rose to tun 70/–

2013   2015

2012 **Halfgroat.** As illus. but larger crown on *obv.; mm.* lis to
coronet 30/–

2013 — Similar but smaller crown on *obv.; mm.* coronet to cross   40/–

2014 **Penny.** As halfgroat but no crowns; *mm.* lis to cross
and none 30/–

2014A — As before but TVEATVR legend both sides; *mm.* mullet
Extr. rare

2015 **Halfpenny.** As illus.; *mm.* lis to mullet, cinquefoil .. 37/6

Third coinage, 1619-25

2016 **Crown.** As 2005, but mostly with bird-headed harp,
colon stops on *obv.*, no stops on *rev.; mm.* 33-46 ..   .. £75

2017 — — plume over shield; *mm.* 125-46 ..   ..   ..£82/10/–

2018 **Halfcrown.** As 2016; all have bird-headed harp   .. £12

2019 — — plume over shield; *mm.* 125-46 ..   ..   .. £15

2020 **Shilling.** Sixth (large) bust, hair longer and very curly;
mm. 24-46 ..   .. 80/–

2021 — — plume over shield; *mm.* 125-46 ..   ..   .. £7

2022   2024

2022	**Sixpence.** Sixth bust; 1621-4; *mm.* 33-46	..	..	90/-
2023	**Halfgroat.** As 2013 but no stops on *rev.*; *mm.* 24-46 and none	..	..	22/6
2024	**Penny.** As illus.; *mm.* 24, 105, 46 and none ..	..		30/-
2025	**Halfpenny.** As 2015 but no *mm.*	..	..	30/-

COPPER

For mintmarks, see our *British Copper Coins and Their Values,* or *English Copper, Tin and Bronze Coins in the British Museum,* 1558-1958.

2026   2029

2026	**Farthing.** " Harrington," small size ..	..	..	£5
2027	— — letter below crown	..	..	..	£6
2028	— — *mm.* below crown ..	..	..	..	£7
2029	" Harrington," normal size; *mm.* on *rev.*	..	..	40/-

2032

2030	" Lennox "; *mm. rev.* only	..	..	..	..	40/-
2031	— *mm.* both sides	..	..	..	..	25/-
2032	— *mm. obv.* only ..	..	..	..	..	17/6
2033	— — larger crown	..	..	..	..	17/6
2034	— oval type, legend starts at bottom l. ..	..	..	60/-

CHARLES I, 1625-1649

Numismatically, this reign is one of the most interesting of all the English monarchs. Some outstanding machine-made coins were produced by Nicholas Briot, a French die-sinker, but they could not be struck at sufficient speed to supplant hand-hammering methods. In 1637 a branch mint was set up at Aberystwyth to coin silver extracted from the Welsh mines. After the king's final breach with Parliament the Parliamentary Government continued to issue coins at London with Charles's name and portrait until the king's trial and execution. The licence to coin " royal " farthings was revoked by Parliament in 1644.

During the Civil Wars coins were struck at a number of towns to supply coinage for those areas of the country under Royalist control. Amongst the more spectacular pieces are the gold triple unites and the silver pounds and half-pounds struck at Shrewsbury and Oxford, and the emergency coins made from odd-shaped pieces of silver plate during the seiges of Newark, Scarborough, Carlisle and Pontefract.

Mintmarks

1625	Lis (105)
1625-6	Cross Calvary (10)
1626-7	Negro's head (96)
1627-8	Castle (71)
1628-9	Anchor (57)
1629-30	Heart (88)
1630-1	Plume (101)
1631-2	Rose (35)
1631-2	Flower and B (59, *Briot*)
1632	B (*Briot*)
1632-3	Harp (87)
1633-4	Portcullis (107)
1634-5	Bell (60)
1635-6	Crown (75)
1636-8	Tun (123)
1638-9	Anchor (57)
	Anchor and B (58, *Briot*)
	Anchor and mullet (*Briot*)
1638-42	Book (61, *Aberystwyth*)
1639-40	Triangle (119a)
1640-1	Star (23)
1641-3	Triangle in circle (119b)
1642	Plume (104, *Shrewsbury*)
	Pellet or pellets „
1642-3	Rose (35, *Truro*)
1642-4	Lion (92, *York*)
1642-6	Plume (103, *Oxford*)
	Pellet or pellets (*Oxford*)
	Lis (105, *Oxford*)
1643	Cross pattée (6, *Bristol*)
1643-4	P in brackets (98, *Parliament*)
	Acorn (65b *Bristol*)
	Castle (71, *Weymouth*)
	Helmet (89, *Weymouth* and ? *Salisbury*)

1643-4	Leopard's head (? *Wey.*)
	Two lions (92 over 92, *Weymouth*)
	Lis (105, *Wey.* or *Sal.*)
	Bunch of grapes (84, *Weymouth* or *Salisbury*)
	Bird (*Wey.* or *Sal.*)
	Boar's head (*Wey.* or *Sal.*)
	Lion rampant (93) „
	Rosette (34, *Wey.* or *Sal.*)
1643-5	Plume (103, *Bristol*)
	Br (67, *Bristol*)
	Pellets (*Bristol*)
	Rose (35, *Exeter*)
	Rosette (34, *Oxford*)
1643-6	Floriated cross (*Oxford*)
1644	Cross pattée (6, *Oxford*)
	Lozenge (*Oxford*)
	Billet (*Oxford*)
	Mullet (25, *Oxford*)
1644-5	R in brackets (112, *Parliament*)
1644-6	Gerb (83, *Chester*)
	Pear (100, *Worcester*)
1645	Eye (81, *Parliament*)
	Lis (105, *Combe-Martin ?*)
	Castle (71, *Exeter*)
1645-6	Sun (120, *Parliament*)
	Plume (102-4, *Lundy*)
	A (*Appledore* or *Lundy*)
1646	B (*Barnstaple* or *Lundy*)
1646-8	Sceptre (109, *Parliament*)
1647-8	Crown (75, *Combe Martin*)

GOLD
Tower mint, under the King, 1625-43

2039

2035	**Angel.** As for Jas. I last issue, without mark of value; *mm.* lis and cross calvary	£180
2036	— — pierced for use as touch-piece	£100
2037	— x in field to r.; *mm.* 96-88	£150
2038	— — — pierced for use as touch-piece	£85
2039	— x in field to l.; *mm.* 96, 88, 35-119a, 119b	£125
2040	— — — pierced for use as touch-piece	£75

2041	**Unite** (=20s.). First bust with ruff and collar of order, high double arched crown. ℞. Square-topped shield; *mm.* 105, 10	£35
2042	— similar but flat single-arched crown	£35
2043	Second bust with ruff and in armour nearly concealed with scarf; *mm.* 10-101	£32/10/–
2043A	— — *mm.* anchor below bust .. .. *Extr. rare*	
2044	Third bust, more armour visible. ℞. Oval shield with CR at sides; *mm.* 101, 35	£37/10/–
2045	Fourth bust, small lace collar, Garter ribbon on breast. ℞. Oval shield with crowned CR at sides; *mm.* 87-23 ..	£37/10/–
2046	Sixth (Briot's) bust, large lace collar. ℞. Similar; *mm.* 57-119b	£50
2046A	— — with Briot's *rev.*; *mm.* 57 .. .. *Extr. rare*	

2048

2047	**Double-crown.** First bust. ℞. Square-topped shield; *mm.* 105, 10	£25
2048	Second bust. ℞. Similar; *mm.* 10-101	£22/10/-
2049	Third bust. ℞. Oval shield with CR at sides; *mm.* 101, 35	£27/10/-
2050	Fourth bust. ℞. Oval shield with crowned CR at sides; *mm.* 87-57	£25
2051	Fifth bust as Aberystwyth silver. ℞. Similar; *mm.* 57, 119a	£40
2052	Sixth bust. ℞. Normal; *mm.* 57-119b	£35
2052A	— ℞. Briot's square-topped shield; *mm.* 57 *Extr. rare*	

2053	**Crown.** First bust. ℞. Square-topped shield; *mm.* 105, 10	£16
2054	Second bust. ℞. Similar; *mm.* 10-101	£16
2055	— — ℞. As next; 101, 35	£37/10/-
2056	Third bust. ℞. Oval shield with CR at sides; *mm.* 101 *Extr. rare*	
2057	Fourth bust. ℞. Oval shield with crowned CR at sides; *mm.* 87-119b	£20
2058	Fifth (Aberystwyth) bust. ℞. Similar; *mm.* 57	£30
2059	Sixth (Briot's) bust. ℞. Similar; *mm.* 57 *Unique*	

Tower mint, under Parliament, 1643-8. All Charles I types

2060	**Unite.** Fourth bust, as 2045; *mm.* (P)	£40
2061	Sixth bust, as 2046; *mm.* (P), (R)	£45
2062	Seventh bust, cruder style; *mm.* 81-109	£60
2063	**Double-crown.** Fourth bust, as 2050; *mm.* eye *Extr. rare*	
2064	Fifth bust, as 2051; *mm.* sun, sceptre	£50
2065	Sixth bust, as 2052; *mm.* (P)	£65
2065A	Seventh bust, as 2062; *mm.* sun *Unique*	
2066	**Crown.** Fourth bust, as 2057; *mm.* (P) to sceptre	£40

Nicholas Briot's coinage, 1631-2
2067   **Angel.**   As Tower but smaller and neater; *mm.* −/B
                                                                   Extr. rare

2068	**Unite.** As illustration but xx. R. FLORENT etc.	..	£300
2069	**Double-crown.** Similar but x. R. CVLTORES, etc.		£200
2070	**Crown.** Similar; *mm.* B .. .. *Extr. rare*		

Provincial issues, 1638-49
  Aberystwyth mint, 1638-42
2071 **Unite.** As Tower. Sixth bust but CR not crowned; *mm.*
      plume   ..   ..   *Unique?*

  Shrewsbury mint, 1642
2072 **Triple unite,** 1642. Half-length figure l. holding sword
      and olive-branch; *mm.* :. R. EXVRGAT, etc., around RELIG
      PROT, etc., in two wavy lines, III and three plumes above,
      date below   ..   ..   *Unique?*

  Oxford mint, 1642-6   *Fine*
2073 **Triple unite.** As last but *mm.* plume, tall narrow bust,
      1642   ..   ..   £650
2074 Similar but " Declaration " on continuous scroll, 1642-3   £600
2075 As last but larger bust, with scarf behind shoulder, 1643   £750
2076 Similar but without scarf, 1643 ..   ..   ..   £650
2077 Similar but OXON below 1643, rosette stops   *Extr. rare*
2078 Smaller size, 1644 / OXON £800
2079 — 1644 / OX £850

2080 **Unite.** Tall thin bust. ℞. " Declaration " in two
wavy lines, 1642 .. .. £85
2081 — ℞. " Declaration " in three lines on continuous
scroll, 1642-3 .. .. £100
2082 Larger bust. ℞. Similar, 1643 .. .. .. £125
2083 Shorter bust. ℞. Similar, 1643, 1645; *mm.* plume .. £85

2084 — — 1644 / ox; *mm.* plume £110
2085 Tall bust to edge of coin. ℞. Similar, 1643 .. £150
2086 As 2083. ℞. " Declaration " in three straight lines,
1644 / ox .. .. *Extr. rare*
2086A Longer, narrower bust. ℞. Similar £120
2087 — ℞. Single plume above " Declaration," 1645-6 / ox £150
2088 **Half-unite.** " Declaration " in three straight lines, 1642
Extr. rare
2089 " Declaration " on scroll; *mm.* plume; 1642-3 .. .. £175

2090 Bust to bottom of coin, 1643 .. .. £140
2091 — 1644 / ox .. .. *Extr. rare*

Bristol mint, 1645
2092 **Unite.** Somewhat as 2083; *mm.* Br; 1645 *Extr. rare*
2093 **Half-unite.** Similar .. .. .. *Unique ?*

Truro mint, 1642-3
2094 **Unite.** *Mm.* rose. ℞. FLORENT, etc., crowned oval
shield between C R .. .. .. *Unique*
2094A — ℞. CVLTORES, etc., similar but no C R *Extr. rare*

Weymouth mint, 1643-4
2095 **Unite.** No *mm.* ℞. FLORENT, etc., double annulet stops,
crowned oval shield, lion's paws on either side of garniture .. .. *Extr. rare*

Salisbury (or Sandsfoot Castle) mint, 1644

2096 **Unite.** As last but *mm.* lis   ..   ..   *Unique ?*

Colchester besieged, 1648

2097 **Ten shillings.** Gateway of castle between CR; below
OBS COL 16 $\frac{s}{x}$ 48 ..   ..   ..   *Extr. rare*

Pontefract besieged, 1648-9. After the death of Chas. I,
in the name of Chas. II.

2098 **Unite.** DVM : SPIRO : SPERO around CR crowned. ℞.
CAROLVS : SECVNDVS : 1648, castle, OBS on l., PC above.
Octagonal ..   ..   *Extr. rare*

2099 CAROL : II, etc., around HANC : DEVS, etc. ℞. POST :
MORTEM, etc., around castle. *Octagonal*   *Extr. rare*

SILVER

Tower mint, under the King, 1625-43

2106

Fine

2100 **Crown.** King on horseback with raised sword. 1a.
Horse caparisoned with plume on head and crupper. ℞.
Square-topped shield over long cross fourchée; *mm.*
105, 10 ..   ..   £52/10/-

2101 — 1b. Similar but plume over shield, no cross; *mm.*
105, 10, 71 ..   ..   £250

2102 — 2a. Smaller horse, plume on hd. only, cross on
housings, king holds sword on shoulder. ℞. Oval garnished shield over cross fourchée, CR above; *mm.* harp ..   £50

2103 — 2b¹. — — plume divides CR, no cross; *mm.* 101, 35   £60

2104 — 2b². — — — with cross; *mm.* harp £80

2105 — 3a. Horse with caparisons. ℞. Oval shield without
CR; *mm.* 60-23 ..   ..   £52/10/-

2106 — 3b. — — plume over shield; *mm.* 107, 75, 123 .. £57/10/-

2106A " Briot " horse with ground-line; *mm.* 119b £200

2117

2107 **Halfcrown.** As 2100. 1a¹. Rose on housings, ground-
line; *mm.* lis £12/10/-
2108 — 1a². Similar but no rose or ground-line; *mm.* lis ..   £16
2109 — 1a³. As last but clumsier horse and shield not over
cross; *mm.* 10-71 ..   ..   £11
2110 — 1a⁴. — — with ground-line; *mm.* lis £200
2111 — 1b. — — plume over shield; *mm.* lis to anchor ..   £80
2112 — 2/1b. As 2102 but rose on housings. R. As last;
mm. heart, plume £140

2113 — 2a. As 2102. R. Flattened oval garnished shield
without cross, CR above; *mm.* plume, rose £8
2114 — 2b. Similar but plume between the CR £50
2115 — 2c. As 2a but differently garnished oval shield with
CR at sides; *mm.* harp, portcullis £6/10/-
2116 — 2d. Similar but with plume over shield; *mm.* harp   £75
2117 — 3a¹. No caparisons on horse, upright sword, scarf
flies out from waist. R. Round garnished shield, no CR;
mm. 57, 60-123   ..   .. £5/10/-
2118 — 3b. — — plume over shield; *mm.* 107-123   ..   £25
2119 — 3a². — cloak flies from king's shoulder; *mm.* 123-23   £6
2120 — — — — rough ground beneath horse; *mm.* 119a, 23   £6
2121 — 4. Foreshortened horse, mane before chest, tail between legs; *mm.* 23, 119b 85/-

2122	**Shilling.** 1. Bust in ruff. ℞. Square-topped shield over cross fourchée; *mm.* lis, cross Calvary	£5/10/-
2123	— — — light weight (81¾ grs.); *mm.* 10	£20
2124	— 1b¹. — — plume over shield, no cross; *mm.* 105, 10	£37/10/-
2125	— 1a. Bust in ruff and armour concealed by scarf. ℞. As 2122; *mm.* 10-71	£9
2126	— — — — light weight; *mm.* cross Calvary	£25
2127	— 1b². — — plume over shield, no cross; *mm.* 10-101	£11
2128	— 1b³. — — — cross; *mm.* negro's head	£42/10/-
2129	— 2a. More armour visible. ℞. Oval shield, CR above; *mm.* plume, rose	£5/5/-
2130	— 2b. — — plume over shield; *mm.* 101, 35	£20
2131	— 3¹. Bust with lace collar. ℞. Flattish oval shield, CR at sides; *mm.* harp, portcullis	75/-
2132	— 3². — — plume over shield; *mm.* harp	£55
2133	— 3a. — no inner circles, rounder shield without CR; *mm.* 60-123	65/-
2134	— 3b. — — plume over shield; *mm.* 60-123	£20

2133   2139

2135	— 4¹. Large Aberystwyth bust, small XII. ℞. Square-topped shield over cross fleury; *mm.* tun	£5/10/-
2136	— 4¹ var. Similar but rounder shoulders, large XII; *mm.* 57, 119a	65/-
2137	— 4². Smaller Aberystwyth bust with small double-arched crown, small XII; *mm.* tun	70/-
2138	— 4³. — single-arched crown, large XII; *mm.* 57, 119a	65/-
2139	— 4⁴. Older (Briot's style) bust, very pointed beard; *mm.* 57-119b	50/-

2143   2145

2140	**Sixpence.** 1. As 2122, but dated 1625-6; *mm.*, 105, 10	£9/10/–
2141	— 1a¹. As 2125, but dated 1625-9; *mm.* 10-88	£7
2142	— 1a². — no cross, 1630; *mm.* 88, 101..	£11
2143	— 2a. As 2129, no date; *mm.* plume, rose	£8/10/–
2144	— 2b. — plume dividing CR; *mm.* plume and rose	£7/10/–
2145	— 3. As 2131; *mm.* harp, portcullis	£6/10/–
2146	— 3a. — no inner circles; *mm.* 60-123	80/–
2147	— 4¹. As first Aberystwyth sixpence, large VI. ℞. Square-topped shield over cross; *mm.* tun	£5/10/–
2148	— 4¹ var. — similar but small VI; *mm.* tun and anchor	£11
2149	— 4². Second Aberystwyth bust, double-arched crown; *mm.* 57, 119a	70/–
2150	— 4² var. — single-arched crown; *mm.* 119a	£10
2151	— 4³. Older (Briot's style) bust; *mm.* 119a-119b	50/–

2152   2164

2152	**Halfgroat.** 1. Crowned rose type; *mm.* 105-96	25/–
2153	— 1a. — without inner circles; *mm.* 96-101	25/–
2154	— 2a. King's bust in ruff and mantle. ℞. Oval shield; *mm.* plume, rose	30/–
2155	— 2b. Similar but with plume over shield	£5
2156	— 3¹. Bust with lace collar. ℞. Oval shield between CR; no inner circles; *mm.* harp, crown, portcullis	25/–
2157	— 3². — — inner circles; *mm.* harp, portcullis	30/–
2158	— 3³. — — inner circle on *rev.*; *mm.* similar	37/6
2159	— 3⁴. — — inner circle on *obv.*; *mm.* similar..	30/–
2160	— 3⁵. — — no CR, no i.cs.; *mm.* portcullis	25/–
2161	— 3⁶. — — i.c. on *obv.*; *mm.* portcullis	25/–
2162	— 3a¹. — ℞. Rounder shield, different garniture, no i.cs.; *mm.* 60-119b	20/–
2163	— 3a². — — i.c. on *obv.*; *mm.* triangle	30/–
2164	— 3a³. — — i.cs. both sides; *mm.* 119a-119b	20/–
2165	— 3a⁴. Aberystwyth bust, no i.cs.; *mm.* anchor	30/–
2166	— 3a⁵. — i.c. on *rev.*; *mm.* anchor	30/–
2167	— 3a⁶. Very small bust, no i.cs.; *mm.* anchor	30/–

2168   2175

2168	**Penny.** 1. Rose each side; i.cs.; *mm.* negro's head, lis/:, one or two pellets	25/–
2169	— 1a. — no i.cs.; *mm.* lis, one or two pellets	20/–
2170	— 1b. — i.c. on *rev.*; *mm.* negro's head/two pellets ..	40/–
2171	— 2. Bust in ruff and mantle. ℞. Oval shield; i.cs.; *mm.* plume	35/–
2172	— 2¹. — — no i.cs.; *mm.* plume	40/–
2173	— 2a¹. More armour visible; no i.cs.; *mm.* plume, rose	30/–
2174	— 2a². — i.c. on *obv.*; *mm.* plume, rose	40/–
2175	— 2a³. — i.cs. both sides; *mm.* plume, rose	35/–
2175A	— 2a⁴ — i.c. on *rev.*; *mm.* rose/plume	80/–
2176	— 3¹. Bust in lace collar. ℞. CR at sides of shield; no i.cs.; *mm.* harp, one or two pellets	25/–
2177	— 3². — similar but no CR; *mm.* as last and 107 ..	35/–
2178	— 3³. — — i.c. on *obv.*; *mm.* harp	35/–
2179	— 3⁴. — — i.c. on *rev.*; *mm.* harp	35/–
2180	— 3a¹. — similar but shield almost round and with scroll garniture; no i.cs.; *mm.* bell, triangle, one or two pellets	25/–
2181	— 3a³. Aberystwyth bust; *mm.* one or two pellets or none..	25/–
2182	**Halfpenny.** Rose each side; no legend or *mm.* ..	35/–

Tower mint, under Parliament, 1643-8. All Charles I type

2183	**Crown.** 4. Foreshortened horse; *mm.* (P) to sun	..£52/10/–
2184	— 5. Tall spirited horse; *mm.* sun	£85
		Fair
2185	**Halfcrown.** 3a³. As 2119 but coarse work; *mm.* (P) to sun	57/6
2186	— 4. Foreshortened horse; *mm.* (P) .. *Extr. rare*	
2187	— 5. Tall horse; *mm.* sun, sceptre	80/–
2188	**Shilling.** 4⁴. Briot style bust but coarse work; *mm.* (P) to sun	55/–
2189	— 4⁵. Long narrow coarse bust; *mm.* sun, sceptre ..	75/–
2190	— 4⁶. Short broad older bust; *mm.* sceptre	80/–
2191	**Sixpence.** 4³. Briot style bust; *mm.* (P) to sun ..	..£5/5/–
2192	— 4⁴. Late Aberystwyth bust; *mm.* (R) to sceptre ..	50/–
2192A	— 4⁵. Squat bust of crude style; *mm.* eye and sun	..£13/10/–
2193	**Halfgroat.** 3a³. As 2164; *mm.* (P) to sceptre ..	35/–
2194	— 3a⁷. Older, shorter bust, pointed beard; *mm.* eye to sceptre	30/–
2195	**Penny.** 3a². Older bust; *mm.* pellets	27/6

Nicholas Briot's coinage, 1631-9.
   First milled issue, 1631-2.
2196   **Crown.**   King on horseback.   ℞.   Crowned shield
            between C R crowned; *mm.* flower and B / B £90
2197   **Halfcrown.**   Similar £30
2198   **Shilling.**   Briot's early bust with falling lace collar.
            ℞.   Square-topped shield over long cross fourchée; *mm.*
            as before £18/10/–
2199   **Sixpence.**   Similar, but VI behind bust £9

                    2199   2200

2200   **Halfgroat.**   Briot's bust, B below, II behind.   ℞.
            IVSTITIA, etc., square-topped shield over long cross
            fourchée £5/10/–
2201   **Penny.**   Similar, but I behind bust £7
   Second milled issue, 1638-9.
2202   **Halfcrown.**   As 2197, but *mm.* anchor and B £27/10/–

                              2202

2203   **Shilling.**   Briot's late bust, the falling lace collar is plain
            with broad lace border, no scarf.   ℞.   As 2198 but cross
            only to inner circle; *mm.* anchor and B £11/10/–
2204   **Sixpence.**   Similar, but VI; *mm.* 57, anchor and mullet   85/–
   Hammered issue, 1638-9.   *Fine*
2205   **Halfcrown.**   King on Briot's style horse with ground
            line.   ℞.   Square-topped garnished shield; *mm.* anchor,
            triangle over anchor £60
2206   **Shilling.**   As 2203; *mm.* anchor, triangle over anchor.
            ℞.   Square-topped shield over short cross fleury ..   £35

Provincial and Civil War issues, 1638-49.
York mint, 1642-4. *Mm.* lion.

2207	**Halfcrown.** 1. Ground-line below horse. ℞. Square-topped shield between CR	£20
2208	— 2. — ℞. Oval shield as Tower 3a..	£22/10/-
2209	— 3. No ground-line. ℞. Shield somewhat flattened	£15
2210	— 4. As last, but EBOR below horse with head held low. Base metal, often very base	£11
2211	— 5. Tall horse, mane in front of chest, EBOR below. ℞. Crowned square-topped shield between CR, flowers in legend	£8/10/-
2212	— 6. As last, but shield is oval, garnished	£6

2213	— 7. Similar, but horse's tail shows between legs. ℞. Shield as last, but with lion's skin garniture, no CR or flowers	85/-
2214	**Shilling.** 1. Bust as Tower 3¹. ℞. EBOR above square-topped shield over cross fleury	80/-
2215	— 2. Similar, but bust in plain armour, mantle; coarse work..	£6
2216	— 3. — ℞. EBOR below oval shield	£5/10/-
2217	— 4. — Similar, but crowned oval shield	80/-
2218	— 5. — As last, but lion's skin garniture	80/-

2220   2221

2219	**Sixpence.** Crowned oval shield	£16
2220	— — C R at sides	£8/10/-
2221	**Threepence.** As type 1 shilling, but III behind bust	90/-

Aberystwyth mint, 1638-42. *Mm.* book.
plume 1 = with coronet and band.   2 = with coronet only.

2222 **Halfcrown.** King on horseback, small pl. 2 behind.
R. Oval garnished shield with large plume above .. £30
2223 — plume 1 behind King, ground below horse £35
2224 As 2222, but more spirited horse, ground, FRAN ET HIB.. £57/10/-
2225 **Shilling.** Bust with large square lace collar, pl. 2
before, small XII. R. As before. No inner circles .. £7
2226 — inner circle on *rev.* £10
2227 As 2225, but large plume 1, large XII, inner circles .. £6/10/-
2228 As last, but small head, rounded lace collar .. £9
2229 Briot's bust as Tower 3¹, small square lace collar, plume
2, inner circles £11

2230 **Sixpence.** As 2225, but small VI; no inner circles .. £12
2231 As 2228, but plume 2, inner circle *obv.* £15
2232 Similar, but with inner circles both sides £11
2233 — — later *rev.* with smaller square-shaped plume .. £9
2234 Bust as the first Oxford sixpence; with crown cutting
inner circle £15/10/-
Very Fine

2235 **Groat.** Large bust, lace collar, no armour on shoulder.
Crown breaks inner circle. R. Shield, plume 1 or 2. £7
2236 — Similar, armour on shoulder, shorter collar. R.
Similar. £8
2237 — Smaller, neater bust not breaking circle. R,
Similar. £7

2236   2240   2241-3

2240 **Threepence.** Small bust, reads M . B . FR . ET . H. R.
Shield, plume 1 or 2 above 85/-
2241 — Similar, but HI. R. Shield, plume 2 above .. 90/-
2242 — M : B : FR : ET . HI: R. Similar 95/-
2242A — M . B . F . ET . HIB. R. Similar £5/10/-
2242B — M : B : F : ET : HIB: R. Similar £5/10/-
2243 — MAG : B : F : ET . H: R. Similar £5

Charles I Silver. Aberystwyth mint *Very Fine*

2244 **Halfgroat.** Bust as 2225. ℞. Large plume. No i.cs. £5
2245 Bust with round lace collar; inner circles £6
2246 Briot's bust, square lace collar; inner circles £6

2249   2251

2247 **Penny.** As 2244; CARO; no inner circles £12
2248 As 2245; CARO; inner circles £12
2249 As 2247; CAROLVS; inner circles £10
2250 Similar, but Briot's bust; inner circles £18
2251 **Halfpenny.** No legend. *O.* Rose. ℞. Plume .. £12

Combe Martin mint, 1645-8. *Mm.* crown.

2255   2257

Fine

2252 **Halfcrown.** King on horseback ℞. Aberystwyth type £140
2253 **Shilling.** Aberystwyth type, but *mm.* crown £130
2254 **Sixpence**. Similar £100
2255 **Groat.** Similar £20
2256 **Threepence.** Similar £25
2257 **Halfgroat.** Similar. ℞. Large plume £30
2258 **Penny.** Similar £40

Combe Martin mint?

2259 **Halfcrown.** As illustration, dated 1645 *fair* £120
2260 — — undated .. .. *Extr. rare*

163

Charles I Silver

Shrewsbury mint, 1642. *Mm.* plume without band.

2261	**Pound.** King on horseback, pl. behind, Aberystwyth style. ℞. Declaration between two straight lines, xx and three Shrewsbury plumes above, 1642 below ..	£200
2262	Similar, but Shrewsbury horse walking over pile of arms	£180
2263	As last, but cannon amongst arms and only single plume and xx above Declaration ..	£250
2264	**Half-pound.** As 2261, but x ..	£75
2265	Similar, but only two plumes on *rev.*	£120
2266	Shrewsbury horseman with ground-line..	£70
2267	— with cannon and arms below horse ..	£65
2268	— as last, but no plume on *obv.*	£65

2270

2269	**Crown.** Aberystwyth horseman .. *Unique*	
2270	Shrewsbury horseman with ground-line	£65
2271	**Halfcrown.** *O.* From Aberystwyth die; *mm.* book. ℞. Single plume above "Declaration," 1642	£75
2272	Aberystwyth horseman, fat plume behind. ℞. Three plumes above Declaration	£21
2273	Shrewsbury horseman. ℞. As 2271, single plume ..	£40
2274	— ℞. 2: plume: 6. above Declaration	£75
2275	— with ground-line. ℞. Similar £67/10/-
2276	— — ℞. As 2271, single plume	£40
2277	— — ℞. Three thin plumes above Declaration ..	£16
2278	— — — no plume behind king £22/10/-
2279	**Shilling.** *O.* from Aberystwyth die; *mm.* book. ℞. Declaration type £32/10/-
2280	*O.* from Shrewsbury die. ℞. Similar £37/10/-

Oxford mint, 1642-6. *Mm.* usually plume with band, except on the smaller denominations when it is lis or pellets. There were so many dies used at this mint that we can only give a selection of the more differing varieties.

2281	**Pound.** Large horseman over arms, no exergual line, fine workmanship. R̶. Three Shrewsbury plumes and xx above Declaration, 1642 below	£300
2282	— Similar, but three Oxford plumes, 1643	£300
2283	Shrewsbury horseman trampling on arms, exergual line. R̶. As last, 1642	£245
2284	— — cannon amongst arms, 1642-3	£210
2285	— as last but exergue is chequered, 1642	£280
2286	Briot's horseman, 1643	£450
2287	*O.* As 2281. R̶. Declaration in cartouche, single large plume above, 1644 ox below	£500
2288	**Half-pound.** As next. R̶. Shrewsbury die, 1642 ..	£75

2289	Oxford dies both sides, 1642-3	£60
2290	**Crown.** *O.* Shrewsbury die with ground-line. R̶. As last but v	£70
2291	Oxford horseman with grass below, 1643	£110
2292	By Rawlins. King riding over a view of the city. R̶. Floral scrolls above and below Declaration, 1644 / oxon below (Beware forgeries) .. .. ..*Extr. rare*	

Charles I Silver. Oxford mint *Fine*

2293 **Halfcrown.** *O.* from Shrewsbury die, 1642 .. .. £42/10/–

2294 ℞. From Shrewsbury die, 1642 .. .. .. £27

2295 Both Oxford dies, but Shrewsbury type horse, ground-line, 1642 .. .. £15

2296 — — without ground-line, 1642 .. .. .. £18

2297 Oxford type horse, ground-line, 1643 .. .. .. £12

2298 — without ground-line, 1643 .. .. £9

2299 Briot's horse, grass below, 1643 .. .. £12/10/–

2300 — — large central plume, 1643, 1644 / ox .. £15

2301 — lumpy ground, 1643, 1643 / ox £12/10/–

2302 — — large central plume, 1643-4 / ox £15

2303 — plain ground, 1644-5 / ox £15

2304 — — large central plume, 1644 / ox £15

2305 — — — two small plumes at date, 1644 / ox .. £75

2306 Large horse (as Briot's, but clumsier), plain ground, 1644-5 / ox £18

2307 — lumpy ground, 1644-5 / ox £18

2308 — — large central plume, 1644 / ox £18

2309 — pebbly ground, 1645-6 / ox £18

2309A — — pellets or annulets by plumes and at date, 1645 / ox £18

2310 — grass below, 1645-6 / ox £21

2310A — — rosettes by plumes and at date, 1645 / ox .. £20

2311 **Shilling.** *O.* From Shrewsbury die. ℞. Declaration type, 1642 .. .. £15

2312 Both Oxford dies. Small bust, 1642-3 .. .. £10/10/–

2313 Similar, but coarser work, 1643 .. .. .. £11

2314 Large bust of fine work, 1643 .. .. .. £11

2315 — 1644-6 / ox £12/10/–

2316 Bust with bent crown, 1643 .. .. .. £12/10/–

2317 — 1644 / ox £12/10/–

2318 Rawlins' dies. Fine bust with R on truncation, 1644 .. £16/10/–

2319 — — 1644 / ox £18

2320 Small size, 1646, annulets or pellets at date £24

2321 **Sixpence.** *O.* Aberystwyth die. ℞. With three Oxford plumes, 1642-3 .. .. £6/10/–

2322 — ℞. With three Shrewsbury plumes, 1643 .. £16

2323 — ℞. With Sh. plume and two lis, 1644 / ox .. £22/10/–

166

2325   2331

2324	**Groat.** *Obv.* Aberystwyth die R. As 2325 ..	80/–
2324A	As last but three plumes above Declaration	£15
2325	As illustration, with lion's head on shoulder	90/–
2326	Large bust reaching to top of coin. R. As last ..	£5
2327	Large bust to bottom of coin, lion's head on shoulder, legend starts at bottom l. R. As last..	£6
2328	Rawlins' die; similar, but no i.c., and with R on shoulder. R. As last	£7
2329	O. As 2325. R. Large single plume and scroll above Declaration, 1645	£6
2330	O. As 2327. R. As last	£10
2331	O. As 2328. R. Large single plume above Declaration, which is in cartouche, 1645-6	£12
2332	**Threepence.** O. Aberystwyth die. R. Declaration type, 1644 / ox	80/–
2333	Rawlins' die, R below shoulder. R. Aberystwyth die with oval shield; *mm.* book	85/–
2334	— R. "Dec." type, three lis above, 1644 below..	80/–
2335	— Similar, without the R, 1646 (over 1644)	80/–
2336	**Halfgroat.** R. Aberystwyth type with large plume	£9
2337	— R. Declaration type, 1644 / ox	£15

2339

2338	**Penny.** O. Aberystwyth die; *mm.* book. R. type, small plume	£25
2339	— — R. type, large plume	£25
2340	— Rawlins' die with R. R. type, small plume ..	£25
2341	— Wider bust like halfgroat. R. Similar	£32/10/–
2342	— — R. Declaration type, 1644	£90

Charles I   Silver   *Fine*

Bristol mint, 1643-5.   *Mm.* usually plume or Br., except on
small denominations.

2343	**Halfcrown.** *O.* Oxford die. Ŗ. Declaration, three Bristol plumes above, 1643 below ..	£16
2344	— — Br. *mm.* on *rev.*, 1643	£10/10/-
2345	King wears unusual flat crown, *obv. mm.* acorn ? between four pellets. Ŗ. As 2343, 1643	£18
2346	— Br. *mm.* on *rev.* 1643-4	£18
2347	Shrewsbury plume behind king. Ŗ. As last ..	£14
2348	— Br. below date, 1644	£16

2350	Br. below horse and below date, 1644-5..	£16
2351	Br. also *mm.* on *rev.*, 1644-5	£14
2352	**Shilling.** *O.* Oxford die. Ŗ. Declaration, 1643 ..	£9
2352A	— — Similar, but *Br.* as *rev. mm.*, 1643-4	£9
2353	Crude bust. Ŗ. As 2352, 1643	£9
2353A	— — Similar, but *Br.* as *rev. mm.*, 1644	£9
2354	Bust of good style, plumelet before. Ŗ. As last, 1644-5	£9
2355	— — Similar, but *Br.* below date instead of as *mm.*, 1644	£9/10/-
2356	Bust with round collar, *mm.* Br. on its side. Ŗ. As last, 1644-5	£9/10/-
2357	Bust with square collar. Ŗ. *Br.* as *mm.*, 1645 ..	£9
2358	**Sixpence.** Coarse bust, nothing before. Ŗ. Declaration, 1643	£15
2359	— Plumelet before face, 1644	£18
2360	**Groat.** Bust l. Ŗ. Declaration, 1644	£9
2361	— Plumelet before face, 1644	£12
2362	— Br. below date, 1644	£9

2363	**Threepence.** *O.* Aberystwyth die, *mm.* book. Ŗ. Declaration, 1644	£20
2364	Bristol die, plume before face, no *mm.*, 1644 ..	£15
2365	**Halfgroat.** Br. in place of date below Declaration ..	£25
2366	**Penny.** Similar bust, I behind. Ŗ. Large plume with bands	£50

Exeter mint, Sept. 1643–Apr. 1646. *Mm.* rose except where stated.

2409 **Crown.**   As 2385, but 1644 divided by *rev. mm.*   ..   £40
2410 Similar but 1644 to 1. of *mm.* £30
2411 Similar, but 1645 and *rev. mm.* EX £40
2412 King's sash in two loose ends; *mm.* castle/rose, 1645 ..   £32
2413 — *mm.* castle/EX, 1645   ..   ..   £45
2414 — *mm.* castle, 1645   ..   ..   £30

2415 **Halfcrown.**   As 2388, but 1644 in legend   *Extr. rare*
2416 Similar but *mm.* castle, 1645   ..   ..   *Unique*
2417 Short portly figure, leaning backwards on ill-proportioned horse, 1644, 16 rose 44   ..   ..£52/10/–
2418 Briot's horse and groundline; 1644   ..   ..   ..   £37

2419 Horse with twisted tail; 1644-5 ..   ..£32/10/–
2420 — R. *Mm.* castle, 1645..   ..   ..   £45
2421 — R. *Mm.* EX, 1645   ..   ..   £45
2422 — R. Declaration type; *mm.* EX, 1644-5   ..   ..   £300
2423 — — — EX also below 1644   ..   ..   £150

2424 **Shilling.**   As 2400.   1644, 16 rose 44, 1645 ..   ..   £16
2425 — R. Declaration type, 1645 ..   ..   £120

2426 **Sixpence.**   As 2424.   1644, 16 rose 44   ..   ..   £20

2427 **Groat.**   Somewhat similar but 1644 at beginning of *obv.* legend £8

2428   2430

2428 **Threepence.**   As illustration, 1644   ..   ..   ..   £7

2429 **Halfgroat.**   Similar but II. R. Oval shield, 1644 ..   £25
2430 — R. Large rose, 1644 ..   ..   £30

2431 **Penny.**   As last but I behind head £40

2435

2432	**Halfcrown.** King on horseback l., w below; *mm.* two lions. R. Declaration type, 1644		£70
2433	— R. Square-topped shield; *mm.* helmet, castle ..		£36
2434	— R. Oval shield; *mm.* helmet		£42/10/-
2435	Similar but grass indicated; *mm.* castle. R. Square-topped shield; *mm.* helmet or none		£35
2436	— R. Oval draped shield, lis or lions in legend ..		£47/10/-
2437	— R. Oval shield, CR at sides, roses in legend		£50
2438	— R. FLORENT etc., oval garnished shield with lion's paws each side		£85
2439	Tall king, no W or *mm.* R. Oval shield, lis, roses, lions or stars in legend		£30
2440	— R. Square-topped shield; *mm.* helmet		£65
2441	— R. FLORENT, etc., oval shield		£85
2442	Briot type horse, sword slopes foreward, ground-line. R. Oval shield, roses in legend		£37/10/-
2443	— similar but CR at sides		£55

2444	Dumpy, portly king, crude horse. R. As 2439	£30
2445	Thin king and horse. R. Oval shield, stars in legend ..	£32/10/-

Weymouth or Salisbury (or Sandsfoot Castle) mint

2450

2446	**Shilling.** Bust of king l., faithfully rendered. ℞. Square-topped shield; *mm.* castle	£50
2447	— ℞. CR above shield; *mm.* helmet and lion	£50
2448	— ℞. Oval shield; *mm.* lion, pear	£30
2449	Bust a somewhat crude copy of last; *mm.* bird, lis. ℞. Square-topped shield with lion's paws above and at sides; *mm.* boar's head, helmet	£35
2450	— — CR above; *mm.* scroll	£35
2451	— ℞. Oval shield, lis in legend; *mm.* lis	£20
2452	— ℞. Round shield; *mm.* various	£25
2453	Bust r.; *mm.* pear. ℞. Oval shield, rose and lis in legend	*Unique*
2454	**Sixpence.** As 2449; *mm.* castle, castle/boar's hd.	£52/10/-
2455	**Groat.** As 2451; *mm.* lis/helmet, rose/helmet..	£30
2456	**Threepence.** Similar; *mm.* lis *obv.*	£18
2457	**Halfgroat.** Similar; *mm.* lis (*O.*) various (℞.)	£30

Salisbury (or Sandsfoot Castle) mint, 1644

2458	**Halfcrown.** King on horseback l., SA below; *mm.* lis. ℞. Oval shield; *mm.* helmet	*Extr. rare*
2459	— ℞. FLORENT, etc., oval shield, no *mm.*	*Extr. rare*
2460	— SA erased or replaced by large pellet or cannon ball; *mm.* lis in legend, helmet ..	£100
2461	Tall horse and king, nothing below; *mm.* lis. ℞. Large round shield with crude garniture; *mm.* helmet	£47/10/-
2462	— ℞. Small uncrowned square-topped shield with lion's paw above and at sides; *mm.* helmet	£60
2463	— ℞. Small oval shield; *mm.* various	£50
2464	— ℞. As 2459 ..	£85
2465	Cruder work with little or no mane before horse. ℞. Round shield	£52/10/-
2466	Grass beneath horse. ℞. Similar; *mm.* lis or rose	£52/10/-
2467	Ground below horse. ℞. As 2459 ..	£70

2468   **Halfcrown.** *O. Mm.* pear. ℞. HC (Hartlebury Castle)
in garniture below shield; *mm.* three pears £55

Chester mint, 1644

2469   2472

2469	**Halfcrown.** As illus. ℞. Oval shield; *mm.* three gerbs	£60
2470	As last. ℞. Crowned oval shield; *mm.* prostrate gerb, −/cinquefoil, −/∴	£70
2471	— ℞. Crowned square-topped shield with CR at sides both crowned; *mm.* cinquefoil, rose in *rev.* legend ..	£90
2472	As 2469, but without plume or CHST. ℞. Declaration type, 1644; *mm.* pl., ∴	£75
2473	**Threepence.** ℞. Square-topped shield; *mm.* prostrate gerb	£75

Coventry or Corfe Castle mint??   *Mm.* two interlocked c's

2474   **Halfcrown.** King on horseback l. ℞. Oval shield
Extr. rare

Carlisle besieged, 1644-5

2475 **Three shillings.** Large crown above C . R / . III . S.
      R. OBS . CARL / · 1645 ..   ..   ..   *Extr. rare*

2476 Similar but : OBS : / · : CARL : · / · 1645 · £500

2477 **Shilling.** As illustration £200
2478 R. Legend and date in two lines £300

Newark besieged, several times, surrendered May 1646

2479 **Halfcrown.** Large crown between CR; below, XXX. R.
      OBS / NEWARK / 1645 or 1646   ..   ..£32/10/-

2480 **Shilling.** Similar but curious flat shaped crown,
      NEWARKE, 1645   ..   ..£32/10/-
2481 Similar but high arched crown, 1645   ..   ..   ..   £25
2482 — NEWARK, 1645 or 1646..   ..   ..   £22

2483 **Ninepence.** As halfcrown but IX, 1645 or 1646   ..   £27
2484 — NEWARKE, 1645   ..   ..   £30

2485 **Sixpence.** As halfcrown but VI, 1646 ..   ..   ..   £30

Pontefract besieged, June 1648-March, 1649

2486   **Two shillings** (lozenge shaped). DVM : SPIRO : SPERO
around CR crowned. ℞. Castle surrounded by OBS, PC,
sword and 1648   ..   ..   *Extr. rare*

2487   **Shilling** (lozenge shaped, octagonal or round). Similar   £40
2488   — Similar but XII to r. dividing PC £35

After the death of Charles I, in the name of Charles II

2489   **Shilling** (octagonal). *O.* As last. ℞. CAROLVS :
SECVNDVS : 1648, castle gateway with flag dividing PC,
OBS on l., cannon protrudes on r. £32/10/-
2490   CAROL : II : etc., around HANC : DEVS : etc. ℞. POST
MORTEM, etc., gateway etc. as last £32/10/-

Scarborough besieged, July 1644-July 1645

2491   **Five shillings and eightpence.** View of castle, value
punched below   ..   ..   *Extr. rare*

2492   **Crown.** Similar but SC also punched ..   *Extr. rare*

2493   **Three shillings and fourpence.** As 2491   *Extr. rare*

2494   **Three shillings.** Similar   ..   ..   *Extr. rare*

2495   **Two shillings and tenpence.** Similar   *Extr. rare*

2496   **Halfcrown.** Similar   ..   ..   ..   *Extr. rare*

2497   **Two shillings and fourpence.** Similar   *Extr. rare*

2498   **Two shillings and twopence.** Similar   *Extr. rare*

2499   **Two shillings.** Similar ..   ..   ..   *Extr. rare*

2500   **One shilling and ninepence.** Similar   *Extr. rare*

2501   **One shilling and sixpence.** Similar ..   *Extr. rare*

2502   **One shilling and fourpence.** Similar   *Extr. rare*

2503   **One shilling and threepence.** Similar   *Extr. rare*

2504	**Shilling.** As illustration	*Extr. rare*
2505	**Sixpence.** Similar	£250
2506	**Groat.** Similar	£250
2507	**Two shillings.** Castle gateway, value punched below	
		Extr. rare
2508	— Similar but gateway stamped twice ..	*Extr. rare*
2509	**One shilling and sixpence.** As 2507	*Extr. rare*
2510	**One shilling and fourpence.** Similar	*Extr. rare*
2511	**One shilling and threepence.** Similar	*Extr. rare*
2512	**One shilling and twopence.** Similar	*Extr. rare*
2513	**One shilling and one penny.** Similar	*Extr. rare*
2514	**Shilling.** Similar	*Extr. rare*
2515	**Elevenpence.** Similar	*Extr. rare*
2516	**Tenpence.** Similar	*Extr. rare*
2517	**Ninepence.** Similar	*Extr. rare*
2518	**Sevenpence.** Similar	*Extr. rare*
2519	**Sixpence.** Similar	£250

COPPER

For mintmarks see our *British Copper Coins and Their Values* or Peck.

2525

2520	**Royal farthing.** " Richmond " round, colon stops. 1a.	
	CARO over IACO; *mm.* on *obv.*	25/–
2521	— — 1b. CARA; *mm.* on *obv.*	80/–
2522	— — 1c. CARO; *mm.* on *obv.*	10/–
2523	— apostrophe stops. 1d. Eagle-headed harp ..	20/–
2524	— 1e. Beaded harp	17/6
2525	— 1f. Scroll-fronted harp, 5 jewels on circlet ..	25/–
2526	— 1g. — — 7 jewels on circlet	15/–
2527	Transitional issue, double-arched crowns	30/–

2530

2528	" Maltravers " round, 3a; *mm.* on *obv.* only	..	..	52/6
2529	— 3b. *Mm.* both sides	..	..	17/6
2530	— 3c. Different *mm.* either side	..	..	20/-

2533

2531	" Richmond " oval. 4a. CARO over IACO; *mm.* both sides	45/-
2532	— — — *mm.* on *obv.*	45/-
2533	— 4b. CARO, colon stops; *mm.* on *obv.* ..	45/-
2533A	— — — — *mm.* on *rev.*	45/-
2533B	— — — — *mm.* both sides	52/6
2534	— 4c. — apostrophe stops; *mm.* rose on *obv.*	50/-
2534A	— — — — *mm.* rose both sides	65/-
2534B	— — — — *mm.* rose (*obv.*); scroll (*rev.*) ..	60/-
2535	" Maltravers " oval. 5. CAROLVS; *mm.* lis both sides ..	55/-

2536   2541

2536	**Rose farthing.** 1a. Double-arched crowns; double rose; sceptres within inner circle, BRIT	40/-
2537	— 1b. — — sceptres just break circle, BRIT	32/6
2538	— 1c. — — sceptres almost to outer circle, BRIT ..	15/-
2539	— 1d. — — — BRI	10/6
2540	— 2. Single-arched crowns; single rose	8/6
2541	— 3. Sceptres below crown	40/-

COMMONWEALTH, 1649-1660

The coins struck during the Commonwealth have inscriptions in English instead of Latin which was considered to savour too much of Papacy. St. George's cross and the Irish harp take the place of the royal arms. The silver halfpenny was issued for the last time.

Mintmarks

1649-57 Sun   1658-60 Anchor

GOLD

		Fine
2542	**Unite.** As illus. but xx; *mm.* sun, 1649-57 ..	.. £52/10/–
2543	— *mm.* anchor, 1658, 1660	.. £160
2544	**Double-crown.** As illus.; *mm.* sun, 1649-55, 57	.. £57/10/–
2545	— *mm.* anchor, 1660	.. £200
2546	**Crown.** As illus. but v; *mm.* sun, 1649-55, 57	.. £40
2547	— *mm.* anchor, 1658, 1660	.. £125

SILVER

2548	**Crown.** Same type; *mm.* sun, 1649, 51-4, 56..	..	£75
2549	**Halfcrown.** Similar; *mm.* sun, 1649, 1651-6 ..	..	£15
2550	— *mm.* anchor, 1658, 1660 .. .. *Fair*	£50	
2551	**Shilling.** Similar; *mm.* sun, 1649, 1651-7 ..	..	£8
2552	— *mm.* anchor, 1658-60 .. .. *Fair*	£15	
2553	**Sixpence.** Similar; *mm.* sun, 1649, 1651-7 ..	..	£8/10/–
2554	— *mm.* anchor, 1658-60 .. .. *Fair*	£15	

2555	**Halfgroat.** As illustration	..	60/–
2556	**Penny.** Similar but I above shields	..	60/–
2557	**Halfpenny.** As illustration	..	70/–

Oliver Cromwell. All said to be only patterns, but some circulated, especially the 1656 halfcrown and the shillings.

GOLD

2559

Very Fine

2558	**Fifty shillings.** Hd. l. ℞. Shield, 1656. Inscribed edge	..	..	..	*Extr. rare*
2559	**Broad** (=20s.). Similar, but grained edge	..	..		£200

SILVER

2560	**Crown.** Bust l. ℞. Shield, 1658. Inscribed edge	£150
2561	**Halfcrown.** Similar, 1656, 1658	£60
2562	**Shilling.** Similar, but grained edge, 1658	£52/10/-
2563	**Sixpence.** Similar .. .. .. *Extr. rare*	

COPPER

2564	**Farthing.** Dr. bust l. ℞. CHARITIE AND CHANGE, shield	£140

There are also other reverses.

SEVENTEENTH CENTURY TOKENS

As there was no authorized copper coinage under the Commonwealth, towns and traders took it into their own hands to issue small change. Between 1648 and 1672 there was an enormous and very varied issue of these tokens. They were mostly farthings and halfpennies, but there were also some pennies. No collection is representative unless it contains at least a few. Many collectors specialize in those of their own town or county. The average price is about 12/6.

CHARLES II, 1660–85

For the first two years after the Restoration the same denominations, apart from the silver crown, were struck as were issued during the Commonwealth. In 1662 the hand hammering of coins was abandoned in favour of manufacture by the Roettiers improved mill and screw presses. As a prevention against clipping the larger coins were made with the edge inscribed DECVS ET TVTAMEN and the regnal year and the medium sized coins were given a grained edge.

The new gold coins were current for 100s., 40s., 20s. and 10s., and they came to be called " guineas " as the gold from which some of them were made was imported from Guinea by the Africa Company (whose badge was the Elephant and Castle). It was not until some years later that the guinea increased in value to 21s. and more. The Africa Co. badge is also found on some silver, as so is the plume symbol indicating silver from the Welsh mines. The four smallest silver denominations, though known today as " Maundy Money," were actually issued for general circulation: at this period the silver penny was probably the only coin distributed at the royal Maundy ceremonies.

A good regal copper coinage was issued for the first time in 1672, but later in the reign farthings were struck in tin (with a copper plug) in order to help the Cornish tin industry.

GOLD

Hammered coinage, 1660-62. *Mintmark:* Crown　　　　　　　　*Fine*

First issue. Without mark of value.

2566　　　　　　　　　　　　　　　2569

2565	**Unite.** (=20s.) Type as illustration	..	..	..	£60
2566	**Double-crown.** As illustration	..	..	.. £62/10/–
2567	**Crown.** Similar	..	..	..	.. £62/10/–

Second issue. With mark of value.

2568	**Unite.** Type as illustration	..	..	..	£50
2569	**Double-crown.** As illustration	..	..	.. £52/10/–
2570	**Crown.** Similar ..	..	..	..	..	£60

181

Milled coinage

2571	**Five guineas.** First bust, pointed and with lovelock, 1668-78	£170
2572	— with elephant below, 1668, 69, 75	£200
2573	— with elephant and castle below, 1675-78	£240
2574	Second bust, rounded truncation, no lovelock, 1678-84	£160
2575	— with elephant and castle below, 1680-84	£185
2576	**Two guineas.** First bust, pointed, 1664, 65, 69, 71 ..	£120
2577	— with elephant below, 1664	£65
2578	Second bust, 1675-84	£75
2579	— with elephant and castle below, 1676, 78, 82-84 ..	£90
2580	— with elephant only below, 1678 .. *Extr. rare*	

2586   2588

2581	**Guinea.** First bust, 1663	£75
2582	— with elephant below, 1663	£65
2583	Second bust, 1664	£50
2584	— with elephant below, 1664 .. .. *Extr. rare*	
2585	Third bust, normal portrait, 1664-73	£32
2586	— with elephant below, 1664, 1665, 1668	£50
2587	Fourth bust, rounded, 1672-84	£28
2588	— elephant and castle below, 1674-84	£40
2589	— elephant below, 1677, 1678 .. .. *Extr. rare*	
2590	**Half-guinea.** First bust, pointed, 1669-72	£35
2591	Second bust, rounded, 1672-84	£25
2592	— elephant and castle below, 1676-78, 80, 82-84 ..	£50

SILVER

Hammered coinage, 1660-62. The smaller " machine made " coins were perhaps minted later than 1662.

First issue. Without inner circles or mark of value.

2593	**Halfcrown.** Crowned bust, as 2595	£35
2594	**Shilling.** Similar	£7

| 2595 | 2601 | 2609 |

2595	**Sixpence.** Similar	..	..	..	..	..	£7
2596	**Twopence.** Similar	..	..	..	..	..	45/–
2597	**Penny.** Similar ..	..	..	..	..	..	60/–
2598	As last, but without mintmark	..	..	..	..	60/–

Second issue. Without inner circles, but with mark of value.

2599	**Halfcrown.** Crowned bust	..	..	..	..	£30
2600	**Shilling.** Similar	..	..	..	..	£17/10/–
2601	**Sixpence.** Similar	..	..	..	..	£55
2602	**Twopence.** Similar, but *mm.* on *obv.* only	..	..	£5
2603	Similar, but *mm.* both sides (machine made)	..	..	80/–
2604	Bust to edge of coin, legend starts at bottom l. (machine made)	..	..	..	..	..	45/–
2605	**Penny.** As 2603 ..	..	..	..	..	..	80/–
2606	As 2604	..	..	..	..	..	35/–

Third issue. With inner circles and mark of value.

2607	**Halfcrown.** Crowned bust	..	..	*Fair*	45/–
2608	**Shilling.** Similar	..	..	*Fair*	45/–
2609	**Sixpence.** Similar	..	..	*Fair*	45/–
2610	**Fourpence.** Similar	..	..	..	..	40/–
2611	**Threepence.** Similar	..	..	..	..	60/–
2612	**Twopence.** Similar	..	..	..	..	35/–
2613	**Penny.** Similar ..	..	..	..	..	45/–

Milled coinage

2614	**Crown.** First bust, rose below, edge not dated, 1662..	£12
2615	— — edge dated, 1662 ..	..	..	..	£22/10/–
2616	— no rose, edge dated, 1662	..	..	..	£35
2617	— — edge not dated, 1662	..	..	..	£15
2618	— — new reverse, shields altered, regnal date on edge in Roman figures, 1663	..	..	..	..	£12
2619	Second bust, 1664–66	..	..	..	£13/10/–
2620	— elephant below, 1666 ..	..	..	..	£65
2621	— regnal date on edge in words, 1667–71	..	..	£18
2622	Third bust, 1671–80	..	..	..	£10/10/–
2623	Fourth bust, 1679–84	..	..	..	..	£14
2624	— elephant and castle below, 1680–81 ..	*Extr. rare*	

	2625				2631-4

2625	**Halfcrown.** First bust, regnal date on edge in Roman figures, 1663	..	..	..	..	..	£12
2626	Second bust, 1664	..	..	..	..	..	£20
2627	Third bust, 1666 ..	..	..	..	..	..	£200
2628	— elephant below, 1666 ..	..	..	..	..	£125
2629	— regnal date on edge in words, 1667-70		..	..	£10
2630	Third bust variety, 1671-2	..	..	..	..	£8
2631	Fourth bust, 1672-84	..	..	..	..	..	£7/10/-
2632	— plume below, 1673, 1683	..	..	*Extr. rare*	
2633	— plume below and in centre or *rev.*, 1673	*Extr. rare*	
2634	— elephant and castle below, 1681	..	*Extr. rare*	

2640

2635	**Shilling.** First bust, 1663	..	..	..	..	£7
2636	— First bust variety, 1663, 1668, 1669 ..	..	..	£6/10/-
2637	— elephant below, 1666 ..	..	..	..	£47/10/-
2638	Guinea-head, elephant below, 1666	..	..	..	£80
2639	Second bust, 1666, 1668-83	..	..	..	..	£8
2640	— plume below bust and in centre of *rev.*, 1671, 73-6, 79-80	..	..	..	..	£28
2641	— plume *rev.* only, 1674	..	..	..	£80
2642	— plume *obv.* only, 1677, 1679 ..	..	..	£52/10/-
2643	— elephant and castle below, 1681	..	*Extr. rare*	
2644	Third (large) bust, 1674-5	..	..	..	..	£25
2645	Fourth (large) bust, older features, 1683-4	..	..	£12

Charles II Silver   *Fine*

2646 **Sixpence.** 1674-84 .. .. 90/–

2647 **Fourpence.** Undated. Crowned bust l. to edge of
coin, value behind. ℞. Shield 37/6

| 2648 | 2650 | 2652 | 2654 |

2648 Dated. *O.* As illus. ℞. Four interlinked c's, 1670-84.. 27/6

2649 **Threepence.** Undated. As 2647 .. .. .. 37/6

2650 Dated. As illus., 1670-84 .. .. 20/–

2651 **Twopence.** Undated. As 2647 .. .. .. 32/6

2652 Dated. As illus., 1668, 1670-84 .. .. .. 15/–

2653 **Penny.** Undated. As 2647 .. .. 42/6

2654 Dated. As illus., 1670-84 .. .. 80/–

2655 **Maundy set.** Undated. The four coins £7/10/–

2656 Dated. The four coins. Uniform dates, 1670-84 .. £8

2657 — — Mixed dates £6/10/–

COPPER and TIN

2659

2658 Copper **Halfpenny.** As illus., but larger, 1672, 73, 75 .. 50/–

2659 Copper **Farthing.** As illustration, 1672-5, 1679 .. 10/–

2660 Tin **Farthing.** Somewhat similar, but with inscribed
edge and copper plug, 1684-5 .. .. *Fair* 65/– £10

Prices are for coins in "fine" condition. Coins in less good
condition may be worth less than half the prices quoted, but
coins in "very fine" or better condition would be priced at
more than double the quoted values.

JAMES II, 1685-88

Tin halfpennies and farthings provided the only base metal coinage during this short reign.

GOLD

Fine

2661	**Five guineas.** Bust l., sceptres wrongly placed, 1686 ..	£220
2662	— with sceptres normal, 1687-8	£180
2663	— elephant and castle below bust 1687-8	£225
2664	**Two guineas.** Similar, 1687-8	£140

2668

2665	**Guinea.** First bust, 1685, 1686	£45
2666	— elephant and castle below, 1685	£60
2667	Second bust, 1686-8	£38
2668	— elephant and castle below, 1686-8	£55
2669	**Half-guinea,** 1686-8	£50
2670	Elephant and castle below, 1686	£90

SILVER

2671	**Crown.** First bust, 1686	£30
2672	Second bust, 1687-8	£18/10/-

2673	**Halfcrown.** First bust, 1685-7	£9
2674	Second bust, 1687-8	£12

James II Silver

							Fine
2675	**Shilling,** 1685-8	..	..	..	..	..	£12
2676	Plume in centre of *rev.*, 1685	..	..	*Two known*			
2677	**Sixpence,** early type shields, 1686-7	..	..	..	£15		
2677A	Late type shields, 1687-8 ..	..	..	..	..	£12/10/–	

	2678	2679	2680	2681

2678	**Fourpence.** *O.* As illus. ℞. IIII crowned, 1686-8 ..		30/–
2679	**Threepence.** As illustration, 1685-8		25/–
2680	**Twopence.** As illustration, 1686-8		25/–
2681	**Penny.** As illustration, 1685-8		65/–
2682	**Maundy set.** As last four. Uniform dates, 1686-8 ..		£8
2683	— Mixed dates		£7

TIN

						Fair
2684	**Halfpenny,** 1685-7	..	..	..	..	95/–
2685	**Farthing.** Cuirassed bust, 1684-7	..	..	..	80/–
2686	Draped bust, 1687	..	..	..	..	£6

All genuine tin coins of this period have a copper plug.

As this is a type catalogue, dates are given as a guide for distinguishing busts and types. The price is for the most common date in each case.

WILLIAM AND MARY, 1688-94

Due to the poor state of the silver coinage, much of it worn hammered coin, the guinea, which was valued at 21s. 6d. at the beginning of the reign, circulated for as much as 30s. by 1694. The tin halfpennies and farthings were replaced by copper coins in 1694. The rampant lion of Orange is now placed as an inescutcheon on the centre of the royal arms.

GOLD

Fine

2687	**Five guineas.** Conjoined heads r., 1691-4	£165
2688	— elephant and castle below, 1691-4	£175
2689	**Two guineas.** Conjoined heads r., 1693-4	£100
2690	— elephant and castle below, 1691, 93, 94	£135
2691	**Guinea.** Conjoined heads r., 1689-94	£45
2692	— elephant and castle below, 1689-94	£55
2693	— elephant only below, 1692-3	£60

2696

2694	**Half-guinea.** First heads, 1689	£40
2695	Second heads, normal portraits, 1690-94	£35
2696	— — elephant and castle below, 1691, 1692 ..	£50
2696A	— — elephant only below, 1692 .. *Extr. rare*	

SILVER

2697	**Crown.** As illustration; 1691, 1692	£47/10/-

2698   2699

2698	**Halfcrown.** First busts and first shield, 1689	..	85/-
2699	— and second shield, 1689, 1690	.. ..	£5/5/-
2700	Second busts. ℞. As crown; 1691-3	.. ..	£6
2701	**Shilling.** As crown; 1692, 1693	.. .. ..	£8/10/-
2702	**Sixpence.** As crown; 1693, 1694	.. .. ..	£8
2703	**Fourpence.** First busts, no tie to wreath, 1689-91, 94	..	17/6
2704	Second busts, tie to wreath, 1692-4	.. .. ..	62/6
2705	**Threepence.** First busts, no tie, 1689-90	.. ..	15/-
2706	Second busts, tie to wreath, 1691-4	.. .. ..	42/6
2707	**Twopence.** 1689-94	.. ..	22/6
2708	**Penny,** 1689. Legend continuous over head	.. ..	£20
2708A	Legend broken by heads, 1690-94	.. ..	£5
2709	**Maundy set.** As last pieces. Uniform date, 1689, 91-94		£12/10/-
2710	— mixed dates	.. ..	£7/10/-

TIN and COPPER

Fair

2711	Tin **Halfpenny.** Small draped busts, 1689	.. ..	£20
2712	Large cuirassed busts; date only on edge, 1690	.. ..	75/-
2713	— date in exergue and on edge, 1691-2	.. ..	75/-
2714	Tin **Farthing.** Small draped busts, 1689, 1689/90	..	£10
2715	Large cuirassed busts, 1689/90, 1690-2	.. ..	62/6

Fine

2716	Copper **Halfpenny,** 1694	.. ..	20/-
2717	Copper **Farthing,** 1694	.. ..	17/6

Prices are for coins in " fine " condition. Coins in less good condition may be worth less than half the prices quoted, but coins in " very fine " or better condition would be priced at more than double the quoted values.

WILLIAM III, 1694-1702

In 1696 a great recoinage was undertaken to replace the hammered silver that still made up most of the coinage in circulation, much of it being clipped and badly worn. Branch mints were set up at Bristol, Chester, Exeter, Norwich and York to help with the recoinage. For a short time before they were finally demonetized unclipped hammered coins were allowed to circulate freely providing they were officially pierced in the centre. Silver coins with roses between the coats of arms were made from silver obtained from the West of England mines.

GOLD

		Fine
2718	**Five guineas.** First bust, 1699, 1700	£185
2719	— elephant and castle below, 1699	£250
2720	Second bust (" fine work "), 1701	£165
2721	**Two guineas,** 1701	£125

2722   2724

2722	**Guinea.** First bust, 1695-7	£25
2723	— elephant and castle below, 1695-6	£40
2724	Second bust, 1697-1701	£22/10/-
2725	— elephant and castle below, 1697-1700	£40
2726	— ℞. Large lettering and large date, 1698	£27
2727	— ℞. Scrolled harp, 1701	£25
2728	— — elephant and castle, 1701	£55
2729	Third bust (" fine work "), 1701	£42/10/-
2730	**Half-guinea.** ℞. With early harp, 1695	£20
2731	— elephant and castle, 1695-6	£27/10/-
2732	℞. With late harp, 1697-1701	£17/10/-
2733	— elephant and castle, 1698	£35

SILVER

2734	**Crown.** First bust, first harp, 1695-6	£7
2735	Second bust (hair across breast), 1696 .. _Unique_	
2736	Third bust, first harp, 1696	£10
2737	— second harp, 1697 .. .. .. _Fair_ £115	
2738	Third bust variety, third harp, 1700	£16

2742(E)

2739	**Halfcrown.** Small shields, 1696	£5
2739A	— — B (*Bristol*) below bust, £6/10/–; C (*Chester*), £12; E (*Exeter*), £21; N (*Norwich*), £12; Y (*York*), £14	
2740	Large shields, early harp, 1696	£7
2740A	— — — B below bust, £10; C, £11/10/–; E, £12; N, £22/10/–; Y, £8	
2741	Large shields, ordinary harp, 1696-1697	£6
2742	— — B below bust, 1697, £5/10/–; C, 1696-7, £7; E, 1696-7 £6/10/–; N, 1696-7, £8/10/–; Y, 1697, £5/10/–	
2743	Second bust (hair across breast), 1696 .. *Unique*	
2744	Modified large shields, 1698-1701	67/6
2745	Elephant and castle below bust, 1701 .. *Extr. rare*	
2746	Plumes in angles on *rev*, 1701	£14

2747   2752   2756-9

2747	**Shilling.** First bust, 1695-7	47/6
2748	— B below bust, 1696-7, 67/6; C, 1696-7, £5/10/–; E, 1696-7, 75/–; N, 1696-7, 80/–; Y, 1696-7, 87/6; Y, 1696-7, £9/10/–	
2749	Second bust (hair across breast), 1696 .. *Unique*	
2750	Third bust, 1697	60/–
2751	— B below bust, 1697, £11; C, 1696-7, 90/–; E, 1697, £9; N, 1697, £6/15/–; Y, 1696-7, £6/15/–	
2752	Third bust variety, 1697-8	£5/5/–
2753	— B below bust, 1697, £10; C, 1697, £15/10/–	
2754	— ℞. Plumes in angles, 1698 .. .. £62/10/–	

2755 **Shilling.** Fourth bust (" flmaing hair "), 1698-9   .. £12/10/–
2756 Fifth bust (hair high), 1699-1701   ..   ..   ..   52/6
2757 — R.   Plumes in angles, 1699, 1701 ..   ..   .. £13/10/–
2758 — R.   Roses in angles, 1699 ..   .. £40
2759 — plume below bust, 1700   ..   .. *Extr. rare*

2760   2768A

2760 **Sixpence.** First bust, early harp, 1695-6   ..   ..   27/6
2761 — — B below bust, 1696, 47/6; C, 1696, 67/6; E, 1696,
        90/–; N, 1696, 60/–; Y, 1696, 52/6; Y, 1696, £5
2762 — later harp, large crowns, 1696   ..   ..   ..   47/6
2763 — — — B below bust, 1696-7, £5/10/–; C, 1696-7,
        £6/10/–; E, 1697, £5
2764 — — small crowns, 1696-7   ..   ..   30/–
2765 — — — B below bust, 1696-7, 47/6; C, 1697, 35/–;
        E, 1697, 47/6; N, 1696-7, 50/–; Y, 1697, 95/–
2766 Second bust, 1696-7   ..   ..   £16
2767 Third bust, large crowns, 1697-1701 ..   ..   ..   27/6
2768 — — B below bust, 1697, 57/6; C, 1697, £10; E, 1697,
        £13/10/–
2768A — small crowns, 1697   ..   ..   80/–
2769 — — C below bust, 1697, £12/10/–; E, 1697, £5/10/–; Y,
        1697, £8
2770 — R.   Plumes in angles, 1698-9   ..   ..   .. £6/10/–
2771 — R.   Roses in angles, 1699 ..   ..   £14
2772 — plume below bust, 1700   ..   .. *Extr. rare*

2773   2774   2775   2776

2773 **Fourpence.** R.   4 crowned, 1697-1702   ..   ..   85/–
2774 **Threepence.** R.   3 crowned, 1698-1701   ..   ..   60/–
2775 **Twopence.** R.   2 crowned, 1698-1701   ..   ..   40/–
2776 **Penny.** R.   1 crowned, 1698-1701 ..   ..   ..   £5
2777 **Maundy set** as last four. Uniform dates, 1698-1701   ..   £16
2778 — — mixed dates £13

COPPER

2782   2783

				Fine
2779	**Halfpenny.** First issue; r. hand up, 1695-8	..	..	45/-
2780	— Second issue; date in legend, 1698-9	..	..	35/-
2781	— Third issue; r. hand on knee, 1699-1701	..	..	15/-
2782	**Farthing.** First issue, 1695-1700	..	..	20/-
2783	— Second issue; date in legend, 1698-9	..	..	25/-

> As this is a type catalogue, dates are given as a guide for distinguishing busts and types. The price is for the most common date in each case.

ANNE 1702-14

The Act of Union of 1707, which effected the unification of the ancient kingdoms of England and Scotland into a single realm, resulted in a change in the royal arms—on the after-Union coinage the English leopards and Scottish lion are emblazoned per pale on the top and bottom shields. After the Union the rose in the centre of the reverse of the gold coins is replaced by the Garter star.

Following a successful Anglo-Dutch expedition against Spain, bullion seized in Vigo Bay was sent to be minted into coin, and the coins made from this metal had the word VIGO placed below the queen's bust.

GOLD

					Fine
Before Union with Scotland					
2784	**Five guineas.** 1705-6 ..	..	..	..	£250
2785	VIGO below bust, 1703 ..	..	..	*Extr. rare*	
2786	**Guinea.** 1702, 1705-7 (Illustrated on page 188).			..	£37/10/-
2787	VIGO below bust, 1703 ..	..	..	..	£275
2788	**Half-guinea,** 1702, 1705	..	..	..	£60
2789	VIGO below bust, 1703 ..	..	..	..	£250

2786   2796

After Union with Scotland.   The shields on *rev*. are changed.

2790	**Five guineas.** Ordinary bust, 1706	..	..	..	£225
2791	— broader shields, 1709	..	..	..	£250
2792	Last (coarse) bust, 1711, 1713-14	..	..	..	£200
2793	**Two guineas,** 1709, 1711, 1713-14	..	..	..	£90
2794	**Guinea.** First bust, 1707	..	..	..	£42/10/–
2795	— elephant and castle below, 1707	..	..	..	£65
2796	Second bust, 1707-9	..	..	..	£30
2797	— elephant and castle below, 1708-9	..	..	..	£60
2798	Third bust, 1710-14	..	..	..	£24
2799	**Half-guinea,** 1707-14	..	..	..	£17/10/–

SILVER

Before Union with Scotland

2800	**Crown.** VIGO below bust, 1703..	..	..	..	£42/10/–
2801	℞. Plumes in angles, 1705	..	..	..	£90
2802	℞. Roses and plumes in angles, 1706-7	..	..	£27
2803	**Halfcrown.** No marks below bust or on *rev*. (i.e. plain), 1703..	..	..	..	£52/10/–
2804	VIGO below bust, 1703	..	..	..	£9
2805	℞. Plumes in angles, 1704-5	..	..	..	£11
2806	℞. Roses and plumes in angles, 1706-7	..	..	£6/15/–

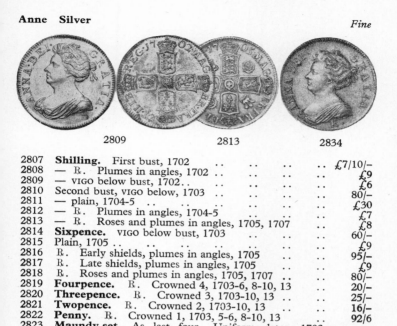

2809 2813 2834

2807	**Shilling.** First bust, 1702	..	..	..	£7/10/-
2808	— ℞. Plumes in angles, 1702 ..	..	..	..	£9
2809	— VIGO below bust, 1702..	..	..	..	£6
2810	Second bust, VIGO below, 1703	..	..	..	80/-
2811	— plain, 1704-5 ..	..	..	..	£30
2812	— ℞. Plumes in angles, 1704-5	..	..	..	£7
2813	— ℞. Roses and plumes in angles, 1705, 1707		..	..	£8
2814	**Sixpence.** VIGO below bust, 1703	..	..	..	60/-
2815	Plain, 1705 ..	..	..	..	£9
2816	℞. Early shields, plumes in angles, 1705		..	..	95/-
2817	℞. Late shields, plumes in angles, 1705		..	..	£9
2818	℞. Roses and plumes in angles, 1705, 1707 ..		..	..	80/-
2819	**Fourpence.** ℞. Crowned 4, 1703-6, 8-10, 13		..	..	20/-
2820	**Threepence.** ℞. Crowned 3, 1703-10, 13 ..		..	..	25/-
2821	**Twopence.** ℞. Crowned 2, 1703-10, 13 ..		..	..	16/-
2822	**Penny.** ℞. Crowned 1, 1703, 5-6, 8-10, 13		..	..	92/6
2823	**Maundy set.** As last four. Uniform dates, 1703, 1705-6, 8-10, 13	..	..	..	£12
2824	— Mixed dates ..	..	..	..	£7/10/-

After Union with Scotland. The shields on *rev.* are changed. The Edinburgh coins have been included here as they are now coins of Great Britain.

2825	**Crown.** Second bust, E (Edinburgh) below, 1707-8 ..			..	£15
2826	— plain, 1707-8 ..	..	..	..	£22/10/-
2827	— ℞. Plumes in angles, 1708 ..	..	..	..	£27
2828	Third bust. ℞. Roses and plumes, 1713	..	..	..	£25

2830

Anne Silver. After Union *Fine*

2829 **Halfcrown.** Plain, 1707-9, 1713 .. .. .. 80/-
2830 E below bust, 1707-9 (illustrated on page 189). .. 60/-
2831 ℞. Plumes in angles, 1708 .. .. .. £6/10/-
2832 ℞. Roses and plumes in angles, 1710, 1712-14 .. £5/15/-

2833 **Shilling.** Second bust, E below, 1707-8 .. .. 52/6
2834 — E★ below, 1707-8 .. .. 60/-
2835 Third bust, plain, 1707-9, 1711 .. .. .. 47/6
2836 — ℞. Plumes in angles, 1707-8 .. .. £5/10/-
2837 — E below, 1707-8 .. .. 80/-
2838 Second bust. ℞. Roses and plumes, 1708 .. £18/10/-
2839 Third bust. ℞. Roses and plumes, 1708, 1710 .. £5/10/-
2840 " Edinburgh " bust, E★ below, 1707-9 .. .. £5/10/-
2841 — E below, 1709 .. .. £14
2842 Fourth bust. ℞. Roses and plumes, 1710, 12-14 .. 55/-
2843 — plain, 1711 .. .. 40/-

2848   2845

2844 **Sixpence.** Normal bust. ℞. Plain, 1707-8, 1711 .. 35/-
2845 — E below bust, 1707-8 .. .. 52/6
2846 — E★ below bust, 1708 .. .. 67/6
2847 " Edinburgh " bust, E★ below, 1708 .. .. 90/-
2848 Normal bust. ℞. Plumes in angles, 1707-8 .. .. 85/-
2849 — ℞. Roses and plumes in angles, 1710 .. .. £6

The type of the Maundy was not changed after the Union, for dates
and prices see 2819-2824.

COPPER

2850 **Farthing,** 1714 .. .. £10

GEORGE I, 1714-27

The coins of the first of the Hanoverian kings have the arms of the Duchy of Brunswick and Luneberg on one of the four shields, the object in the centre of the arms being the Electoral cap. The king's German titles also appear, in abbreviated form, and name him "Duke of Brunswick and Luneberg, Arch-treasurer of the Holy Roman Empire, and Elector," and on the guinea of 1714, "Prince Elector." A quarter-guinea was struck for the first time in 1718, but it was an inconvenient size and the issue was discontinued.

Silver coined from bullion supplied to the mint by the South Sea Company in 1723 shows the company's initials s.s.c.; similarly Welsh Copper Company bullion has the letters w.c.c. below the king's bust and plumes and an interlinked cc on the reverse. Roses and plumes together on the reverse indicate silver supplied by the Company for Smelting Pit Coale and Sea Coale.

GOLD

2852

			Fine
2851	**Five guineas,** 1716, 17, 20, 26		£325
2852	**Two guineas,** 1717, 20, 26		£90
2853	**Guinea.** First head. ℞. Legend ends ET . PR . EL (Prince Elector), 1714		£50
2854	Second head, tie with two ends, 1715		£30
2855	Third head, no hair below truncation, 1715, 1716 ..		£30
2856	Fourth head, tie with loop and one end, 1716-23 ..		£30
2857	— elephant and castle below, 1721-2		£85
2858	Fifth (older) head, tie with two ends, 1723-7		£35
2859	— elephant and castle below, 1726		£60

2863

2860	**Half-guinea.** First bust, 1715, 1717-24	£20
2861	— elephant and castle below, 1721	£80
2862	Second (older) bust, 1725-7	£20
2863	**Quarter-guinea,** 1718 only	£9

SILVER

2864	**Crown.** ℞. Roses and plumes in angles, 1716, 18, 20, 26	..£47/10/–
2865	— ℞. ssc (South Sea Company) in angles, 1723	..£52/10/–
2866	**Halfcrown.** Plain (proof only), 1715 EF £400	
2867	℞. Roses and plumes in angles, 1715, 17, 20 ..	£15
2868	℞. ssc in angles, 1723	£18
2869	℞. Small roses and plumes, 1726	£140

2872   2875

2870	**Shilling.** First bust. ℞. Roses and plumes, 1715-23 ..	£6/15/–
2871	— plain (i.e. no marks either side), 1720-1	90/–
2872	— ℞. ssc in angles, 1723	32/6
2873	Second bust, bow to tie. ℞. Similar, 1723	65/–
2874	— ℞. Roses and plumes, 1723-7	£7
2875	— w.c.c. (Welsh Copper Company) below, 1723-6	..£32/10/–
2876	**Sixpence.** ℞. Roses and plumes in angles 1717, 20	£8
2877	℞. ssc in angles, 1723	52/6
2878	℞. Small roses and plumes, 1726	£6/15/–

2879	**Fourpence,** 1717, 1721, 1723, 1727	45/–
2880	**Threepence,** 1717, 1721, 1723, 1727	60/–
2881	**Twopence,** 1717, 1721, 1723, 1726-7	20/–
2882	**Penny,** 1716, 1718, 1720, 1723, 1725-7	27/6
2883	**Maundy set.** As last four. Uniform dates, 1723, 1727	£17/10/–
2884	— Mixed dates	..£7/10/–

COPPER

2887   2888

2885	**Halfpenny,** " Dump issue," 1717-8	..	..	..	15/–
2886	Second issue, 1719-24	..	..	..	15/–
2887	**Farthing,** " Dump " issue, 1717	..	..	..	*£7
2888	Second issue, 1719-24	..	..	..	12/6

GEORGE II, 1727-60

Silver was only coined spasmodically by the Mint during this reign and no copper was struck after 1754. Gold coins made from bullion supplied by the East India Company bear the company's initials; and some of the treasure seized by Admiral Anson during his circumnavigation of the globe, 1740-44, and by other privateers, was made into coin which had the word LIMA below the king's bust to celebrate the expedition's successful harassment of the Spanish colonies in the New World. Hammered gold was finally demonetized in 1733.

GOLD

Fine

2889	**Five guineas.** Young head, 1729, 31, 35, 38, 41 ..	£150
2890	— E.I.C. (East India Company) below, 1729 ..	£135
2891	Old head, LIMA below, 1746	£165
2892	— plain, 1748, 1753	£150
2893	**Two guineas.** Young head, 1734-5, 1738-39 ..	£42/10/–
2894	Intermediate head, 1739-40	£40
2895	Old head, 1748, 1753	£55

2896	**Guinea.** First young head, small lettering, 1727	..	..	£45
2897	— larger lettering, smaller shield, 1727-8	..	..	£40
2898	Second (narrower) young head, 1729-32	..	..	£30
2899	— E.I.C. below, 1729, 1731-2	..	..	£35
2900	— larger lettering on *obv.*, 1732-8	..	..	£27/10/-
2901	— — E.I.C. below, 1732	..	..	£40
2902	Intermediate head, 1739-41, 1743	..	..	£32/10/-
2903	— E.I.C. below, 1739	..	..	£40
2904	— larger lettering on *obv.* 1745-6	..	..	£30
2905	— LIMA below, 1745	..	..	£90
2906	Old head, 1747-53, 1755-6, 1758-60	..	..	£25

2907   2905   2911

2907	**Half-guinea.** Young head, 1728-39	..	..	£21
2908	— E.I.C. below, 1729-32, 1739	..	..	£45
2909	Intermediate head, 1740, 1743, 1745-6	..	..	£24
2910	— LIMA below, 1745	..	..	£75
2911	Old head, 1747-53, 1755-6, 1758-60	..	..	£17/10/-

SILVER

2912	**Crown.** Young bust. ℞. Roses and plumes in angles, 1732, 1734-6	..	..	£52/10/-
2913	— ℞. Roses in angles, 1739, 1741	..	..	£35
2914	Old head. ℞. Roses in angles, 1743	..	..	£40
2915	— LIMA below, 1746	..	..	£45
2916	— plain (i.e. no marks either side), 1750-1	..	..	£70

		EF	
2917	**Halfcrown.** Young bust; plain (proof only), 1731	£160	
2918	— ℞. Roses and plumes, 1731-2, 1734-6	..	£7/10/-
2919	— ℞. Roses, 1739, 1741	..	£6/10/-
2920	Old bust. ℞. Roses, 1743, 1745	..	£7
2921	— LIMA below, 1745-6	..	60/-
2922	— plain, 1750-1	..	£8/10/-

2923	**Shilling.** Young bust. ℞. Plumes, 1727, 1731	..	£10
2924	— ℞. Roses and plumes, 1727-9, 1731-2	..	85/-
2925	— — larger lettering, 1734-7	..	70/-
2926	— plain, 1728	..	£15
2927	— ℞. Roses, 1739, 1741	..	47/6
2928	Old bust. ℞. Roses, 1743, 1745, 1747	..	65/-
2929	— LIMA below, 1745-6	..	30/-
2930	— plain, 1750-1, 1758	..	17/6

2934   2936

2931	**Sixpence.** Young bust; plain, 1728	..	..		..	£12
2932	— ℞. Plumes, 1728	..	..		..	£6/10/–
2933	— ℞. Roses and plumes, 1728, 1731-2, 1734-6				..	55/–
2934	— ℞. Roses, 1739, 1741	..	..		..	47/6
2935	Old bust. ℞. Roses, 1743, 1745	..	..		..	52/6
2936	— LIMA below, 1745-6	..	..	..	..	32/6
2937	— plain, 1750-1, 1757-8 ..	..	..	..	..	12/–

Very Fine

2938 **Fourpence.** Young head. ℞. Crowned 4, 1729, 31-2,
1735, 37, 39, 40, 43, 46, 60   ..   ..   50/–

2939 **Threepence** — ℞. Crowned 3, similar dates   ..   40/–

2940 **Twopence** — ℞. Crowned 2, similar dates and 56, 59   30/–

2941 **Penny** — ℞. Crowned 1, similar dates and 50, 52-60..   22/6

2942 **Maundy set.** As last four. Uniform dates, 1729, 31-2,
1735, 37, 39, 40, 43, 46, 60   ..   ..   £10
2943 — — mixed dates £7

COPPER

2947   2949

Fine

2944	**Halfpenny.** Young bust, 1729-39	..	..	..	10/–
2945	Old bust, GEORGIUS, 1740, 1742-5	..	..	..	12/6
2946	— GEORGIVS, 1746-54	..	..	..	10/6
2947	**Farthing.** Young bust, 1730-37, 1739		..	..	7/6
2948	Old bust. GEORGIUS, 1741, 1744	..	..	..	12/6
2949	— GEORGIVS, 1746, 1749-50, 1754	..	..	..	5/–

GEORGE III, 1760-1820

During the second half of the 18th century very little silver or copper was minted. In 1797 Matthew Boulton's " cartwheels," the first copper pennies and twopences, demonstrated the improvement that could be effected as a result of the application of steam power to the coining press.

During the Napoleonic Wars bank notes came into general use when the issue of guineas was stopped between 1797 and 1813, but gold 7s. pieces were minted to help relieve the shortage of smaller money. As an emergency measure Spanish " dollars " were put into circulation for a short period after being countermarked, and in 1804 Spanish dollars were overstruck and issued as Bank of England dollars.

The transition to a " token " silver coinage began in 1811 when the Bank of England had 3s. and 1s. 6d. tokens made for general circulation. Private issues of token money in the years 1788-95 and 1811-15 helped to alleviate the shortage of regal coinage. A change over to a gold standard and a regular "token" silver coinage came in 1816 when the Mint, which was moved from its old quarters in the Tower of London to its present site on Tower Hill, began a complete recoinage. The guinea was replaced by a 20s. sovereign, and silver coins were made which had an intrinsic value lower than their face value. British silver is still legal tender back to 1816. The St. George design used on the sovereign and crown was the work of Benedetto Pistrucci.

GOLD

				Very Fine
2950	**Five guineas,** 1770, 73, 77. Pattern only	..	..	£1800
2951	**Two guineas,** 1768, 73, 77. Pattern only	..	..	£800

2952   2956

2952	**Guinea.** First head, 1761	..	..	..	..	£65
2953	Second head, 1763-4	..	..	..	..	£70
2954	Third head, 1765-73	..	..	..	..	£27
2955	Fourth head, 1774-79, 1781-86 ..	..	..	..	£22
2956	Fifth head. R. " Spade " shaped shield, 1787-99	..	£17
2957	Sixth head. R. Shield in Garter, 1813; known as the Military guinea	£45

2961   2964

2958	**Half-guinea.** First head, 1762-3	..	..	..	£40
2959	Second head, 1764-66, 1768-9, 1772-75		..	..	£25
2960	Third head (less fine style), 1774-5	..	..	..	£65
2961	Fourth head, 1775-79, 1781, 1784-86	..	..	..	£18/10/–
2962	Fifth head. ℞. " Spade " type, 1787-98, 1800		..	..	£15
2963	Sixth type. ℞. Shield in Garter, 1801-3		..	..	£13
2964	Seventh type. Hd. with short hair. ℞. As last, 1804, 1806, 1808-11, 1813				£12

2965   2968

2965	**Third-guinea.** I. First head, 1797-1800	..	..	£9
2966	II. Similar but date not in legend, 1801-3	..	..	£10
2967	III. Second head with short hair, 1804, 06, 08-11, 13			£8
2968	**Quarter-guinea,** 1762				£14

Last or new coinage, 1817-20. See Page 215.

SILVER

| 2973 | **Shilling.** Young bust, 1763; known as the " Northumberland " shilling .. .. | £30 |

2973   2974

| 2974 | Older bust, 1787, without semée of **hearts in the** Hanoverian shield .. .. | 22/6 |

203

George III   Silver.

2975	**Shilling,** 1787, without hearts, no stop over head ..	80/-
2976	— — — no stops at date	£6/10/-
2977	— — with semée of hearts	20/-
2978	— 1798, no stop over head; known as the " Dorrien and Magens " shilling .. .. .. *Extr. rare*	
2979	**Sixpence,** 1787, without hearts	13/6
2980	— with hearts	16/-
2981	**Fourpence.** Young bust; 1763, 5, 6, 70, 2, 6, 80, 4, 6	60/-
2982	Older bust. ℞. Thin 4; 1792	75/-
2983	— ℞. Normal 4; 1795, 1800	£5/5/-

2984   2985   2986

2984	**Threepence.** Young bust; 1762, 3, 5, 6, 70, 2, 80, 4, 6	12/6
2985	Older bust. ℞. Thin 3; 1792	75/-
2986	— ℞. Normal 3; 1795, 1800	27/6
2987	**Twopence.** Young bust; 1763, 5, 6, 72, 6, 80, 4, 6 ..	32/6
2988	Older bust. ℞. Thin 2; 1792	75/-
2989	— ℞. Normal 2; 1795, 1800	30/-
2990	**Penny.** Young bust; 1763, 5, 6, 70, 2, 6, 9, 80, 1, 4, 6 ..	27/6
2991	Older bust. ℞. Thin 1; 1792	25/-
2991A	— ℞. Normal 1; 1795, 1800	17/6
2992	**Maundy set,** 1763, 5, 6, 72, 80, 4, 6. Uniform dates ..	£9/10/-
2993	Older bust. ℞. Thin numerals, 1792 (" Wire money ")	£13/10/-
2994	— ℞. Normal numerals; 1795, 1800, uniform dates ..	£9/10/-

---

Prices are for coins in " very fine " condition.   Coins in less
good condition may be worth less than half the prices quoted,
but coins in " extremely fine " or better condition would be
priced at more than double the quoted values.

2995   2996

2995 **Dollar** (current for 4s. 9d.). Spanish American 8 *reales*
     countermarked with Geo. III hd. in oval £30

2996 — — octagonal countermark £60

2997 **Half-dollar** with similar oval countermark £30

Bank of England issue

2998 **Dollar** (current for 5s.), 1804. Laureate bust of king. ℞
     Britannia seated l. £9

     These dollars were re-struck from Spanish-American 8 *reals* until
     at least 1811. Dollars that show dates of original coin are worth
     rather more.

3008 **Three shillings.** Dr. bust in armour r. ℞ BANK/TOKEN/
     3 SHILL/ date (in oak wreath). 1811-12 ..   ..   ..   45/-

3014 Laureate head r. ℞. As before but wreath of oak and
     laurel, 1812-6   ..   ..   40/-

George III Silver. *Very Fine*

3016 3017

3016	**Eighteen pence.** Dr. bust in armour; 1811-12 ..	35/-
3017	Laureate head; 1812-6	30/-
3018	**Ninepence.** Similar, 1812 (pattern only) FDC £35	

Last or new coinage, 1816-20 See page 216

COPPER

First issue—London

3029	**Halfpenny.** Cuir. bust r. ℞ Britannia, 1770-5 ..	27/6
3030	**Farthing,** 1771, 1773-5	25/-

Second issue—Soho. " Cartwheel " coinage.

3031 Twopence. Legends incuse on raised rim, 1797. As illustration of the penny below *Fine* 22/6   60/-

3032 Penny, 1797 .. .. *Fine* 15/-   50/-

George III   Copper.   *Very Fine*

Third issue—Soho

| 3033 | **Halfpenny.** Draped bust r., 1799 | .. | .. | .. | 10/6 |
| 3034 | **Farthing,** 1799 | .. .. .. | .. | .. | 12/6 |

3033   3037

Fourth issue—Soho

3035	**Penny.** Different bust, 1806, 1807	..	..	..	20/–
3036	**Halfpenny,** 1806, 1807	.. ..	..	..	..	7/6
3037	**Farthing,** 1806, 1807	.. ..	..	..	..	10/–

EIGHTEENTH CENTURY TOKENS

In 1787, the regal copper coinage being very scanty, pennies and half-pennies were struck by the Anglesey Copper Mining Company and there began a fresh token epoch. They present an immense variety of types, persons, buildings, coats of arms, local legends, political events, etc., all drawn upon for subjects of design. They were struck by many firms in most cities and towns in the country and are to be found in good condition. Circulated specimens are so common that they have little value

Price of commoner pennies ..   ..   ..   VF 15/–; EF 40/–

Coventry Halfpenny. ℞ Lady Godiva

| — — — halfpennies | .. | .. | .. | VF 4/–; | EF 10/6 |
| — — — farthings .. | .. | .. | .. | VF 5/–; | EF 10/6 |

NINETEENTH CENTURY TOKENS

With the issue of the copper coinage of 1797 tokens were made illegal, but the dearth of silver currency was still felt. Spanish coins were, however, abundant and circulated freely; these were re-struck by the Bank of England (c.f. no. 2998 above) and also officially countermarked (c.f. nos. 2995-7 above). During the Napoleonic wars there came a small wave of prosperity in the industrial districts and the inevitable need of small change, so in 1811 tokens again made their appearance. On this occasion silver ones were made as well as copper. These, with two exceptions, were suppressed before the last coinage of George III.

Withymoor Scythe Works Penny, 1813

Price of the commoner pennies	..	..	VF	7/6;	EF	25/–
— — — halfpennies	..	..	..	VF	5/–;	EF 12/6
— — — farthings ..	..	..	..	VF	6/–;	EF 17/6

For further details of 18th and 19th century tokens see our *British Copper Coins and Their Values*, part II.

Part II

BRITISH COINS

1816 — 1967

A catalogue of modern coins
with prices for each date

B. A. SEABY LTD.

59-65 GREAT PORTLAND STREET, LONDON, W.1

1968 EDITION

BRITISH COINS 1816-1967

IN recent years there has been a growing interest in Britain's modern coinage, particularly in those coins issued since 1816— the date from which our silver coins are legal tender. Seaby's *Standard Catalogue of British Coins* had formerly been a *type* catalogue, giving values for the commonest date or variety of each different type of coin. However, in response to requests from collectors, we are now giving prices for every date of each denomination from 1816 to the present day.

We have omitted mintage figures as they can be misleading. The figures published in the Royal Mint Reports prior to 1953 refer to the number of coins struck during the operating year, but not necessarily to the number which bear that year's date. In many cases unused dies dated the previous year were used during the year for which figures are given. Also, particularly when a new coinage was to be introduced, minting sometimes began during the previous year.

We have included the gold coins struck at the branch mints in the Commonwealth as they were current and circulated with those struck at the London mint.

The values given here are our *selling prices* at the time of going to press for coins in the particular grades of preservation marked at the top of each page (or in other appropriate places). It cannot be stressed too strongly that the value of a coin depends largely on its state of preservation, and we would emphasise that it is the sharpness of the detail of the design that is more important than the colour or brilliance of the coin. Coins minted a hundred years ago or more were sometimes issued in large quantities, and in worn condition they are worth little more than their face value. Speaking generally, coins issued during the past thirty years or so have to be practically uncirculated to be worth appreciably more than their face value.

CONDITIONS OF A COIN

Grades in order of merit as generally used in Great Britain.

FDC = *Fleur-de-coin.* Mint state, unused, flawless, without any wear, scratches or marks.

Unc. = *Uncirculated.* A coin in new condition as issued by the Royal Mint, but, owing to modern mass-production methods of manufacture, not necessarily perfect.

Proof. Specially struck coin from new dies with a mirror-like or matt surface. The raised part of the design is sometimes "frosted" in order to contrast with the polished field. (In this country 'Proof' is not a term used to describe the state of preservation).

EF = *Extremely Fine.* A coin that shows little sign of having been in circulation, but which may exhibit slight surface marks on very close inspection.

VF = *Very Fine.* Only slight traces of wear on the raised surfaces; a coin that has had only slight circulation.

F = *Fine*. Considerable signs of wear on the raised surfaces, or design weak through faulty striking.

Fair. A coin that is worn, but which has the inscriptions and main features of the design still distinguishable, or a piece that is very weakly struck.

Poor. A very worn coin, of no value as a collector's piece unless extremely rare.

CLEANING COINS. Speaking generally *don't* clean coins. More coins are ruined by cleaning than by any other cause, and a badly cleaned coin loses most of its value. A nicely toned piece is usually considered desirable. Really dirty gold and silver can, however, be carefully washed in soap and water. Copper coins should never be cleaned or washed, they should be brushed.

DESIGNERS AND ENGRAVERS INITIALS.

On some coins the initials of the designer or engraver are inserted, either below the head or in some part of the reverse design.

B.P.	Benedetto Pistrucci	Geo. III, Geo. IV
J.B.M.	Jean Baptiste Merlen	Geo. IV
W.W.	William Wyon	Wm. IV, Victoria
L.C.W.	Leonard Wyon	Victoria
J.E.B.	Joseph Boehm	Victoria
T.B.	Thomas Brock	Victoria
De S.	G. W. De Saulles	Edw. VII
B.M.	Bertram Mackennal	Geo. V
P.M.	Percy Metcalfe	Geo. V
K.G.	Kruger Gray	Geo. V, Geo. VI
H.P.	T. Hugh Paget	Edw. VIII, Geo. VI
W.P.	Wilson Parker	Geo. VI, Eliz. II
M.G.	Mary Gillick	Elizabeth II
W.G.	William Gardner	Elizabeth II
E.F.	Edward Fuller	Elizabeth II
C.T.	Cecil Thomas	Elizabeth II

NOTE. Exchange Control Order, 1966 No. 438, which came into force on 27th April 1966, prohibits the sale to collectors resident in the U.K. of gold coins dated after 1837, unless they have the necessary Bank of England authorisation.

214

GEORGE III, 1760-1820

A change over to a gold standard and a regular "token" silver coinage came in 1816 when the Mint, which was moved from its old quarters in the Tower of London to its present site on Tower Hill, began a complete recoinage. The guinea was replaced by a 20s. sovereign, and silver coins were now made with an intrinsic value lower than their face value. British silver is still legal tender back to 1816. The St. George design used on the gold and the crown was the work of Benedetto Pistrucci.

Last or new coinage, 1816-20

GOLD

2969	**Five pounds,** 1820 (Pattern only)	..	FDC £3500
2970	**Two pounds,** 1820 (Pattern only)	..	FDC £750

2971   2972

2971 Sovereign. ℞ St. George

	F	VF	EF			F	VF	EF
1817	..	£10	£20	£40	1819	..	£600	£1000 £1500
1818	..	£15	£30	£60	1820	..	£9	£17 £35

2972 Half-sovereign. ℞ Crowned shield

	F	VF	EF			F	VF	EF
1817	..	£8	£15	£28	1820	..	£10	£18 £35
1818	..	£9	£16	£32					

215

3019 Crown. Laureate head r. ℞ Pistrucci's St. George and dragon within Garter.

					F	VF	EF
1818, edge LVIII	..	..	..	..	70/–	£12	£27
— — LIX	..	..	..	..	70/–	£13	£30
1819 — LIX	..	..	..	..	60/–	£11	£25
— — LX	..	..	..	..	80/–	£15	£32
1820 — LX	..	..	..	..	70/–	£12	£27

3020 Halfcrown. Large or " bull " head.

	F	VF	EF			F	VF	EF
1816	..	30/–	85/–	£9	1817	..	27/6	80/–	£8

3021

George III   Silver

3021 Halfcrown.   Small head.

	F	VF	EF		F	VF	EF
1817 ..	21/–	70/–	£7	1819 ..	25/–	75/–	£8
1818 ..	25/–	75/–	£8	1820 ..	35/–	£5	£14

3022　　　　　　　　　　　3023

3022 Shilling.   ℞   Shield in Garter.

	F	VF	EF		F	VF	EF
1816 ..	13/6	40/–	80/–	1819 ..	16/–	50/–	£5
1817 ..	14/–	42/–	90/–	1820 ..	16/–	50/–	£5
1818 ..	20/–	67/6	£8				

3023 Sixpence.   ℞   Shield in Garter.

	F	VF	EF		F	VF	EF
1816 ..	10/–	27/6	60/–	1819 ..	11/6	32/6	75/–
1817 ..	10/–	27/6	65/–	1820 ..	11/6	32/6	75/–
1818 ..	16/–	47/6	90/–				

3024 Maundy set (4d., 3d., 2d. and 1d.).

	EF	FDC		EF	FDC
1817 ..	£12/10/–	£15	1820 ..	£12/10/–	£15
1818 ..	£12/10/–	£15			

		EF	FDC
3025	— **fourpence,** 1817, 1818, 1820	£5	£7
3026	— **threepence,** 1817, 1818, 1820	65/–	80/–
3027	— **twopence,** 1817, 1818, 1820	35/–	50/–
3028	— **penny,** 1817, 1818, 1820	22/6	25/–

GEORGE IV, 1820-30

The Mint resumed the coinage of copper farthings in 1821, and pennies and halfpennies in 1825. A gold two pound piece was first issued for general circulation in 1823.

GOLD

3038 Five pounds, 1826 (Proof only). ℞   Shield   FDC   £750

3039 Two pounds, 1823. Large bare head. ℞ St. George

	F £38	VF £65	EF £85

3040 — 1826. Type as 3038 (Proof only)   ..   FDC   £325

3041   3042

3041 Sovereign. Laureate head. ℞ St. George.

	F	VF	EF		F	VF	EF
1821	.. £10	£20	£40	1824	.. £15	£30	£60
1822	.. £11	£24	£45	1825	.. £30	£55	£100
1823	.. £45	£90	£200				

3042 — Bare head. ℞ Crowned shield.

	F	VF	EF		F	VF	EF
1825	.. £9	£18	£40	1828	.. £250	£400	£650
1826	.. £9	£18	£40	1829	.. £11	£22	£45
1827	.. £10	£24	£50	1830	.. £11	£22	£45

| | 3043 | | 3044 | | 3045 | |

3043 Half-sovereign.   Laureate head.   ℞ Ornately garnished shield

	F	VF	EF		F	VF	EF
1821	..	£18	£40	£70			

3044 — As last.   ℞   Plain shield.

| 1823 | .. | £9 | £18 | £35 | 1825 | .. | £8 | £16 | £30 |
| 1824 | .. | £8 | £17 | £32 | | | | | |

3045 — Bare head.   ℞   Garnished shield.

| 1826 | .. | £9 | £18 | £32 | 1828 | .. | £8 | £16 | £30 |
| 1827 | .. | £10 | £20 | £38 | | | | | |

SILVER

3046 Crown.   Laureate head.   ℞   St. George.

1821, edge SECUNDO	..	..	..	90/-	£16	£55
1822 — SECUNDO	..	..	..	£5	£20	£70
— — TERTIO	..	..	..	£5	£18	£60

3047 — Bare head.   ℞   Shield with crest (Proof only), 1826
                                        FDC   £275

3048 Halfcrown. Laureate head. ℞ Garnished shield.

	F	VF	EF			F	VF	EF
1820	.. 40/-	£6	£12		1823	.. £27	£75	£150
1821	.. 42/6	£7	£14					

3049 — Similar. ℞ Shield in Garter and collar.

1823	.. 65/-	£9	£20		1824	80/-	£12	£30

3050 — Bare head. ℞ Shield with crest.

1824	.. *Extremely rare*			1828	.. 42/6	£7	£16
1825	.. 35/-	£5	£12	1829	.. 37/6	£6	£13
1826	.. 30/-	£5	£11				

3051   3052

3051 Shilling. Laureate head. ℞ Garnished shield.

1821	..	..	..	..	..	..	40/-	£7	£14

3052 — Similar. ℞ Shield in Garter.

1823	.. 55/-	£8	£30		1825	.. 30/-	£5	£12
1824	.. 27/6	90/-	£10					

George IV   Silver

3053   Shilling. Bare head. ℞ Lion on crown. Type as sixpence, 3056

	F	VF	EF		F	VF	EF
1825 ..	21/–	65/–	£7	1827 ..	40/–	£6	£15
1826 ..	20/–	57/6	£6	1829 ..	27/6	80/–	£10

3054   Sixpence. Laureate head. ℞ Garnished shield.

			F	VF	EF
1821	.. ..	.. ..	30/–	90/–	£9

3055 — Similar. ℞ Shield in Garter.

	F	VF	EF		F	VF	EF
1824 ..	27/6	£5	£10	1826 ..	60/–	£10	£22
1825 ..	21/–	75/–	£8				

3056 — Bare head. ℞ Lion on crown.

	F	VF	EF		F	VF	EF
1826	20/–	57/6	£6	1828 ..	30/–	75/–	£10
1827 ..	50/–	£6	£15	1829 ..	22/6	60/–	£7

3057   Maundy set (4d., 3d., 2d. and 1d.).

	EF	FDC			EF	FDC
1822 ..	£14	£17	1827	..	£12	£15
1823 ..	£12	£15	1828	..	£12	£15
1824 ..	£18	£24	1829	..	£12	£15
1825 ..	£12	£15	1830	..	£12	£15
1826 ..	£12	£15				

				F	VF	EF
3058	**— fourpence,** 1822-30	..	..	20/–	40/–	70/–
3059	**— threepence,** small head, 1822	..		27/6	55/–	£5
3060	**— — normal head,** 1823-1830		..	15/–	27/6	50/–
3061	**— twopence,** 1822-30	..	..	9/–	17/6	30/–
3062	**— penny,** 1822-30	..	..	7/6	15/–	25/–

First issue, 1821-6.
3063 Farthing. Laureate bust, draped.

		F	VF	EF			F	VF	EF
1821	..	3/6	10/6	30/–	1825	..	3/6	10/–	25/–
1822	..	2/6	8/6	20/–	1826	..	6/–	25/–	65/–
1823	..	5/–	15/–	40/–					

Second issue, 1825-30.

3064 Penny. Laureate head. ℞ Britannia.

1825	..	16/–	80/–	£12	1827	..	£9	£30	£80
1826	..	11/–	45/–	£8					

3065 Halfpenny. Similar.

1825	..	25/–	65/–	£9	1827	..	8/6	20/–	60/–
1826	..	7/6	17/6	45/–					

3066   3068

3066 Farthing. Similar.

1826	..	5/–	12/–	30/–	1829	..	10/–	30/–	75/–
1827	..	8/6	22/6	60/–	1830	..	7/6	20/–	47/6
1828	..	4/–	12/–	30/–					

3067 Half-farthing (for use in Ceylon). Similar.

1828	..	32/6	80/–	£10	1830	..	37/6	90/–	£11

3068 Third-farthing (for use in Malta). Similar.

1827	..		7/6	20/–	45/–

WILLIAM IV 1830-37

In order to prevent confusion between the sixpence and half-sovereign the size of the latter was reduced in 1834, but the smaller gold piece was not acceptable to the public and in the following year it was made to the normal size. In 1836 the silver groat was again issued for general circulation: it is the only British silver coin which has a seated Britannia as the type. Crowns were not struck during this reign for general circulation; but proofs or patterns of this denomination were made and are greatly sought after.

GOLD

3069 Two pounds, 1831 (Proof only) .. *FDC* £500

3070   3072

3070 Sovereign. ℞ Crowned shield.

	F	VF	EF		F	VF	EF
1831	£16	£32	£60	1835	£14	£28	£50
1832	£12	£22	£40	1836	£14	£28	£50
1833	£15	£30	£55	1837	£13	£25	£45

3071 Half-sovereign. Similar; small size, 1834.

					£20	£40	£75

3072 — large size.

	F	VF	EF		F	VF	EF
1835	£15	£25	£45	1837	£18	£35	£60
1836	£30	£65	£100				

SILVER

3073 Crown. ℞ Shield on mantle, 1831
(Proof only) .. .. *FDC* £600

3074 Halfcrown. ℞ Shield on mantle.

	F	VF	EF			F	VF	EF
1834 ..	40/–	£6	£13	1836 ..	40/–	£6	£13
1835 ..	75/–	£10	£24	1837 ..	52/6	£8	£16

3075   3076

3075 Shilling. ℞ Value in wreath.

1834 ..	25/–	75/–	£7	1836 ..	27/6	80/–	£8
1835 ..	32/6	85/–	£10	1837 ..	32/6	85/–	£10

William IV Silver

3076 Sixpence. ℞ Value in wreath.

	F	VF	EF		F	VF	EF
1831	20/-	57/6	£6	1836	£5	£12	£27
1834	15/-	42/6	£5	1837	30/-	85/-	£10
1835	30/-	85/-	£10				

3077   3078

3077 Groat. ℞ Britannia.

1836	7/6	17/6	35/-	1837	7/6	17/6	35/-

3077A Threepence (for use in the West Indies). As Maundy three-pence but with a dull surface.

1834	17/6	35/-	70/-	1836	15/-	30/-	60/-
1835	15/-	30/-	60/-	1837	17/6	35/-	70/-

3078 Three-halfpence (for Colonial use). ℞ Value.

1834	4/-	10/-	20/-	1836	5/-	13/6	27/6
1835	5/-	13/6	27/6	1837	15/-	47/6	£5

3079 Maundy set (4d., 3d., 2d., and 1d.).

	EF	FDC		EF	FDC
1831	£14	£17	1835	£13	£16
1832	£13	£16	1836	£13	£16
1833	£13	£16	1837	£13	£16
1834	£13	£16			

				F	VF	EF
3080	— **fourpence,** 1831-7			15/-	30/-	60/-
3081	— **threepence,** 1831-7			25/-	60/-	£6
3082	— **twopence,** 1831-7			10/-	20/-	40/-
3083	— **penny,** 1831-7			10/-	20/-	40/-

COPPER

3084 Penny. No initials on truncation.

	F	VF	EF			F	VF	EF
1831	15/-	80/-	£12	1837	..	45/-	£8	£25
1834	20/-	£5	£15					

3085 — ww on truncation, 1831 .. .. 20/- £6 £18

3086 Halfpenny. As penny.

	F	VF	EF			F	VF	EF
1831	7/6	27/6	75/-	1837	..	7/6	25/-	65/-
1834	7/6	27/6	75/-					

3087   3088

3087 Farthing. Similar.

	F	VF	EF			F	VF	EF
1831	5/-	20/-	55/-	1836	..	5/-	17/6	45/-
1834	5/-	15/-	40/-	1837	..	5/-	17/6	45/-
1835	5/-	17/6	45/-					

3088 Half-farthing (for use in Ceylon). Similar.

1837 .. .. 45/- £7 £20

3089 Third-farthing (for use in Malta). Similar.

1835 .. .. 10/6 25/- 52/6

VICTORIA, 1837-1901

In 1849, as a first step towards decimalization, a silver florin ($\frac{1}{10}$th pound) was introduced, but the coins of 1849 omitted the usual *Dei Gratia* and these so-called " Godless " florins were succeeded in 1851 by the " Gothic " issue. The halfcrown was temporarily discontinued but was minted again from 1874 onwards. Between 1863 and 1880 reverse dies of the gold and silver coins were numbered in the course of Mint experiments into the wear of dies. The exception being the florin when the die number is on the obverse below the bust.

The gold and silver coins were redesigned for the Queen's Golden Jubilee in 1887. The double-florin which was then issued was abandoned after only four years; the Jubilee sixpence of 1887, known as the " withdrawn " type, was changed to avoid confusion with the half sovereign. Gold and silver was again redesigned in 1893 with an older portrait of the Queen, but the " old head " was not used on the bronze coinage until 1895. The heavy copper penny had been replaced by the lighter bronze " bun " penny in 1860. In 1874-6 and 1881-2 some of the bronze was made by Heaton in Birmingham. From 1897 farthings were issued with a dark surface.

Early sovereigns had a shield type reverse, but Pistrucci's St. George design was used again from 1871. In order to increase the output of gold coinage, branches of the Royal Mint were set up in Australia at Sydney and Melbourne, and, later, at Perth, for coining gold of imperial type.

GOLD

Young head coinage, 1838-87.

3090 Five pounds, 1839. ℞ " Una and the lion " (proof only) .. ..   *FDC*   £1000

3091   3092

3091   Sovereign, type I.   R   Shield.

	F	VF	EF			F	VF	EF
1838	£8	£14	£25	1852			£7	£14
1839	£14	£28	£50	1853			£7	£13
1841	£60	£100	£200	1854			£8	£16
1842		£7	£15	1855			£7	£14
1843		£7	£15	1856			£8	£16
1844		£9	£17	1857			£8	£16
1845		£9	£17	1858		£11	£20	£38
1846		£9	£17	1859			£8	£16
1847		£8	£16	1860			£7	£14
1848	£6	£11	£22	1861			£7	£12
1849	£7	£12	£24	1862			£7	£12
1850	£8	£14	£27	1863			£7	£12
1851	£6	£11	£22	1872			£7	£13

3092   — — die number below wreath.

	F	VF	EF			F	VF	EF
1863		£7	£14	1870			£7	£13
1864		£7	£12	1871			£7	£12
1865		£8	£16	1872			£6	£9
1866		£7	£12	1873		£6	£11	£20
1868		£8	£16	1874		£16	£35	£70
1869		£7	£12					

3093   3094

3093   — — M below wreath for Melbourne mint.

			F	VF	EF					F	VF	EF
1872	M			£10	£18	1883	M			£7	£12
1874	M			£6	£10	1884	M			£6	£9
1875	M			*Rare*		1885	M			£6	£11
1880	M			£10	£18	1886	M			£7	£12
1881	M			£7	£12	1887	M			£6	£11
1882	M			£8	£14						

Victoria Gold

3094 Sovereign. ℞. Shield s below wreath for Sydney mint.

		F	VF	EF				F	VF	EF
1871	s		£6	£10		1881	s		£14	£25
1872	s		£7	£12		1882	s		£7	£11
1873	s		£6	£10		1883	s		£10	£18
1875	s		£10	£18		1884	s		£7	£11
1877	s		£6	£10		1885	s		£7	£11
1878	s		£6	£9		1886	s		£6	£10
1879	s		£6	£9		1887	s		£7	£12
1880	s		£6	£10						

3095 — Type II. ℞ St. George.

		F	VF	EF				F	VF	EF
1871	..		£6	£10		1878	..		£7	£10
1872	..		£6	£9		1879	..	£40	£80	£150
1873	..		£8	£12		1880	..		£6	£9
1874	..	£8	£18	£35		1884	..		£7	£10
1876	..		£6	£9		1885	..		£8	£12

3096   3097

3096 — — M below head for Melbourne mint.

			F	VF	EF					F	VF	EF
1872	M	..	..	£16	£30		1880	M	..	..	90/–	£7
1873	M	..	..	90/–	£8		1881	M	..	..	90/–	£7
1874	M	..	..	90/–	£8		1882	M	..	..	90/–	£8
1875	M	..	..	90/–	£8		1883	M	..	..	90/–	£8
1876	M	..	..	90/–	£8		1884	M	..	..	90/–	£8
1877	M	..	..	90/–	£7		1885	M	..	..	90/–	£7
1878	M	..	..	90/–	£8		1886	M	..	..	90/	£7
1879	M	..	..	90/–	£8		1887	M	..	..	90/–	£8

3097 — — s below head for Sydney mint.

			F	VF	EF					F	VF	EF
1871	s	..	..	£10	£18		1881	s	..	..	£5	£9
1872	s	..	..	£5	£10		1882	s	..	..	95/–	£8
1873	s	..	..	£6	£12		1883	s	..	..	£5	£9
1874	s	..	..	£5	£10		1884	s	..	..	£5	£9
1875	s	..	..	£6	£12		1885	s	..	..	£5	£9
1876	s	..	..	£5	£10		1886	s	..	..	£5	£9
1879	s	..	..	£6	£12		1887	s	..	..	95/–	£8
1880	s	..	..	£5	£10							

3098   3099

3098   Half-sovereign.   R   Shield.

	F	VF	EF			F	VF	EF
1838	£5	£10	£20	1852	65/–	£5	£9
1839	? only proofs			1853		75/–	£6
1841	90/–	£8	£15	1854	£12	£35	£60
1842		85/–	£7	1855		80/–	£7
1843		90/–	£8	1856		80/–	£7
1844		90/–	£8	1857		90/–	£8
1845	70/–	£6	£10	1858		85/–	£7
1846	65/–	£5	£9	1859		75/–	£6
1847	65/–	£5	£9	1860		85/–	£7
1848	75/–	£7	£12	1861		85/–	£7
1849	70/–	£6	£10	1862	£9	£16	£30
1850	£20	£50	£85	1863	65/–	£5	£9
1851		90/–	£8				

3099 — — die number below shield.

		VF	EF				VF	EF
1863		75/–	£6	1873			75/–	£6
1864		75/–	£6	1874			75/–	£6
1865		75/–	£6	1875			85/–	£7
1866		65/–	£5	1876			75/–	£6
1867		65/–	£5	1877			65/–	£5
1869		75/–	£6	1878			65/–	£5
1870		75/–	£6	1879	£5	£10	£17	
1871		75/–	£6	1880			90/–	£8
1872		75/–	£6					

3100 — — As 3098 but head in slightly lower relief.

		VF	EF				VF	EF
1880		75/–	£6	1884			62/6	95/–
1883		62/6	95/–	1885			60/–	90/–

3101   3102

3101 — — s below shield for Sydney mint.

			VF	EF					VF	EF
1871	s		£6	£10	1881	s			£8	£15
1872	s		£6	£10	1882	s			£7	£12
1875	s		£6	£10	1883	s			£5	£8
1879	s		£10	£20	1886	s			£6	£10
1880	s		£6	£10	1887	s			£5	£8

Victoria Gold

3102 Half-sovereign. As 3098, but M below shield for Melbourne
mint.

			VF	EF					VF	EF
1873	M	..	.. £8	£13	1884	M	..	.. £6	£10
1877	M	..	.. £6	£10	1885	M	..	.. £15	£30
1881	M	..	.. £20	£40	1886	M	..	.. £6	£10
1882	M	..	.. £6	£10	1887	M	..	.. £7	£12

Jubilee coinage, 1887-93

			F	VF	EF
3103	**Five pounds.** ℞ St. George, 1887		£50	£75	£100
3104	**Two pounds.** Similar, 1887	..	£25	£40	£48

3105 Sovereign. ℞. St. George

1887	..	£6	£10	1890	..	£6	£12
1888	..	£6	£12	1891	..	£6	£12
1889	..	£5	£9	1892	..	£6	£10

3106 — — M on ground for Melbourne mint.

1887	M	..	.. £5	£7	1891	M	..	.. 92/6	£6
1888	M	..	.. 92/6	£6	1892	M	..	.. 92/6	£6
1889	M	..	.. 92/6	£6	1893	M	..	.. 92/6	£6
1890	M	..	.. 92/6	£6					

3107 — — s on ground for Sydney mint.

1887	s	..	.. £5	£8	1891	s	..	.. 95/-	£7
1888	s	..	.. 95/-	£7	1892	s	..	.. 95/-	£7
1889	s	..	.. 95/-	£7	1893	s	..	.. £5	£8
1890	s	..	.. 95/-	£7					

3108 Half-sovereign. ℞ Shield.

	VF	EF		F	VF	EF
1887 ..	.. 75/–	£5	1892 ..		65/–	85/–
1890 ..	.. 75/–	£6	1893 ..	£5	£9	£16
1891 ..	.. 70/–	£5				

3109 — — M below shield for Melbourne mint.

	VF	EF			VF	EF
1887 M..	.. £7	£10	1893 M..		.. £7	£10

3110 — — S below shield for Sydney mint.

	VF	EF			VF	EF
1887 s ..	.. £6	£9	1891 s ..		.. £6	£9
1889 s ..	.. £7	£11				

Old head coinage, 1893-1901

3112

				F	VF	EF
3111	**Five pounds.** ℞ St. George, 1893	..		£70	£100	£120
3112	**Two pounds.** Similar, 1893	..		£27	£42	£58

3113 Sovereign. ℞ St. George.

	VF	EF			VF	EF
1893 ..	.. £7	£10	1898 ..		.. 95/–	£7
1894 ..	.. £5	£8	1899 ..		.. 90/–	£7
1895 ..	.. 95/–	£7	1900 ..		.. 90/–	£7
1896 ..	.. 92/6	£7	1901 ..		.. £5	£8

3115   3116

3114   Sovereign. R. St. George. M on ground for Melbourne mint.

	VF	EF			VF	EF
1893 M..	.. £5	£7	1898 M..	..	87/6	£6
1894 M..	.. 90/–	£6	1899 M..	..	87/6	£6
1895 M..	.. 90/–	£6	1900 M..	..	90/–	£6
1896 M..	.. 90/–	£6	1901 M..	..	90/–	£6
1897 M..	.. 87/6	£6				

3115   — — P on ground for Perth mint.

1899 P ..	.. £8	£15	1901 P ..	.. £5	£8
1900 P ..	.. £5	£8			

3116   — — S on ground for Sydney mint.

1893 S ..	.. £5	£8	1898 S ..	.. £12	£25
1894 S ..	.. 92/6	£7	1899 S ..	.. 95/–	£7
1895 S ..	.. £5	£8	1900 S ..	.. 95/–	£7
1896 S ..	.. £6	£10	1901 S ..	.. £5	£8
1897 S ..	.. 95/–	£7			

3117   Half-sovereign. R. St. George.

1893 ..	.. 70/–	£5	1898 ..	.. 65/–	90/–
1894 ..	.. 65/–	90/–	1899 ..	.. 65/–	90/–
1895 ..	.. 65/–	90/–	1900 ..	.. 65/–	90/–
1896 ..	.. 65/–	90/–	1901 ..	.. 65/–	90/–
1897 ..	.. 65/–	90/–			

3118   — — M on ground for Melbourne mint.

1893 M ? proofs only			1899 M..	.. £5	£8
1896 M..	.. £5	£8	1900 M..	.. £6	£10

3119   — — P on ground for Perth mint.

1899 P ? proofs only			1900 P ..	.. £6	£10

3120   — — S on ground for Sydney mint.

1893 S ..	.. 95/–	£8	1900 S ..	.. 95/–	£8
1897 S ..	.. 95/–	£8			

Victoria
Young head coinage

3121 Crown. Young head. R Crowned shield.
1839 (Proof only) FDC £250

	F	VF	EF			F	VF	EF
				1845	..	£5	£15	£45
1844	.. £5	£15	£45	1847	..	£6	£16	£48

	VF	EF	FDC

3122 — "Gothic" type, as illustration;
inscribed edge, mdcccxlvii = 1847.   £50   £75   £100
Probably not issued for general circulation

3123

<table>
<tr><td></td><td></td><td></td><td></td><td></td><td>*F*</td><td>*VF*</td><td>*EF*</td></tr>
</table>

3123   Halfcrown, type A¹. Young head with one ornate and one plain fillet binding hair. ww in relief on truncation, 1839 .. .. .. £22 £70 £150

3125   — type A³. Two plain fillets, ww incuse, 1840 .. .. £5 £16 £45

3126   — type A⁴. Similar but no initials on truncation.

	F	VF	EF			F	VF	EF
1841	£7	£20	£60	1846	..	£5	£14	£40
1842	70/–	£10	£30	1848	..	£8	£25	£75
1843	£7	£20	£60	1849	..	£5	£14	£42
1844	70/–	£10	£30	1850	..	£5	£14	£42
1845	70/–	£10	£30					

3127   — type A⁵. As last but inferior workmanship.

1874	30/–	£6	£17	1881	..	27/6	£5	£15
1875	30/–	£6	£17	1882	..	27/6	£5	£15
1876	35/–	£7	£20	1883	..	27/6	£5	£15
1877	35/–	£7	£20	1884	..	32/6	£6	£18
1878	35/–	£7	£20	1885	..	27/6	£5	£15
1879	45/–	£8	£24	1886	..	27/6	£5	£15
1880	32/6	£6	£18	1887	..	27/6	£5	£15

3128   3129

3128   Florin "Godless" type (i.e. without D.G.) 1849 .. .. .. 37/6 £5 £11

3129   — " Gothic " type B¹, reads bꞧit:, ww below bust, date of obverse legend in gothic numerals (1851 to 1863)

mdcccli	£5	£15	£32	mdccclvii	45/–	£7	£14
mdccclii	30/–	£5	£10	mdccclviii	32/6	£5	£11
mdcccliii	32/6	£5	£11	mdccclix	45/–	£7	£14
mdcccliv	£5	£15	£32	mdccclx	60/–	£9	£18
mdccclv	45/–	£7	£14	mdccclxii	80/–	£12	£25
mdccclvi	60/–	£9	£18	mdccclxiii	80/–	£12	£25

3130   — — type B²; as last but die number below bust (1864 to 1867)

mdccclxiv	32/6	£5	£11	mdccclxvi	60/–	£9	£18
mdccclxv	60/–	£9	£18	mdccclxvii	80/–	£12	£25

Victoria Silver

3131 Florin " Gothic " type B³; reads britt:, die number (1868 to 1877)

	F	VF	EF		F	VF	EF
mdccclxviii	45/-	£7	£14	mdccclxxiii	30/-	90/-	£9
mdccclxix	32/6	£5	£11	mdccclxxiv	32/6	92/6	£10
mdccclxx	32/6	£5	£11	mdccclxxv	42/-	£7	£14
mdccclxxi	32/6	£5	£11	mdccclxxvi	42/-	£7	£14
mdccclxxii	30/-	90/-	£9	mdccclxxvii	42/-	£7	£14

3132 — — type B⁴. As last but with border of 48 arcs and no ww.
1877 mdccclxxvii 90/- £13 £27

3133 — — type B⁵. Similar but 42 arcs, (1877 to 1878)
mdccclxxvii 80/- £10 £22 mdccclxxviii 40/- £5 £11

3134 — — type B⁵/⁶. As last but no die number.
1879 mdccclxxix 80/- £12 £27

3135 — — type B⁶. reads britt. ; ww; 48 arcs,
1879 mdccclxxix 65/- £10 £20

3136 — — type B⁷. As last but no ww; 38 arcs,
1879 mdccclxxix 65/- £10 £20

3137 — — typeB⁸. Similar but 33 arcs, (1880 to 1887)

mdccclxxx	30/-	90/-	£9	mdccclxxxv	25/-	75/-	£7
mdccclxxxi	25/-	75/-	£7	mdccclxxxvi	30/-	90/-	£9
mdccclxxxiii	25/-	75/-	£7	mdccclxxxvii	40/-	£5	£13
mdccclxxxiv	25/-	75/-	£7				

3138 — — type B⁹. Similar but 46 arcs,
1887 mdccclxxxvii 70/- £10 £20

3144

3139 Shilling, type A¹. First head, ww on truncation.
1838 .. 40/- £6 £14   1839 .. 40/- £6 £14

3140 — type A². Second head, ww
(Proof only), 1839 .. .. .. *FDC* £42

3141 — type A³. Second head, no initials on truncation.

1839	..	20/-	45/-	£6	1852	..	25/-	65/-	£9
1840	..	40/-	£5	£16	1853	..	25/-	65/-	£9
1841	..	30/-	80/-	£12	1854	..	40/-	£5	£16
1842	..	25/-	65/-	£9	1855	..	25/-	65/-	£9
1843	..	30/-	80/-	£12	1856	..	25/-	65/-	£9
1844	..	25/-	65/-	£9	1857	..	25/-	65/-	£9
1845	..	30/-	80/-	£12	1858	..	25/-	65/-	£9
1846	..	25/-	65/-	£9	1859	..	25/-	65/-	£9
1848 over 6		40/-	£5	£16	1860	..	30/-	80/-	£12
1849	..	25/-	65/-	£9	1861	..	30/-	80/-	£12
1850	..	50/-	£7	£21	1862	..	40/-	£5	£16
1851	..	40/-	£5	£16	1863	..	40/-	£5	£16

Victoria Silver

3142 Shilling type A⁴. As before but die number above date.

	F	VF	EF			F	VF	EF
1864	..	30/-	90/-	£12	1866	..	30/-	90/-	£12
1865	..	30/-	90/-	£12	1867	..	35/-	£5	£15

3144 — type A⁶. Third head, die number above date.

1868	..	20/-	60/-	£6	1874	..	20/-	60/-	£6
1869	..	35/-	£5	£12	1875	..	20/-	60/-	£6
1870	..	35/-	£5	£12	1876	..	25/-	75/-	£8
1871	..	20/-	60/-	£6	1877	..	20/-	60/-	£6
1872	..	17/6	50/-	£5	1878	..	20/-	60/-	£6
1873	..	17/6	50/-	£5	1879	..	35/-	£5	£12

3145 — type A⁷. Fourth head; no die number.

1879	..	35/-	£5	£12	1884	..	14/-	40/-	£5
1880	..	14/-	40/-	£5	1885	..	14/-	40/-	£5
1881	..	14/-	40/-	£5	1886	..	14/-	40/-	£5
1882	..	70/-	£10	£25	1887	..	21/-	65/-	£7
1883	..	14/-	40/-	£5					

3150   3147

3146 Sixpence, type A¹. First head.

1838	..	15/-	45/-	£5	1852	..	20/-	60/-	£7
1839	..	16/-	50/-	£6	1853	..	16/-	50/-	£6
1840	..	20/-	60/-	£7	1854	..	30/-	90/-	£10
1841	..	20/-	60/-	£7	1855	..	16/-	50/-	£6
1842	..	20/-	60/-	£7	1856	..	16/-	50/-	£6
1843	..	16/-	50/-	£6	1857	..	20/-	60/-	£7
1844	..	16/-	50/-	£6	1858	..	20/-	60/-	£7
1845	..	20/-	60/-	£7	1859	..	16/-	50/-	£6
1846	..	16/-	50/-	£6	1860	..	20/-	60/-	£7
1848	..	30/-	90/-	£10	1862	..	30/-	90/-	£10
1849	..	(? exists)			1863	..	30/-	90/-	£10
1850	..	20/-	60/-	£7	1866	..	45/-	£7	£16
1851	..	20/-	60/-	£7					

3147 — type A². First head; die number above date.

1864	..	25/-	75/-	£8	1866	..	28/-	80/-	£9
1865	..	35/-	90/-	£10					

3148 — type A³. Second head; die number above date.

1867	..	40/-	£5	£10	1874	..	20/-	60/-	£7
1868	..	40/-	£5	£10	1875	..	20/-	60/-	£7
1869	..	40/-	£5	£10	1876	..	40/-	£5	£10
1870	..	40/-	£5	£10	1877	..	20/-	60/-	£7
1871	..	30/-	75/-	£8	1878	..	20/-	60/-	£7
1872	..	30/-	75/-	£8	1879	..	40/-	£5	£10
1873	..	20/-	60/-	£7					

Victoria Silver

3149 Sixpence type A[4]. Second head; no die number.

	F	VF	EF			F	VF	EF
1871	..	40/-	£5	£10	1879	..	20/-	60/-	£6
1877	..	20/-	60/-	£6	1880	..	32/-	80/-	£9

3150 — type A[5]. Third head.

1880	..	20/-	50/-	£5	1884	..	20/-	50/-	£5
1881	..	20/-	50/-	£5	1885	..	20/-	50/-	£5
1882	..	35/-	£5	£10	1886	..	16/-	42/6	90/-
1883	..	20/-	50/-	£5	1887	..	12/6	35/-	75/-

3151   3152   3153

3151 Groat (4d.). ℞ Britannia

1838	..	7/-	21/-	40/-	1847 over 6		£5	£15	£30
1839	..	9/-	27/6	55/-	1848	..	9/-	27/6	55/-
1840	..	7/-	21/-	40/-	1849	..	10/6	32/6	65/-
1841	..	12/6	45/-	80/-	1851	..	12/6	45/-	80/-
1842	..	8/6	25/-	50/-	1852	..	£7	£20	£37
1843	..	9/-	27/6	55/-	1853	..	65/-	£10	£20
1844	..	10/6	32/6	65/-	1854	..	7/-	21/-	40/-
1845	..	9/-	27/6	55/-	1855	..	8/6	25/-	50/-
1846	..	9/-	27/6	55/-					

3152 Threepence. ℞ Crowned 3; as Maundy threepence but with a dull surface.

1838	..	10/-	30/-	£5	1864	..	8/-	24/-	75/-
1839	..	10/-	30/-	£5	1865	..	10/-	30/-	£5
1840	..	10/-	30/-	£5	1866	..	8/-	24/-	75/-
1841	..	10/-	30/-	£5	1867	..	8/-	24/-	75/-
1842	..	10/-	30/-	£5	1868	..	8/-	24/-	75/-
1843	..	10/-	30/-	£5	1870	..	8/-	24/-	75/-
1844	..	10/-	30/-	£5	1871	..	8/-	24/-	75/-
1845	..	7/-	20/-	63/-	1872	..	8/-	24/-	75/-
1846	..	8/-	24/-	75/-	1873	..	8/-	24/-	75/-
1849	..	15/-	40/-	£6	1874	..	7/-	20/-	63/-
1850	..	8/-	24/-	75/-	1875	..	7/-	20/-	63/-
1851	..	8/-	24/-	75/-	1876	..	7/-	20/-	63/-
1853	..	10/-	30/-	£5	1877	..	7/-	20/-	63/-
1854	..	8/-	24/-	75/-	1878	..	8/-	24/-	75/-
1855	..	15/-	40/-	£6	1879	..	8/-	24/-	75/-
1856	..	8/-	24/-	75/-	1880	..	8/-	24/-	75/-
1857	..	10/-	30/-	£5	1881	..	7/-	20/-	63/-
1858	..	8/-	24/-	75/-	1882	..	8/-	24/-	75/-
1859	..	8/-	24/-	75/-	1883	..	7/-	20/-	63/-
1860	..	8/-	24/-	75/-	1884	..	7/-	20/-	63/-
1861	..	8/-	24/-	75/-	1885	..	7/-	20/-	63/-
1862	..	8/-	24/-	75/-	1886	..	7/-	20/-	63/-
1863	..	10/-	30/-	£5	1887	..	15/-	40/-	£6

3153   Threehalfpence (For Colonial use).   R   Value, etc.

	F	VF	EF		F	VF	EF
1838	.. 7/6	15/–	30/–	1842	.. 7/6	15/–	30/–
1839	.. 5/–	10/–	20/–	1843	.. 3/–	6/6	15/–
1840	.. 15/–	32/6	75/–	1860	.. 7/–	13/6	27/6
1841	.. 8/6	17/6	35/–	1862	.. 6/–	12/6	25/–

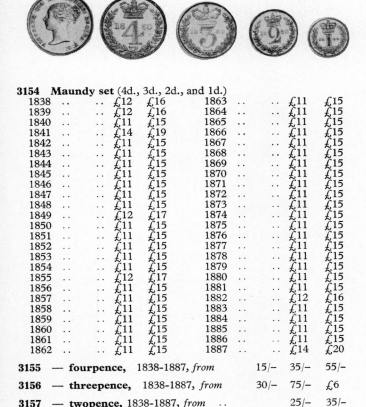

3154   Maundy set (4d., 3d., 2d., and 1d.)

1838	..	.. £12	£16	1863	..	.. £11	£15
1839	..	.. £12	£16	1864	..	.. £11	£15
1840	..	.. £11	£15	1865	..	.. £11	£15
1841	..	.. £14	£19	1866	..	.. £11	£15
1842	..	.. £11	£15	1867	..	.. £11	£15
1843	..	.. £11	£15	1868	..	.. £11	£15
1844	..	.. £11	£15	1869	..	.. £11	£15
1845	..	.. £11	£15	1870	..	.. £11	£15
1846	..	.. £11	£15	1871	..	.. £11	£15
1847	..	.. £11	£15	1872	..	.. £11	£15
1848	..	.. £11	£15	1873	..	.. £11	£15
1849	..	.. £12	£17	1874	..	.. £11	£15
1850	..	.. £11	£15	1875	..	.. £11	£15
1851	..	.. £11	£15	1876	..	.. £11	£15
1852	..	.. £11	£15	1877	..	.. £11	£15
1853	..	.. £11	£15	1878	..	.. £11	£15
1854	..	.. £11	£15	1879	..	.. £11	£15
1855	..	.. £12	£17	1880	..	.. £11	£15
1856	..	.. £11	£15	1881	..	.. £11	£15
1857	..	.. £11	£15	1882	..	.. £12	£16
1858	..	.. £11	£15	1883	..	.. £11	£15
1859	..	.. £11	£15	1884	..	.. £11	£15
1860	..	.. £11	£15	1885	..	.. £11	£15
1861	..	.. £11	£15	1886	..	.. £11	£15
1862	..	.. £11	£15	1887	..	.. £14	£20

3155   — fourpence, 1838-1887, *from*   15/–   35/–   55/–

3156   — threepence, 1838-1887, *from*   30/–   75/–   £6

3157   — twopence, 1838-1887, *from*   ..   25/–   35/–

3158   — penny, 1838-1887, *from*   ..   20/–   30/–

3159 Crown. ℞ St. George.

	F	VF	EF			F	VF	EF
1887	..	30/–	80/–	£11	1890	..	50/–	£6	£20
1888	..	£5	£14	£32	1891	..	50/–	£6	£20
1889	..	35/–	£5	£17	1892	..	50/–	£6	£20

3160 Double-florin (4s.). ℞ Cruciform shields.

1887	Roman I in date ..	..	..	20/–	60/–	£8

3161 — Similar but Arabic 1 in date.

1887	..	20/–	50/–	£7	1889	..	25/–	70/–	£9
1888	..	35/–	£5	£15	1890	..	25/–	85/–	£12

3162

Victoria Silver

3162 Halfcrown. ℞ Shield in collar.

	VF	EF			VF	EF
1887	40/–	80/–	1890		60/–	£6
1888	50/–	£5	1891		60/–	£6
1889	50/–	£5	1892		60/–	£6

3163 Florin. ℞ Cruciform shields.

	VF	EF			VF	EF
1887	50/–	£5	1890		90/–	£9
1888	60/–	£6	1891		£10	£25
1889	60/–	£6	1892		£12	£30

3164   3165

3164 Shilling. Small head. ℞ Shield in garter.

	VF	EF			VF	EF
1887	8/–	15/–	1889		£5	£15
1888	15/–	30/–				

3165 — Large head. ℞ As before.

	VF	EF			VF	EF
1889	37/6	90/–	1891		40/–	£5
1890	40/–	£5	1892		40/–	£5

3166   3167

3166 Sixpence. ℞ Shield in garter (withdrawn
type), 1887 .. .. 7/– 14/–

3167 — ℞ Value in wreath.

	VF	EF			VF	EF
1887	8/–	17/6	1891		12/6	30/–
1888	9/–	20/–	1892		12/6	30/–
1889	9/–	20/–	1893		£10	£20
1890	12/–	30/–				

Victoria   Silver

						F	VF	EF

3168 **Groat** (for use in British Guiana) R
Britannia, 1888 .. .. 30/– 60/–

3169 **Threepence.** As Maundy but dull surface.

						F	VF
1887	..	..	5/–	10/–	1891	7/6	15/–
1888	..	..	10/–	20/–	1892	10/–	20/–
1889	..	..	7/6	15/–	1893	£5 £10	£20
1890	..	..	7/6	15/–			

3170 **Maundy set** (4d., 3d., 2d. and 1d.)

			EF	FDC			EF	FDC
1888	.	..	£16	£21	1891	..	£15	£20
1889	..	..	£15	£20	1892	..	£15	£20
1890	..	..	£15	£20				

			VF	EF
3171	— **fourpence,** 1888-1892, *from* ..	..	42/6	55/–
3172	— **threepence,** 1888-1892, *from* ..	..	£7	£10
3173	— **twopence,** 1888-1892, *from*	..	40/–	52/6
3174	— **penny,** 1888-1892, *from*	..	30/–	40/–

Old   head coinage

3175

Victoria Silver

3175 Crown. ℞ St. George.

	F	VF	EF
1893; regnal date on edge, LVI	50/–	£7	£25
— — — — LVII	£6	£15	£50
1894 — — — LVII	£5	£12	£35
— — — — LVIII	£5	£12	£35
1895 — — — LVIII	£5	£12	£35
— — — — LIX	90/–	£10	£30
1896 — — — LIX	£6	£15	£50
— — — — LX	90/–	£10	£30
1897 — — — LX	90/–	£10	£30
— — — — LXI	50/–	£7	£25
1898 — — — LXI	£6	£15	£50
— — — — LXII	£5	£12	£35
1899 — — — LXII	£5	£12	£35
— — — — LXIII	£5	£12	£35
1900 — — — LXIII	£5	£12	£35
— — — — LXIV	90/–	£10	£30

3176 Halfcrown. ℞ Shield in collar.

	F	VF	EF			F	VF	EF
1893	27/6	52/6	£6		1897	25/–	50/–	£5
1894	32/6	65/–	£7		1898	32/6	65/–	£7
1895	32/6	65/–	£7		1899	32/6	65/–	£7
1896	32/6	65/–	£7		1900	25/–	50/–	£6
					1901	25/–	50/–	£6

3177 Florin. ℞ Three shields within Garter.

	F	VF	EF			F	VF	EF
1893	20/–	45/–	£5		1898	22/6	55/–	£7
1894	22/6	55/–	£7		1899	22/6	55/–	£7
1895	22/6	55/–	£7		1900	20/–	45/–	£5
1896	22/6	55/–	£7		1901	20/–	45/–	£5
1897	20/–	45/–	£5					

3178   Shilling.   R   Three shields within Garter.

	F	VF	EF		F	VF	EF
1893	8/–	25/–	60/–	1898	8/–	25/–	60/–
1894	10/–	30/–	75/–	1899	10/–	30/–	75/–
1895	10/–	30/–	70/–	1900	8/–	25/–	60/–
1896	8/–	25/–	60/–	1901	8/–	25/–	60/–
1897	8/–	25/–	60/–				

3179   Sixpence.   R   Value in wreath.

	F	VF	EF		F	VF	EF
1893	7/6	22/6	50/–	1898	7/–	20/–	45/–
1894	9/6	27/6	60/–	1899	7/–	20/–	45/–
1895	9/6	27/6	60/–	1900	7/–	20/–	45/–
1896	9/6	27/6	60/–	1901	5/–	17/6	40/–
1897	7/–	20/–	45/–				

3180   Threepence.   R   3.   As Maundy but dull surface.

	F	VF	EF
1893-1901, *each*	3/–	10/–	30/–

3181   Maundy set (4d., 3d., 2d. and 1d.)

	EF	FDC		EF	FDC
1893	£9	£12	1898	£8	£10
1894	£8	£10	1899	£8	£10
1895	£8	£10	1900	£8	£10
1896	£8	£10	1901	£8	£10
1897	£8	£10			

	EF	FDC
3182 — **fourpence,** 1893-1901, *from*	30/–	40/–
3183 — **threepence,** 1893-1901, *from*	85/–	£5
3184 — **twopence,** 1893-1901, *from*	25/–	35/–
3185 — **penny,** 1893-1901, *from*	25/–	35/–

Victoria

COPPER AND BRONZE

Young head coinage, 1838-1895
Copper issue

3186 Penny. ℞ Britannia.

	F	VF	EF			F	VF	EF
1841	10/6	21/–	60/–	1853		5/–	15/–	45/–
1843	90/–	£15	£45	1854		7/–	17/6	50/–
1844	15/–	35/–	£5	1855		7/–	18/6	55/–
1845	40/–	£5	£14	1856		30/–	90/–	£15
1846	25/–	65/–	£9	1857		8/–	20/–	55/–
1847	20/–	55/–	£8	1858		6/–	15/–	45/–
1848	15/–	60/–	£8	1859		12/6	35/–	£5
1849	£8	£25	£75	1860			£45	£125
1851	25/–	70/–	£10					

3187 Halfpenny. ℞ Britannia.

	F	VF	EF			F	VF	EF
1838	8/–	20/–	50/–	1852		7/6	22/6	55/–
1841	4/6	12/6	35/–	1853		3/6	10/–	22/6
1843	25/–	60/–	£8	1854		4/–	10/6	25/–
1844	17/6	47/6	£7	1855		4/–	10/6	25/–
1845	£12	£35	£100	1856		10/–	25/–	60/–
1846	15/–	40/–	£6	1857		4/–	10/6	25/–
1847	20/–	55/–	£8	1858		4/–	10/6	25/–
1848	15/–	40/–	£6	1859		12/6	27/6	70/–
1851	10/6	30/–	60/–	1860	*Extremely rare*			

Victoria Copper

3188   3189

3188 Farthing. ℞ Britannia.

	F	VF	EF			F	VF	EF
1838	.. 5/–	15/–	40/–	1850	.. 5/–	15/–	40/–
1839	.. 4/–	10/–	30/–	1851	.. 15/–	40/–	£6
1840	.. 4/–	10/–	30/–	1852	.. 15/–	40/–	£6
1841	.. 4/–	10/–	30/–	1853	.. 4/–	10/–	22/6
1842	.. 10/6	30/–	£5	1854	.. 4/6	12/6	30/–
1843	.. 5/–	12/6	30/–	1855	.. 7/6	17/6	50/–
1844	.. 35/–	£5	£15	1856	.. 10/6	30/–	80/–
1845	.. 5/–	15/–	40/–	1857	.. 4/–	12/6	30/–
1846	.. 10/6	30/–	£5	1858	.. 4/–	10/6	25/–
1847	.. 4/6	11/–	35/–	1859	.. 12/6	35/–	£5
1848	.. 5/·	12/6	35/–	1860	..		£200
1849	.. 15/–	45/–	£8				

3189 Half-farthing. ℞ Value.

	F	VF	EF			F	VF	EF
1839	.. 8/6	20/–	50/–	1851	.. 5/–	15/–	35/–
1842	.. 6/–	15/–	40/–	1852	.. 5/–	15/–	40/–
1843	..	5/–	12/6	1853	.. 12/6	30/–	80/–
1844	..	3/6	8/6	1854	.. 12/6	30/–	80/–
1847	.. 4/–	12/6	30/–	1856	.. 15/–	40/–	£5

3190   3191

3190 Third-farthing (for use in Malta). ℞ Britannia.

1844	..	..	..	..	..	20/–	50/–	£7

3191 Quarter-farthing (for use in Ceylon). ℞ Value.

1839	..	65/–	£7	1852	..	45/–	£5
1851	..	75/–	£8	1853	..	80/–	£9

For further details and varieties of this series see:—
British Copper Coins and Their Values
Hard covers, *price 15/–*

246

3192 Penny. R Britannia.

3192A — — H (Ralph Heaton & Sons, Birmingham) below date

	F	VF	EF			F	VF	EF
1860 ..	20/–	60/–	£8		1877 ..	10/–	35/–	£6
1861 ..	10/6	45/–	£7		1878 ..	20/–	70/–	£12
1862 ..	10/–	30/–	£5		1879 ..	8/6	27/6	£5
1863 ..	10/–	30/–	£5		1880 ..	15/–	50/–	£9
1864 ..	32/6	£6	£25		1881 ..	35/–	90/–	£15
1865 ..	20/–	70/–	£12		1881 H ..	12/6	35/–	£6
1866 ..	15/–	50/–	£8		1882 H ..	7/6	30/–	£5
1867 ..	20/–	60/–	£9		1883 ..	7/6	35/–	£6
1868 ..	32/6	£7	£30		1884 ..	7/6	30/–	£5
1869 ..	£15	£75			1885 ..	4/–	25/–	£5
1870 ..	30/–	£6	£20		1886 ..	5/–	30/–	£5
1871 ..	50/–	£9	£35		1887 ..	5/–	35/–	£5
1872 ..	10/–	40/–	£7		1888 ..	5/–	35/–	£5
1873 ..	10/–	35/–	£6		1889 ..	5/–	35/–	£5
1874 ..	12/6	40/–	£7		1890 ..	3/6	20/–	65/–
1874 H ..	8/6	40/–	£7		1891 ..	3/6	20/–	65/–
1875 ..	10/6	35/–	£6		1892 ..	3/6	20/–	65/–
1875 H ..	60/–	£9	£35		1893 ..	3/6	20/–	65/–
1876 H ..	10/–	30/–	£5		1894 ..	10/6	50/–	£8

3193

Victoria Bronze

3193 Halfpenny. ℞ Britannia.

3193A — — H below date.

	F	VF	EF		F	VF	EF
1860 ..	6/-	17/6	45/-	1877 ..	9/-	25/-	80/-
1861 ..	5/-	10/6	30/-	1878 ..	20/-	45/-	£7
1862 ..	5/-	15/-	40/-	1879 ..	8/-	20/-	60/-
1863 ..	12/6	30/-	£5	1880 ..	10/-	30/-	85/-
1864 ..	12/6	30/-	£5	1881 ..	15/-	35/-	95/-
1865 ..	15/-	35/-	£6	1881 H..	15/-	35/-	95/-
1866 ..	10/-	25/-	90/-	1882 H..	7/6	20/-	60/-
1867 ..	20/-	50/-	£7	1883 ..	10/-	30/-	85/-
1868 ..	15/-	45/-	£6	1884 ..	5/-	15/-	45/-
1869 ..	32/6	80/-	£12	1885 ..	5/-	15/-	45/-
1870 ..	15/-	40/-	£6	1886 ..	5/-	15/-	45/-
1871 ..	£10	£30	£100	1887 ..	3/-	12/6	35/-
1872 ..	15/-	40/-	£6	1888 ..	5/-	15/-	40/-
1873 ..	15/-	40/-	£6	1889 ..	4/-	15/-	40/-
1874 ..	21/-	50/-	£8	1890 ..	2/6	12/6	35/-
1874 H..	10/-	25/-	80/-	1891 ..	3/6	12/6	35/-
1875 ..	7/6	15/-	40/-	1892 ..	10/-	35/-	90/-
1875 H..	21/-	50/-	£7	1893 ..	3/6	12/6	35/-
1876 H..	7/6	22/6	65/-	1894 ..	12/6	35/-	£5

3194   3195

3194 Farthing. ℞ Britannia.

3194A — — H below date.

	F	VF	EF		F	VF	EF
1860 ..		5/-	17/6	1879 ..		6/-	18/6
1861 ..		6/-	18/6	1880 ..	6/-	17/6	40/-
1862 ..		7/6	20/-	1881 ..		5/-	15/-
1863 ..	£5	£12	£35	1881 H..	7/6	17/6	40/-
1864 ..	5/-	15/-	32/6	1882 H..	6/-	15/-	35/-
1865 ..		7/6	21/-	1883 ..	10/6	27/6	70/-
1866 ..		4/6	17/6	1884 ..		5/-	17/6
1867 ..	3/-	8/6	20/-	1885 ..		5/-	16/-
1868 ..	5/-	12/6	30/-	1886 ..		5/-	14/-
1869 ..	8/-	20/-	50/-	1887 ..	5/-	15/-	35/-
1872 ..	8/-	20/-	50/-	1888 ..	4/-	10/6	25/-
1873 ..		6/-	17/6	1890 ..	4/-	10/6	25/-
1874 H..		10/6	25/-	1891 ..		4/6	10/6
1875 ..	50/-	£5	£12	1892 ..	12/6	60/-	£7
1875 H..	3/-	7/6	18/6	1893 ..		5/-	15/-
1876 H..	22/6	80/-	£10	1894 ..		7/6	20/-
1878 ..		6/-	17/6	1895 ..	45/-	£8	£20

Victoria Bronze

3195 Third-farthing (for use in Malta). R Value.

	F	VF	EF			F	VF	EF
1866	7/-	17/-	40/-	1881	..	7/6	20/-	50/-
1868	6/-	15/-	35/-	1884	..	6/-	15/-	35/-
1876	7/6	20/-	50/-	1885	..	6/-	15/-	35/-
1878	7/-	17/6	40/-					

Old head issue

3196 Penny. R Britannia.

	F	VF	EF			F	VF	EF
1895	6/-	15/-	40/-	1899	..	3/-	10/6	30/-
1896	3/-	10/6	30/-	1900	..	3/-	10/6	30/-
1897	3/-	10/6	30/-	1901	..	2/-	6/-	17/6
1898	5/-	17/6	50/-					

3197 Halfpenny. Type as Penny. R Britannia.

	F	VF	EF			F	VF	EF
1895	5/-	15/-	40/-	1899	..	3/-	10/6	30/-
1896	3/-	10/6	30/-	1900	..	3/-	10/6	30/-
1897	3/-	10/6	30/-	1901	..	2/-	6/-	17/6
1898	3/-	15/-	40/-					

3198 Farthing. R Britannia. Bright finish.

	F	VF	EF			F	VF	EF
1895	3/-	7/6	22/6	1897	..	4/-	10/6	30/-
1896	2/-	5/-	17/6					

3199 — — Black finish.

	F	VF	EF			F	VF	EF
1897	..	..	5/6	12/6	1900	..	..	3/6	10/6
1898	..	..	7/-	20/-	1901	..	..	3/-	8/6
1899	..	..	3/6	10/6					

EDWARD VII, 1901-10

Crowns, five pound pieces and two pound pieces were only issued in 1902. A branch of the Royal Mint was opened at Ottawa and coined sovereigns of imperial type from 1908.

GOLD

		VF	EF
3200 Five pounds. ℞ St. George, 1902 ..		£80	£110
3201 Two pounds. Similar, 1902		£42	£55

3202

3202 Sovereign. ℞ St. George.

	VF	EF			VF	EF
1902 ..	.. 95/–	£8	1906 ..	.. 95/–	£7
1903 ..	.. 95/–	£7	1907 ..	.. 90/–	£6
1904 ..	.. 95/–	£7	1908 ..	.. 90/–	£6
1905 ..	.. 95/–	£7	1909 ..	.. 90/–	£6
			1910 ..	.. 90/–	£6

3203 — — c on ground for Ottawa mint.

	VF	EF			VF	EF
1908 c ..	.. £225	£350	1910 c ..	.. £22	£30
1909 c ..	.. £22	£30			

3204   Sovereign.   ℞   St. George.   M on ground for Melbourne mint.

	VF	EF		VF	EF
1902 M..	.. 90/–	£6	1907 M..	.. 90/–	£6
1903 M..	.. 90/–	£6	1908 M..	.. 90/–	£6
1904 M..	.. 90/–	£6	1909 M..	.. 90/–	£6
1905 M..	.. 90/–	£6	1910 M..	.. 90/–	£6
1906 M..	.. 90/–	£6			

3205   — —   P on ground for Perth mint.

1902 P..	.. 90/–	£6	1907 P..	.. 90/–	£6
1903 P..	.. 90/–	£6	1908 P..	.. 90/–	£6
1904 P..	.. 90/–	£6	1909 P..	.. 90/–	£6
1905 P..	.. 90/–	£6	1910 P..	.. 90/–	£6
1906 P..	.. 90/–	£6			

3206   — —   S on ground for Sydney mint.

1902 S..	.. £5	£7	1907 S..	.. £5	£7
1903 S..	.. £5	£7	1908 S..	.. £5	£7
1904 S..	.. £7	£10	1909 S..	.. £5	£7
1905 S..	.. £5	£7	1910 S..	.. £5	£7
1906 S..	.. £5	£7			

3207   Half-sovereign.   ℞   St. George.

1902	..	.. 65/–	85/–	1907	..	.. 60/–	75/–
1903	..	.. 60/–	75/–	1908	..	.. 60/–	75/–
1904	..	.. 65/–	85/–	1909	..	.. 60/–	75/–
1905	..	.. 60/–	75/–	1910	..	.. 60/–	75/–
1906	..	.. 60/–	75/–				

3208   — —   M on ground for Melbourne mint.

1906 M..	.. £7	£11	1908 M..	.. £5	£8
1907 M..	.. £6	£9	1909 M..	.. £5	£7

3208A   — —   P on ground for Perth mint.

1904 P..	.. £10	£15	1909 P..	.. £10	£15
1908 P..	.. £13	£25			

3209   — —   S on ground for Sydney mint.

1902 S..	.. £7	£10	1908 S..	.. 90/–	£7
1903 S..	.. £6	£9	1910 S..	.. 90/–	£7
1906 S..	.. £5	£8			

SILVER

		F	*VF*	*EF*
3210 Crown. ℞ St. George, 1902

	F	*VF*	*EF*
	£5	£12	£30

3211 Halfcrown. ℞ Shield in Garter.

		F	*VF*	*EF*			*F*	*VF*	*EF*
					1906	..	45/-	90/-	£10
1902	..	42/-	90/-	£10	1907	..	50/-	£5	£12
1903	..	£12	£25	£50	1908	..	50/-	£5	£12
1904	..	£10	£20	£45	1909	..	50/-	£5	£12
*1905	..	£40	£125	£225	1910	..	45/-	90/-	£10

* Worth much less if in only *fair* condition. Beware of counterfeits of this date.

3212   3213

Edward VII Silver

3212 Florin. ℞ Britannia standing.

	F	VF	EF			F	VF	EF
1902	.. 30/–	80/–	£9	1907	..	32/6	90/–	£10
1903	.. 32/6	90/–	£10	1908	..	40/–	£5	£12
1904	.. 40/–	£5	£12	1909	..	40/–	£5	£12
1905	.. 40/–	£5	£12	1910	..	32/6	90/–	£10
1906	.. 32/6	90/–	£10					

3213 Shilling. ℞ Lion on crown.

	F	VF	EF			F	VF	EF
1902	.. 16/–	35/–	85/–	1907	..	16/–	35/–	85/–
1903	.. 25/–	60/–	£7	1908	..	25/–	60/–	£7
1904	.. 25/–	60/–	£7	1909	..	16/–	35/–	85/–
1905	.. 40/–	£5	£12	1910	..	15/–	30/–	75/–
1906	.. 15/–	30/–	75/–					

3214 Sixpence. ℞ Value in wreath.

	F	VF	EF			F	VF	EF
1902	.. 10/–	25/–	50/–	1907	..	10/–	27/6	60/–
1903	.. 10/–	27/6	60/–	1908	..	15/–	37/6	85/–
1904	.. 15/–	37/6	85/–	1909	..	10/–	27/6	60/–
1905	.. 10/–	27/6	60/–	1910	..	10/–	22/6	45/–
1906	.. 10/–	27/6	60/–					

3215 Threepence. As Maundy but dull finish.

	VF	EF			VF	EF
1902	.. .. 12/6	30/–	1907	.. ..	12/6	30/–
1903	.. .. 12/6	30/–	1908	.. ..	10/6	25/–
1904	.. .. 12/6	30/–	1909	.. ..	12/6	30/–
1905	.. .. 12/6	30/–	1910	.. ..	12/6	30/–
1906	.. .. 12/6	30/–				

3216 Maundy set (4d, 3d, 2d and 1d.)

	EF	FDC			EF	FDC
1902	.. .. £9	£12	1907	.. ..	£8	£10
1903	.. .. £8	£10	1908	.. ..	£8	£10
1904	.. .. £8	£10	1909	.. ..	£12	£15
1905	.. .. £8	£10	1910	.. ..	£12	£15
1906	.. .. £8	£10				

			EF	FDC
3217	— **fourpence**, 1902-10, *from*	.. ..	30/–	40/–
3318	— **threepence**, 1902-10, *from*	.. ..	80/–	£5
3219	— **twopence**, 1902-10, *from*	.. ..	25/–	35/–
3220	— **penny**, 1902-10, *from* ..	.. ..	25/–	35/–

3221 Penny. ℞ Britannia.

	F	VF	EF			F	VF	EF
1902	3/–	12/6	50/–	1907	..	4/–	12/6	50/–
1903	5/–	15/–	60/–	1908	..	5/–	15/–	55/–
1904	10/6	30/–	90/–	1909	..	7/6	25/–	80/–
1905	7/6	25/–	75/–	1910	..	4/–	10/6	45/–
1906	5/–	17/6	65/–					

3222 Halfpenny. ℞ Britannia.

	F	VF	EF			F	VF	EF
1902	3/6	12/6	30/–	1907	..	5/–	15/–	40/–
1903	5/–	15/–	40/–	1908	..	4/–	12/6	35/–
1904	7/6	20/–	50/–	1909	..	5/–	15/–	40/–
1905	5/–	15/–	40/–	1910	..	5/–	17/6	50/–
1906	5/–	15/–	40/–					

3223   3224

3223 Farthing. ℞ Britannia. Blackened finish.

1902	..		4/6	15/–	1907	..	4/–	15/–
1903	..		5/–	17/6	1908	..	5/–	17/6
1904	..	3/–	12/6	30/–	1909	..	3/6	15/–
1905	..		5/–	17/6	1910	.. 6/–	15/–	40/–
1906	..		5/–	17/6				

3224 Third-farthing (for use in Malta). ℞ Value,

                                                 6/–   15/–

GEORGE V, 1910-36

Paper money issued by the Treasury during the first World War replaced gold for internal use after 1915; but the branch mints in Australia and South Africa (the gold producing countries) continued striking sovereigns until 1930-32. Owing to the steep rise in the price of silver in 1919/20 the issue of standard (.925) silver was discontinued and coins of .500 silver were minted.

In 1912, 1918 and 1919, some pennies were made under contract by private mints in Birmingham. In 1918, as half-sovereigns were no longer being minted, farthings were again issued with the ordinary bright bronze finish. Crown pieces had not been issued for general circulation but they were struck in small numbers about Christmas time for people to give as presents in the years 1927-36, and in 1935 a special commemorative crown was issued in celebration of the Silver Jubilee.

GOLD

				FDC
3225	**Five pounds.**	℞	St. George, 1911 (Proof only)	£275
3226	**Two pounds.**	℞	St. George, 1911 (Proof only)	£125

3227 Sovereign. ℞ St. George.

	VF	EF		VF		VF	EF
1911	..	..	95/–	1915	..	..	£5
1912	..	..	90/–	1916*	..	.. £65	£100
1913	..	..	90/–	1917*	..	.. £140	£200
1914	..	..	90/–	1925	..	..	£6

Forgeries exist of these dates as of other dates of London and of other mints.

George V   Gold

3228   Sovereign.   ℞   St. George.   C on ground for the Ottawa mint.

	VF	EF		VF	EF
1911 C ..	..	£6	1917 C ..	..	£8
1913 C ..	.. £200	£250	1918 C ..	..	£8
1914 C ..	.. £22	£28	1919 C ..	..	£9
1916 C *Extremely rare.*					

3228	3229	3240A

3229   — —   I on ground for Indian mint, 1918 ..   ..   £6

3230   — —   M on ground for Melbourne mint.

1911 M..	..	£7	1920 M ? exists.		
1912 M..	..	£6	1921 M ? exists.		
1913 M..	..	£8	1922 M ? exists.		
1914 M..	..	£8	1923 M *Very rare.*		
1915 M..	..	£8	1924 M *Very rare.*		
1916 M..	.. £11	£18	1925 M ..	..	£6
1917 M..	..	£8	1926 M ..	.. £9	£12
1918 M..	.. £7	£10	1927 M ? exists.		
1919 M..	.. £14	£20	1928 M *Very rare.*		

3231   — —   small head.

1929 M	.. £11	£15	1931 M ..	.. £13	£20
1930 M	.. £11	£15			

3232   — —   P on ground for Perth mint.

1911 P..	..	£7	1920 P..	.. £7	£10
1912 P..	..	£7	1921 P..	.. £8	£11
1913 P..	..	£7	1922 P..	.. £7	£10
1914 P..	..	£9	1923 P..	.. £9	£13
1915 P..	.. £8	£13	1924 P..	.. £13	£20
1916 P..	.. £8	£13	1925 P..	.. £13	£20
1917 P..	.. £7	£10	1926 P..	.. £15	£25
1918 P..	..	£9	1927 P..	.. £10	£14
1919 P..	.. £7	£10	1928 P..	.. £9	£13

3233   — — —   small head.

1929 P..	.. £8	£12	1931 P..	.. £9	£13
1930 P .	.. £9	£13			

3234 Sovereign. ℞ St. George's. on ground for Sydney mint.

	VF	EF		VF	EF
1911 s ..	..	£8	1919 s ..	.. £12	£20
1912 s ..	..	£7	1920 s *Extremely rare.*		
1913 s ..	..	£7	1921 s ..	.. £15	£25
1914 s ..	..	£7	1922 s *Extremely rare.*		
1915 s ..	..	£8	1923 s *Extremely rare.*		
1916 s ..	.. £8	£12	1924 s *Extremely rare.*		
1917 s ..	..	£8	1925 s ..	.. £7	£10
1918 s ..	..	£8	1926 s ..	.. £25	£45

3235 — — SA on ground for Pretoria mint.

1924 SA	*Extremely rare.*		1927 SA	..	.. £5
1925 SA	..	.. 95/–	1928 SA	..	.. £5
1926 SA	..	.. 95/–			

3236 — — — small head.

1929 SA	..	.. £5	1931 SA	..	.. £6
1930 SA	..	.. £5	1932 SA	..	.. £7

3237 Half-sovereign. ℞ St. George.

1911 ..	..	.. 67/6	1914 ..	..	.. 62/6
1912 ..	..	.. 65/–	1915 ..	..	.. 70/–
1913 ..	..	.. 65/–			

3238 — — M on ground for Melbourne mint

1915 M	..	..	..	..	..	..	.. £7

3239 — — P on ground for Perth mint.

1911 P ..	..	.. £8	1918 P ?	
1915 P ..	..	.. £6		

3240 — — S on ground for Sydney mint.

1911 s ..	..	.. £6	1915 s ..	..	.. 85/–
1912 s ..	..	.. £5/10/–	1916 s ..	..	.. £7
1914 s ..	..	.. 95/–			

3240A — — SA on ground for Pretoria mint.

1925 SA	..	.. 80/–	1926 SA	..	.. 80/–

George V

First coinage. Sterling silver (.925 fine).

3241 Halfcrown. ℞ Crowned shield in Garter.

	VF	EF		VF	EF
1911	15/–	40/–	1916	13/6	32/6
1912	15/–	40/–	1917	13/6	32/6
1913	30/–	75/–	1918	13/6	32/6
1914	15/–	40/–	1919	13/6	32/6
1915	13/6	32/6			

3242 Florin. ℞ Cruciform shields.

1911	12/6	27/6	1916	10/–	25/–
1912	12/–	30/–	1917	12/–	30/–
1913	12/–	30/–	1918	10/–	25/–
1914	10/–	25/–	1919	10/–	25/–
1915	12/–	30/–			

3243 Shilling. ℞ Lion on crown, inner circles

1911	10/–	25/–	1916	8/6	20/–
1912	8/6	20/–	1917	8/6	20/–
1913	15/–	38/–	1918	8/6	25/–
1914	10/–	25/–	1919	10/–	25/–
1915	8/6	20/–			

3244 Sixpence. ℞ Similar.

	VF	EF			VF	EF
1911	7/–	16/–	1916		7/–	16/–
1912	7/–	16/–	1917		8/–	21/–
1913	10/–	25/–	1918		7/–	16/–
1914	7/–	16/–	1919		7/–	16/–
1915	7/–	16/–	1920		7/–	16/–

3245 Threepence. As Maundy but dull finish.
1911 to 1915, each .. 7/6   1916 to 1920, each .. 6/–

		EF	FDC
3246 Maundy set (4d., 3d., 2d. and 1d.).			
1911 to 1920. Uniform dates .. .. *each set*	£12/10/–	£15	
3247 — fourpence, 1911-1920	40/–	50/–	
3248 — threepence, 1911-1920	£5	£6	
3249 — twopence, 1911-1920	35/–	42/6	
3250 — penny, 1911-1920	35/–	42/6	

Second coinage. Debased silver (.500 fine). Types as before.

		VF	EF
3251 Halfcrown, 1920 to 1926, each		15/–	45/–

3252 Florin

	VF	EF			VF	EF
1920	15/–	40/–	1923 ..	..	12/6	30/–
1921	12/6	30/–	1924 ..	..	15/–	40/–
1922	15/–	40/–	1925 ..	..	15/–	40/–
			1926 ..	..	15/–	40/–

3253 Shilling.

	VF	EF			VF	EF
1920	7/–	21/–	1924 ..	..	10/–	32/6
1921	8/–	25/–	1925 ..	..	10/–	32/6
1922	8/–	25/–	1926 ..	..	8/–	25/–
1923	8/–	25/–				

3254 Sixpence.

	VF	EF			VF	EF
1920	12/6	27/6	1923 ..	..	7/–	17/6
1921	10/–	22/6	1924 ..	..	5/–	12/6
1922	10/–	22/6	1925 ..	..	5/–	12/6

3255 — new beading and broader rim, 1925, 1926   10/–   32/6

George V Silver

3256 Threepence. As Maundy but dull finish.

	VF	EF		VF	EF
1920, 1921	.. 2/6	7/6	1922, 1925, 1926	4/–	12/6

3257 Maundy set (4d., 3d., 2d. and 1d.).

				EF	FDC
1921 to 1927. Uniform dates	..	..	..	£14	£17/10/–
3258 — fourpence, 1921-7	..	..	..	50/–	60/–
3259 — threepence, 1921-7	..	..	..	£5	£6
3260 — twopence, 1921-7	..	..	..	50/–	60/–
3261 — penny, 1921-7 ..	..	..	..	50/–	60/–

Third coinage. As before but **modified effigy.**
The BM on truncation is in a new place, nearer
to the back of the neck and without stops;
beading is more pronounced.

3262 Halfcrown

	VF	EF				VF	EF
1926 ..	.. 27/6	80/–	1927		..	22/6	60/–
3263 Shilling, 1926, 1927, each				..	..	15/–	45/–
3264 Sixpence, 1926, 1927, each				..	..	12/6	32/6
3265 Threepence, 1926		..		..	..	10/–	25/–

Fourth coinage. New types, 1927-35.

3266 Crown. ℞ Crown in wreath.

1927 (Proof only) *FDC* £40

			VF	EF				VF	EF
					1931	..	..	£18	£32
1928	..	..	£17	£30	1932	..	..	£30	£50
1929	..	..	£18	£32	1933	..	..	£15	£27
1930	..	..	£18	£32	1934	..	..	£125	£220

3267 Halfcrown. ℞ Shield.

	F	VF	EF				VF	EF
1928	..	10/–	25/–	1932	..	..	12/6	32/6
1929	..	10/–	25/–	1933	..	..	12/6	32/6
1930	.. 60/–	£6	£20	1934	..	..	12/6	32/6
1931	..	12/6	32/6	1935	..	..	10/–	25/–

3268 Florin. ℞ Cruciform sceptres, shield in each angle.

1927 (Proof only) *FDC* £10

	VF	EF				VF	EF
			1931	..	..	10/6	32/6
1928	.. .. 9/–	25/–	1932	..	..	20/–	45/–
1929	.. .. 9/–	35/–	1933	..	..	10/6	32/6
1930	.. .. 9/–	35/–	1935	..	..	9/–	25/–

3269 Shilling. ℞ Lion on crown, no inner circles.

1927	..	..	.. 22/6	1932	..	..	.. 14/–
1928	..	..	.. 14/–	1933	..	..	.. 14/–
1929	..	..	.. 14/–	1934	..	..	.. 30/–
1930	..	..	.. 30/–	1935	..	..	.. 14/–
1931	..	..	.. 22/6				

3270 3272

3270 Sixpence. ℞ Three oak sprigs with six acorns.

	EF
1928, 1929, 1930, each	10/-

3271 — — closer milling

	VF	EF					EF
1931 ..	..	8/-	1934 ..	..	..	12/6
1932 ..	..	8/-	1935 ..	..	..	8/-
1933 ..	..	8/-				

3272 Threepence. ℞ Three oak sprigs with three acorns.

1927 (Proof only) FDC £25	1930 ..	..	..	10/6
VF EF	1931-5	..	..	4/-
1928 .. .. 7/6 20/-				

3273 Maundy set. As earlier sets.

	EF	FDC
1928 to 1934, each	£14	£17/10/-
1935	£20	£25

3274 — fourpence, 1928-1935 ..	..	..	50/-	60/-
3275 — threepence, 1928-1935	..	..	£5	£6
3276 — twopence, 1928-1935 ..	..	..	45/-	55/-
3277 — penny, 1928-1935	..	..	45/-	55/-

Jubilee issue, 1935.

		VF	EF
3278 Crown. ℞ St. George ..	.. ..	30/-	70/-

BRONZE

3279 Penny. ℞ Britannia.

3280 — — H (The Mint, Birmingham, Ltd.) to l. of date.

3281 — — KN (King's Norton Metal Co.) to l. of date.

	F	VF	EF		F	VF	EF
1911	3/–	12/6	35/–	1918 H	7/6	40/–	£8
1912	2/6	10/–	30/–	1918 KN	15/–	80/–	£25
1912 H	4/–	30/–	£6	1919		7/6	35/–
1913		10/6	35/–	1919 H	10/6	40/–	£8
1914		10/6	35/–	1919 KN	16/–	90/–	£35
1915		12/6	40/–	1920		6/–	25/–
1916		10/6	35/–	1921		6/–	25/–
1917		12/6	40/–	1922	3/–	10/6	40/–
1918		12/6	40/–	1926	6/–	25/–	70/–

3282 — — modified effigy.

	F	VF	EF		F	VF	EF
1926	35/–	85/–	£15	1927		5/–	22/6

3283 — — small head.

			F	VF	EF			F	VF	EF
1928			4/–	20/–		1932	3/6	12/6	50/–
1929			4/–	20/–		1934	2/6	10/–	40/–
1930			5/–	25/–		1935		4/–	20/–
1931			6/–	30/–					

3284 Halfpenny. ℞ Britannia.

	F	VF	EF				VF	EF
1911	..		10/6	30/–	1919	..	.. 7/6	25/–
1912	..		7/6	25/–	1920	..	.. 8/6	27/6
1913	..	7/6	20/–	60/–	1921	..	.. 8/6	27/6
1914	..		7/6	25/–	1922	..	.. 8/6	27/6
1915	..		7/6	25/–	1923	..	.. 8/6	27/6
1916	..		7/6	25/–	1924	..	.. 8/6	27/6
1917	..		7/6	25/–	1925	..	.. 12/6	40/–
1918	..		7/6	25/–				

3285 — — modified effigy.

		VF	EF				VF	EF
1925	..	.. 12/6	32/6	1927	..	.. 11/–	35/–
1926	..	.. 13/6	35/–				

3286 — — small head.

		VF	EF				VF	EF
1928	..	.. 6/–	25/–	1932	..	.. 3/6	17/6
1929	..	.. 3/6	17/6	1933	..	.. 3/6	17/6
1930	..	.. 3/6	17/6	1934	..	.. 5/–	25/–
1931	..	.. 3/6	17/6	1935	..	.. 4/6	20/–

3287   3290

3287 Farthing. ℞ Britannia. Blackened finish.

1911	..	.. 5/–	15/–	1915	..	.. 8/6	25/–
1912	..	.. 4/–	12/6	1916	..	.. 4/–	10/6
1913	..	.. 7/6	17/6	1917	..	.. 5/–	12/6
1914	..	.. 6/–	15/–				

3288 — — Bright finish. 1918-1925 .. .. 4/– 15/–

George V Bronze

3289 Farthing. ℞ Britannia. Modified effigy.

		VF	EF				VF	EF
1926	..	.. 3/6	10/6	1931	..	..	3/-	8/6
1927	..	.. 3/6	10/6	1932	..	..	2/6	7/6
1928	..	.. 3/6	10/6	1933	..	..	3/-	8/6
1929	..	.. 3/-	8/6	1934	..	..	5/-	12/6
1930	..	.. 3/6	10/6	1935	..	..	7/6	20/-

3290 Third-farthing (for use in Malta). ℞
Value, 1913 ..   ..   10/6   25/-

EDWARD VIII, 1936
(Now Duke of Windsor)

No coins were issued for currency in England bearing the name or portrait of Edward VIII. As George V died early in January, probably all the coins bearing the date 1936 were struck during the reign of Edward.

George V posthumous. Types as last issue of George V with his name and portrait but dated 1936.

					VF	EF
3291 SILVER. **Crown,** 1936	..	..	..		£32	£55
3292 — **Halfcrown,** 1936	..	..	..			25/-
3293 — **Florin,** 1936	..	..	..			22/6
3294 — **Shilling,** 1936 ..	..	..	..			12/6
3295 — **Sixpence,** 1936 ..	..	..	..			7/6
3296 — **Threepence,** 1936	..	..	..			4/-

				FDC
3297 — **Maundy set** (4d., 3d., 2d. and 1d.), 1936	..			£30

				VF	EF
3298 BRONZE. **Penny,** 1936	..	..	..	3/6	12/6
3299 — **Halfpenny,** 1936	..	..	..	6/-	20/-
3300 — **Farthing,** 1936	..	..	..	4/-	8/6

Edward VIII portrait

3301 NICKEL BRASS. **Threepence,** dodecagonal. His own name and portrait. ℞. Thrift, 1937. Although dated 1937 some were struck in 1936 in preparation for issue the next year but owing to the King's abdication were mostly melted up. A few, however, did get into circulation. *Exceedingly rare*

GEORGE VI, 1936-52

Though they were at first issued concurrently, the twelve-sided nickel-brass threepence superseded the small silver threepence in 1942. Two different shillings were issued; one, the " Scottish " shilling, has the Scottish lion seated on a crown and was issued as a compliment to the Scottish ancestry of Queen Elizabeth, now Queen Mother. In 1947, as silver was needed to repay the bullion lent by the U.S.A. during the war, silver coins were replaced by coins of the same type and weight made of cupro-nickel. In 1949, after India had attained independence, the title *Indiae Imperator* was dropped from the coinage. Commemorative crown pieces were issued for the Coronation and the 1951 Festival of Britain.

First issue   *FDC*

3302 GOLD. **Five pounds** ℞ St. George, 1937. Proof only

£165

3303 — **Two pounds.** Similar £80

3304 — **Sovereign.** Similar £50

3305 — **Half-sovereign.** Similar £25

3306

266

George VI   First Issue

3306 SILVER (.500 fine). **Crown.** ℞ Shield   *VF*   *EF*
with supporters, 1937 ..   ..   ..   50/–   £6

3307 — Halfcrown. ℞ Shield.

	EF		*EF*		
1937 ..	17/6	1941 .. 17/6		1944 ..	17/6
1938 ..	25/–	1942 .. 17/6		1945 ..	16/–
1939 ..	25/–	1943 .. 17/6		1946 ..	16/–
1940 ..	17/6				

3308 — Florin. ℞ Crowned rose, etc.

1937 ..	15/–	1941 ..	15/–	1944 ..	13/6
1938 ..	22/6	1942 ..	15/–	1945 ..	13/6
1939 ..	22/6	1943 ..	13/6	1946 ..	13/6
1940 ..	15/–				

3309 — Shilling. "English." ℞. Lion over crown.

1937 ..	11/–	1941 ..	11/–	1944 ..	10/–
1938 ..	15/–	1942 ..	11/–	1945 ..	10/–
1939 ..	15/–	1943 ..	10/–	1946 ..	10/–
1940 ..	11/–				

3310 — — "Scottish." ℞. Lion seated facing on crown, etc.

1937 ..	12/6	1941 ..	12/6	1944 ..	11/–
1938 ..	16/–	1942 ..	12/6	1945 ..	11/–
1939 ..	16/–	1943 ..	12/6	1946 ..	11/–
1940 ..	12/6				

George VI First Issue

3311   3312

3311   SILVER.   (500 fine).   **Sixpence.**   R.   GRI crowned.

	EF			EF			EF
1937	.. 7/6		1941	.. 6/–		1944	.. 6/–
1938	.. 10/6		1942	.. 6/–		1945	.. 6/–
1939	.. 10/6		1943	.. 6/–		1946	.. 6/–
1940	.. 7/6						

3312 — **Threepence.**   R.   Shield on rose.

	F	VF	EF		F	VF	EF
1937	..		5/–	1941	..	2/–	5/–
1938	..		6/–	1942	..	5/– 10/6	25/–
1939	.. 2/–	7/6	17/6	1943	..	8/– 17/6	35/–
1940	..	2/–	5/–	1944	..	10/6 20/–	50/–

3313 — **Maundy set.** Uniform dates.

			FDC
1937 to 1946	..	..	£15
3314 — — **fourpence,** 1937-1946, *from*	..	..	55/–
3315 — — **threepence,** 1937-1946, *from*	..	..	55/–
3316 — — **twopence,** 1937-1946, *from*	..	..	55/–
3317 — — **penny,** 1937-1946, *from* ..	..	..	55/–

3318   3342

3318   NICKEL BRASS.   **Threepence** (dodecagonal).   R.   Thrift.

	VF	EF		F	VF	EF
1937	.. .. 3/–	10/6	1943	..	2/6	10/6
1938	.. .. 7/6	30/–	1944	..	2/6	10/6
1939	.. .. 6/–	20/–	1945	..	4/–	12/6
1940	.. .. 4/–	17/6	1946	.. 8/6	40/–	£10
1941	.. .. 2/6	10/6	1948	..	5/–	20/–
1942	.. .. 2/6	10/6				

3319 BRONZE. **Penny.** ℞. Britannia.

	VF	EF					EF
1937	..	..	12/6	1945	..	..	..	8/6
1938	..	..	20/–	1946	..	..	..	15/–
1939	..	..	25/–	1947	..	..	..	7/6
1940	..	.. 7/6	30/–	1948	..	..	..	7/6
1944	..	..	10/6				

3320   3344

3320 — **Halfpenny.** ℞. Ship.

1937	..	10/6	1941	..	8/6	1945	..	8/6
1938	..	12/6	1942	..	6/–	1946	..	25/–
1939	..	12/6	1943	..	8/6	1947	..	7/6
1940	..	15/–	1944	..	8/6	1948	..	7/6

3321 — **Farthing.** ℞. Wren.

1937	..	5/–	1941	..	3/6	1945	..	3/–
1938	..	10/6	1942	..	5/–	1946	..	3/–
1939	..	3/–	1943	..	3/–	1947	..	3/–
1940	..	6/–	1944	..	3/–	1948	..	3/–

Second issue. Types as before but change of metal.

		EF	Unc.
3322	CUPRO-NICKEL. **Halfcrown,** 1947, 1948	15/–	18/6
3323	— **Florin,** 1947, 1948	12/6	16/–
3324	— **Shilling,** " English," 1947, 1948 ..	7/6	10/–
3325	— — " Scottish," 1947, 1948 ..	7/6	10/–
3326	— **Sixpence,** 1947, 1948	5/–	7/–

		FDC
3327	SILVER (.925 fine). **Maundy set.** Uniform dates, 1947, 1948	£16
3328	— — — **fourpence,** 1947, 1948	60/–
3329	— — — **threepence,** 1947, 1948	60/–
3330	— — — **twopence,** 1947, 1948	60/–
3331	— — — **penny,** 1947, 1948	60/–

George VI   Third Issue

Third issue.   Types as before but title IND. IMP. omitted.

	EF	Unc.		EF	Unc.
3332 CUPRO-NICKEL. **Halfcrown**					
1949	12/-	15/-	1951	10/-	12/6
1950	10/-	12/6	1952 *Extr. rare*		
3333 — Florin					
1949	9/-	11/-	1950, 1951 ..	8/-	10/-
3334 — Shilling, " English "					
1949	7/6	9/-	1950, 1951 ..	6/-	7/6
3335 — — " Scottish "					
1949	7/6	9/-	1950, 1951 ..	6/-	7/6

	EF	Unc.		EF	Unc.
3336 — Sixpence					
1949	4/6	6/-	1951	3/6	5/-
1950	3/6	5/-	1952 *VF* 10/6	35/-	60/-

3337 SILVER (.925) **Maundy set** (4d., 3d., 2d. and 1d.)

			FDC				FDC
1949 ..	..	..	£17	1951 ..	..	..	£17
1950 ..	..	..	£17	1952 ..	..	..	£25

The 1952 Maundy was distributed by Elizabeth II.

3338 — fourpence, 1949-1952, *from*	65/-
3339 — threepence, 1949-1952, *from*	65/-
3340 — twopence, 1949-1952, *from*	65/-
3341 — penny, 1949-1952, *from*	65/-

3342 NICKEL BRASS. **Threepence** (dodecagonal).

	F	VF	EF		VF	EF
1949 ..	20/-	£5	£25	1951	12/6	45/-
1950 ..		10/6	40/-	1952		10/6

3343 BRONZE. **Penny.**

			EF			EF
1949 ..			10/6	1951	90/-	£10
1950 ..		25/-	£8			

3344 — Halfpenny.

1949 ..			8/6	1951		12/6
1950 ..			12/6	1952		8/6

3345   BRONZE **Farthing.**

				EF					EF
1949	..	..	..	6/–	1951	..	..	..	5/–
1950	..	..	..	7/6	1952	..	..	..	6/–

The coins dated 1952 were issued during the reign of Elizabeth II.

Festival of Britain, 1951.

3346   CUPRO-NICKEL.   **Crown.**   ℞   St. George.

						VF	EF	Unc.
1951	..	..	..	..	..	25/–	50/–	70/–

ELIZABETH II, 1952-

A coronation commemorative crown was issued in 1953, and another was struck on the occasion of the 1960 British Exhibition in New York. In 1954 the *Britt. Omn.* was dropped from the Queen's titles owing to the changing status of so many Commonwealth territories. Ten million sovereigns were issued in the years 1957-59 to counteract the activities of continental counterfeiters; these sovereigns were mainly sold on the continental bullion markets and owing to the demand further issues have been made each year since 1962. Owing to rising prices the farthing had become virtually worthless; production of these small coins ceased after 1956 and they were finally demonetized at the end of 1960.

3347   3360

First issue, 1953.

		EF	Unc.
3347 CUPRO-NICKEL. **Crown.** Queen on horseback. ℞ Crown in centre of cross, shield in each angle, 1953		21/-	30/-

3348 — **Halfcrown.** ℞ Crowned shield, 1953   12/6   17/6

Elizabeth II   First Issue

	3349		3362

			EF	*Unc.*
3349	Cupro-Nickel **Florin** ℞ Double rose; etc., 1953		10/6	15/–

	3350	3351

3350	— **Shilling.** "English" ℞ Three leopards in shield, 1953	6/6	10/–
3351	— — "Scottish" ℞ Lion rampart in shield, 1953	6/6	10/–

3352	— **Sixpence.** ℞ Garland, 1953 ..	3/6	5/–

	3353	3366

		EF
3353	Nickel-Brass. **Threepence** (dodecagonal). ℞ Crowned portcullis, 1953	12/6

273

			VF	EF
3354 BRONZE. **Penny.** R Britannia, 1953 ..			6/–	30/–

3355   3367

3355 — Halfpenny. R Ship, 1953 ..   ..   ..   12/6

3356   3368

			EF
3356 — Farthing. R Wren, 1953			7/6
			Unc.
3357 Ordinary set, 1953 (2/6 to ¼d.). Nos. 3348 to 3355 in plastic envelope as issued by the Royal Mint ..			60/–

		FDC
3358 SILVER **Maundy set** (4d., 3d., 2d. and 1d.), 1953		£60

Elizabeth II

Second issue. Types as before (except the sovereign and crown but legend changed, BRIT. OMN. omitted.

		EF
3359	GOLD. **Sovereign.** ℞ St. George, 1957 ..	95/–

3359A — — coarser milling.

	EF				*EF*
1958 ..	..	.. 85/–	1964 ..	..	.. 85/–
1959 ..	..	.. £5/5/–	1965 ..	..	.. 85/–
1962 ..	..	.. 85/–	1966 ..	..	.. 85/–
1963 ..	..	.. 85/–	1967 ..	..	.. 85/–

3360 CUPRO-NICKEL. **Crown.** Bust r. ℞ Cruciform shields, 1960 ..   ..   75/–

3361 — **Halfcrown.**

	Unc.			*Unc.*			*Unc.*	
1954 ..	6/–	1958 ..	5/–	1962 ..	4/6	1966
1955 ..	6/–	1959 ..	5/–	1963 ..	4/6	1967
1956 ..	5/–	1960 ..	4/6	1964 ..	4/6	
1957 ..	5/–	1961 ..	4/6	1965		

We are not putting a value against the coins of the last few years as they can be obtained fairly easily from general circulation. Dealers, however, have to charge a premium when selling them to cover their handling expenses.

3362 — **Florin.**

	Unc.			*Unc.*			*Unc.*	
1954 ..	6/–	1958 ..	4/–	1962 ..	3/6	1966
1955 ..	6/–	1959 ..	4/–	1963 ..	3/6	1967
1956 ..	4/–	1960 ..	3/6	1964 ..	3/6	
1957 ..	4/–	1961 ..	3/6	1965		

3363 — **Shilling** " English ".

	Unc.			*Unc.*			*Unc.*	
1954 ..	3/–	1958 ..	2/6	1962 ..	2/–	1966
1955 ..	3/–	1959 ..	2/6	1963 ..	2/–	
1956 ..	3/–	1960 ..	2/–	1964 ..	2/–	
1957 ..	2/6	1961 ..	2/–	1965		

3364 — — " Scottish ".

	Unc.			*Unc.*				
1954 ..	3/–	1958 ..	2/6	1962 ..	2/–	1966
1955 ..	3/–	1959 ..	20/–	1963 ..	2/–	
1956 ..	3/–	1960 ..	2/–	1964 ..	2/–	
1957 ..	2/6	1961 ..	12/–	1965		

Elizabeth

3365 CUPRO-NICKEL. Sixpence.

	Unc.			Unc.			Unc.	
1954	.. 2/6	1958	.. 2/–	1962	.. 1/6	1966		
1955	.. 2/6	1959	.. 2/–	1963	.. 1/6	1967		
1956	.. 2/6	1960	.. 1/6	1964	.. 1/–			
1957	.. 2/–	1961	.. 1/6	1965				

3366 NICKEL-BRASS. Threepence.

	Unc.			Unc.				
1954	.. 4/–	1958	.. 3/–	1962		1966		
1955	.. 4/–	1959	.. 7/6	1963		1967		
1956	.. 4/–	1960	.. 1/6	1964				
1957	.. 10/–	1961	.. 1/–	1965				

3366A BRONZE. Penny.

	Unc.					
1961	.. 2/–	1963		1965		1967
1962		1964		1966		

3367 — Halfpenny.

	Unc.			Unc.			Unc.	
1954	.. 6/–	1958	.. 5/–	1963	.. 1/6	1967		
1955	.. 6/–	1959	.. 2/6	1964	.. 1/6			
1956	.. 6/–	1960	.. 2/6	1965				
1957	.. 5/–	1962	.. 1/6	1966				

3368 — Farthing.

	Unc.		Unc.		Unc.
1954	.. 7/6	1955	.. 6/–	1956	.. 15/–

3369 SILVER. Maundy set (4d., 3d., 2d. and 1d.).

	FDC			FDC			FDC
1954	.. £22/10/–	1959	.. £22/10/–	1964	.. £22/10/–		
1955	.. £22/10/–	1960	.. £22/10/–	1965	.. £22/10/–		
1956	.. £22/10/–	1961	.. £22/10/–	1966	.. £27/10/–		
1957	.. £22/10/–	1962	.. £22/10/–	1967	.. £27/10/–		
1958	.. £22/10/–	1963	.. £22/10/–				

Churchill Commemorative issue

3369a CUPRO-NICKEL. **Crown,** 1965 R Bust of Churchill *unc.* 6/6

PROOF or SPECIMEN SETS

Issued by the Royal Mint in official case from 1887 onwards, but earlier sets were issued privately by the engraver.

All pieces have a finish superior to that of the current coins.

		No. of coins	FDC
3370	**George IV.** New issue, **1826.** Five pounds to farthing	11	£2250
3371	**William IV.** Coronation, **1831.** Two pounds to farthing	14	£2000
3372	**Victoria,** young head, **1839.** "Una and the Lion" five pounds, and sovereign to farthing	15	£2000
3373	— **1853.** Sovereign to quarter-farthing, including Gothic type crown	16	£2000
3374	Jubilee head. Golden Jubilee, **1887.** Five pounds to threepence	11	£800
3374A	— — Crown to threepence	7	£325
3375	Old head, **1893.** Five pounds to threepence	10	£900
3376	— — Crown to threepence	6	£280
3377	**Edward VII.** Coronation, **1902.** Five pounds to Maundy penny. Matt surface	13	£350
3378	— — Sovereign to Maundy penny. Matt surface	11	£110
3379	**George V.** Coronation, **1911.** Five pounds to Maundy penny	12	£600
3380	— — Sovereign to Maundy penny	10	£150
3381	— — Halfcrown to Maundy penny	8	£80
3382	New types, **1927.** Crown to threepence	6	£65
3383	**George VI.** Coronation, **1937.** Gold. Five pounds to half-sovereign	4	£300
3384	— — — Silver, etc. Crown to farthing, including Maundy	15	£45
3385	Mid-Century, **1950.** Halfcrown to farthing	9	£22
3386	Festival of Britain, **1951.** Crown to farthing	10	£38
3387	**Elizabeth II.** Coronation, **1953.** Crown to farthing	10	£24

NOTE. Exchange Control Order, 1966 No. 438, which came into force on 27th April 1966, prohibits the sale to collectors resident in the U.K. of gold coins dated after 1837, unless they have the necessary Bank of England authorisation.

SEABY'S

NUMISMATIC PUBLICATIONS

STANDARD CATALOGUE OF BRITISH COINS.— ENGLAND AND UNITED KINGDOM, edited by P. J. Seaby. A type catalogue from the time of the Ancient Britons to 1813 and a listing by date from 1816 to 1965. It is pocket-size and has over 750 half-tone illustrations; over 4,750 coins are listed with their values. **1968** edition. 280 pages. 25/-

or separately

    Part 2: British Coins 1816-1966. 72 pages, 213 illustrations, 1,780 coins with values 12/6

BRITISH COPPER COINS AND THEIR VALUES, edited by P. J. Seaby and Monica Bussell

    All dates and main varieties listed; 112 pages, 172 half-tone, and 22 line-block illustrations. 1967/8 edition with revised prices. 15/–

ENGLISH SILVER COINAGE from 1649, by H. A. Seaby (Joint editor P. A. Rayner). The standard work of reference for this series; each type is described and every date and main variety is listed and tabulated for easy reference with the comparative rarity. *New edition in preparation*

TRADE TOKENS ISSUED IN THE SEVENTEENTH CENTURY, ed. by G. C. Williamson (Reprint 1967). A catalogue originally issued in 1889-91; 1,590 pages, 20 plates. The standard work on this series. *Three vols.* £12/10/–

NOTES ON NINETEENTH CENTURY SILVER TOKENS, by A. W. Waters. Supplementary and explanatory notes to Dalton's "Silver Token Coinage, 1811 and 1812." 9.7" ×7.2", 32 pages. 10/6

ROMAN COINS AND THEIR VALUES, by David Sear. (1964) A general catalogue of Roman Coins, listing a selection of 4,312 coins from 268 B.C. to 498 A.D. All denominations, including gold, of every reign are given with standard values. Hundreds of line-block illustrations in the text, map, 8 half-tone plates. 30/-

THE COINAGE OF ROMAN BRITAIN, by Gilbert Askew. (Revised 1967). A history and catalogue of Roman coins relating to Britain and coins struck at Roman mints in this country. Over 900 coins listed, 3 maps, illustrated in text. 17/6

A DICTIONARY OF ROMAN COINS. Republican and Imperial By S. W. Stevenson. Reprint 1965. 928 pages, several hundred illustrations in text. £6

ROMAN SILVER COINS, by H. A. Seaby.

Vol. I. The Republic to Augustus. With valuations. 30/-

Vol. II. Tiberius to Commodus. With valuations.

New edition in preparation

GREEK COINS AND THEIR VALUES, by H. A. Seaby. A catalogue listing over 3,150 coins, with chapters on coin types, weights, denominations, dating, gods and goddesses, maps and alphabets. 30/-

THE COINAGE OF ANCIENT BRITAIN, by R. P. Mack. A reference work on Celtic coinage listing 416 types. Twenty-two plates, 19 maps. Cloth 70/-

COINS AND CHRISTIANITY, by K. A. Jacob. Paper covers, 7/-

COLLECTING COINS, by Frank Purvey. 4/-

SEABY'S COIN AND MEDAL BULLETIN. A monthly periodical for all interested in numismatics. *Subscription price 14/- per annum*

Thick binding cover for a year's Bulletins, 2/- each

Bound volume for 1965, 1966, 1967 (ready February 1968).
Cloth, 25/- each

£ STERLING CONVERSION TABLE

12 pence (12d)=1 shilling (1s); 20 shillings (20s)=1 pound (£1)

£	s.	d.		U.S. dollars	German marks	Swiss francs	French francs	Italian lire
		6		.07	.28	.30	.34	44
	1	0		.14	.56	.60	.68	87
	2	0		.28	1.12	1.21	1.37	174
	3	0		.42	1.68	1.82	2.05	262
	4	0		.56	2.23	2.42	2.74	349
	5	0		.70	2.78	3.02	3.43	436
	6	0		.84	3.36	3.ǝ3	4.11	523
	7	6		1.05	4.17	4.53	5.14	654
	10	0		1.40	5.56	6.04	6.86	872
	12	6		1.75	6.95	7.55	8.57	1,090
	15	0		2.10	8.34	9.06	10.29	1,308
	17	6		2.45	9.73	10.57	12.00	1,526
	20	0	(£1)	2.80	11.12	12.08	13.72	1,744
	25	0		3.50	13.90	15.10	17.15	2,180
	30	0		4.20	16.68	18.12	20.58	2,616
	40	0	(£2)	5.60	22.24	24.16	27.44	3,488
	50	0		7.00	27.80	30.20	34.30	4,360
	60	0	(£3)	8.40	33.36	36.24	41.16	5,232
	70	0		9.80	38.92	42.28	48.02	6,104
	80	0	(£4)	11.20	44.48	48.32	54.88	6,976
	90	0		12.60	50.04	54.36	61.74	7,848
5	0	0		14.00	55.60	60.40	68.60	8,720
6	0	0		16.80	66.72	72.48	82.32	10,464
7	0	0		19.60	77.84	84.56	96.04	12,208
8	0	0		22.40	88.96	96.64	109.76	13,952
9	0	0		25.20	100.08	108.72	123.48	15,696
10	0	0		28.00	111.20	120.80	137.20	17,440
20	0	0		56.00	222.40	241.60	274.40	34,880
25	0	0		70.00	278.00	302.00	343.00	43,600
50	0	0		140.00	556.00	604.00	686.00	87,200
100	0	0		280.00	1,112.00	1,208.00	1,372.00	174,400

Published by B. A. Seaby Ltd., 59-65, Great Portland Street, London, W.1.